Instructor's Manual and Test Bank

Elements
of
Ecology

Seventh Edition

Neal J. Voelz

St. Cloud State University

Aimee C. Wyrick

Pacific Union College

Floyd E. Hayes

Pacific Union College

Benjamin Cummings

San Francisco   Boston   New York
Cape Town   Hong Kong   London   Madrid   Mexico City
Montreal   Munich   Paris   Singapore   Sydney   Tokyo   Toronto

VP, Editor-in-Chief, Biology: Beth Wilbur

Acquisitions Editor: Star MacKenzie

Senior Supplements Project Editor: Susan Berge

Assistant Editor: Brady Golden

Managing Editor, Production: Michael Early

Production Supervisor: Jane Brundage

Production Management/Composition: Progressive Publishing Alternatives, Marsha Hall

Image Rights and Permissions Manager: Zina Arabia

Manufacturing Buyer: Michael Penne

Executive Marketing Manager: Lauren Harp

Cover Photo Credit: Getty Images/Gallo Images/Michael Poliza: Elephant (*Loxodonta africana*) Herd & Shadows—Directly Above.

Many of the designations used by manufacturers and sellers to distinguish their products are claimed as trademarks. Where those designations appear in this book, and the publisher was aware of a trademark claim, the designations have been printed in initial caps or all caps.

1 2 3 4 5 6 7 8 9 10—B&B—13 12 11 10 09

Manufactured in the United States of America.

Benjamin Cummings
is an imprint of

www.pearsonhighered.com

ISBN 10: 0-321-56788-9;

ISBN 13: 978-0-321-56788-8

Instructor's Manual Contents

Test Bank Contents

Preface to Instructor's Manual and Test Bank

The purpose of the Instructor's Manual and Test Bank is to serve as a supplement to the text, guiding the instructor in its use, providing perspective, and supplying the instructor with test questions to use in examinations. These purposes are served with the two sections: a summary of each chapter is provided at the beginning, followed by a section of test questions for each chapter (with accompanying software available). The chapter summaries are meant to provide more than just a brief restatement of the material in each chapter of the text. In the commentary, we have tried to not only provide a flowing summary that ties together all the sections of the text chapter, but also to provide suggestions to the instructor regarding the teaching of the material. In particular, we have tried to point out when material is likely to be challenging, exciting, or surprising to students, and to provide occasional suggestions for approaches to take in presenting material.

In the Test Bank, we have attempted to provide test questions that represent the material in the text evenly and thoroughly, highlighting important concepts and vocabulary. Overlap in material covered is not complete between the different types of questions, because different types of questions lend themselves to different classes of material. For example, short answer questions are particularly useful for vocabulary, and essay questions allow the instructor to ask students to synthesize concepts from multiple sections of a chapter. The instructor is encouraged to select questions of each type that match his or her teaching style and that accurately represent the content as presented in the course being taught. We hope that instructors will find the Instructor's Manual and Test Bank to be a useful resource that will help the teaching and administration of a course go more smoothly.

Neal J. Voelz
Aimee C. Wyrick
Floyd E. Hayes

Instructor's Manual

CHAPTER 1 The Nature of Ecology

Commentary

Ecology is the study of interactions among organisms and between organisms and their environment (Section 1.1). This first chapter will help students understand that while a thorough knowledge of ecology is necessary to make sound environmental decisions, ecology is not environmentalism; instead, ecology is a science with a long, diverse, and complex history that continues to change today with the advent of new technology and the growing influence of humans on the planet. Organisms interact with each other and the physical environment in the context of the ecosystem (Section 1.2). Thus, an ecosystem consists of two interacting components: biotic (living) and abiotic (nonliving).

A useful framework for helping students understand ecology is an organizational hierarchy, which ranges from individuals to the biosphere (Section 1.3). A primary unit of this ecological hierarchy is the population—a group of individuals of the same species. Populations of different species that live together form a community, and a community plus the nonliving environment compose an ecosystem (Section 1.2). A landscape is an area that includes a variety of communities and ecosystems, whereas the biosphere considers the Earth as a whole. This hierarchy is more than a way to classify different ecological levels. Unique processes and patterns occur within the levels, dictating the types of questions asked by ecologists (Section 1.4). Sections 1.5 and 1.6 discuss some of the important scientific methods that ecologists use to test hypotheses within the various levels of the ecological hierarchy (see also Quantifying Ecology 1.1 and 1.2).

A common notion among young students and in society in general is that science is a process of cataloging facts. It is important to dispel this notion by emphasizing that uncertainty and debate are key features of ecology and of all branches of science (Section 1.7). Students should see science as a process of collecting evidence to test ideas while eliminating incorrect hypotheses along the way.

Make it clear to students that as a science, ecology is especially interdisciplinary (Section 1.8). In order to understand populations, communities, and ecosystems, ecologists must draw on concepts and techniques from many fields, ranging from genetics to physiology to geology. As the human population grows and exerts greater pressure on our resources it will be increasingly important that we also view ecology as including the study of human populations and their interaction with other species (see Ecological Issues: The Human Factor).

The ecological hierarchy spans a broad range of spatial scales and extends from individual organisms to all species on Earth. However, the individual is the basic unit of ecology because individual organisms are intimately connected with the environment and pass genetic material to the next generation (Section 1.9).

Discussion Topics

1. First, ask students what they think environmentalism is, and then ask them for a definition of ecology. Make a list of the student responses and look for connections. The relationships among ecology, environmentalism, and environmental science can also be developed. Discuss the social factors that have recently shaped our perception of the word "ecology."
2. Discuss the concept of an ecosystem. Why might an ecosystem actually be difficult to delineate in nature? Are there other aspects of the ecological organizational hierarchy that are difficult to precisely define? If so, how do students think ecologists deal with these uncertainties?

3. Ask students what their concept of science is. Do they see science as simply the process of gathering facts? Ask them what they think a fact represents in science (i.e., Do they know of any scientific "facts" that were previously thought true but have now been disproved?). Discuss how science is based on a continual process of refining or rejecting hypotheses.

CHAPTER 2   Climate

Commentary

This chapter introduces the basic concepts of climate. There is an emphasis on solar radiation, which is the climatic factor that provides the foundation for life on Earth. Section 2.1 describes the physical processes that govern how solar radiation is intercepted by the Earth. The importance of the Earth's atmosphere and, in particular, its chemical makeup, should be made clear because it will be important for the students' understanding of global climate change. One major goal of ecology is to understand the distribution and abundance of organisms on Earth. For such an understanding at a global scale, it is essential to realize how intercepted solar radiation and resulting average temperatures vary with latitude (Section 2.2). Temperature also varies greatly with change in altitude (Section 2.3). These fundamental gradients contribute to some of the most striking ecological patterns seen on Earth, including the annual cycle of seasons and the latitudinal gradient in diversity.

The latitudinal gradient in intercepted solar radiation contributes indirectly to important climatic variables such as the circulation of air masses and the currents in the oceans (Sections 2.4 and 2.5). Students should understand the process by which high solar input at the equator causes rising air masses there; the movement of these air masses is subsequently influenced by the Earth's rotation as they flow northward (the Coriolis effect, Section 2.4). Similarly, the major patterns of water flow in the Earth's oceans are influenced by the latitudinal gradient in solar radiation, the Earth's rotation, and the global patterns of airflow (Section 2.5). An important principle involved in understanding global climate patterns is that warm air can hold more moisture than cold air (Section 2.6). A firm understanding of the implications of this principle will help students realize how geographical patterns in climate influence the distribution and abundance of species.

The global pattern of rainfall (Section 2.7) brings together all facets of climate discussed so far, including temperature, winds, and ocean currents. Asking students to understand global patterns of rainfall based on their present knowledge will provide them with an opportunity to examine and apply their basic understanding of important climatic principles. A discussion of more irregular climate occurrences, such as the El Niño–Southern Oscillation (Section 2.9), provides a similar opportunity.

So far, we have discussed large-scale climatic patterns. Students should understand that while these global patterns strongly influence the baseline conditions of a habitat, most organisms experience conditions that vary locally from the regional average (Section 2.10). These local conditions that are experienced by organisms called microclimates are created by a wide variety of factors, including geographical structure (see also Section 2.8), vegetation, slope, and aspect. Ecological Issues describes the microclimate experienced by many organisms: the urban microclimate.

Discussion Topics

1. Assume that you are camping in mountainous or on very hilly terrain. Where would you place your campfire so that smoke will not drift into your tent site?

2. Ask students if they or other organisms in their area are ever influenced by the El Niño–Southern Oscillation. If so, what effects does this phenomenon have and how long do they last?
3. Observe the movements of a local animal. (Even a domesticated animal will do.) What special microclimate situations is it exploiting and why? What factors are creating microclimates that are significantly different from the average climate of the region?
4. Choose an example of a microclimate and ask students to discuss both the global and local influences that determine the microclimatic conditions that are experienced by organisms there.

CHAPTER 3   The Aquatic Environment

Commentary

Water is the most important substance on Earth and covers almost 75 percent of the planet's surface. Its unique properties allow life as we know it. An especially important aspect of water for life on Earth involves the cycling of water between Earth and the atmosphere (Section 3.1). This cycle directly or indirectly links freshwater, marine, and terrestrial environments (see also Ecological Issues). While the previous chapter discussed the method by which incoming solar radiation drives global climate patterns, Section 3.1 shows how solar radiation is linked to the water cycle. Students should understand the unique and important properties of water and why they are so crucial for life (Section 3.2).

The composition of solar radiation changes as it interacts with materials, such as water, on the Earth's surface. Light is reflected, absorbed, or transmitted through objects, and students should note how water can create gradients in light quantity and quality through and among habitats (Section 3.3). As discussed in the previous chapter, incoming solar radiation strongly influences regional temperature trends, while the temperature of local microclimates may be influenced by a number of factors. Temperature is an important environmental variable affecting the activity of organisms. Because of this it is important to understand that temperature varies on many different temporal and spatial scales. For example, due to some of the unique properties of water discussed in Section 3.2, water temperature in freshwater lakes varies in layers with depth (Section 3.4). Furthermore, these layers predictably change position and temperature throughout the course of a year.

Water is often called the "universal solvent" because of its ability to dissolve more substances than any other liquid (Section 3.5). This makes water an extremely important biological material because it is involved in transportation of nutrients and waste products at all levels of the ecological hierarchy. Osmosis and diffusion (Section 3.6), which are important processes that involve water, are terms that all students in the life sciences should understand thoroughly since they have applications in many different branches of biology. An important chemical property that greatly influences the distribution and abundance of organisms in aquatic habitats is acidity (Section 3.7). Many important ecological habitats are also strongly influenced by the mass movements of water, including currents, waves, and tides (Sections 3.8 and 3.9). Estuaries provide an interesting habitat for studying the ecological constraints imposed on organisms (Section 3.10).

Discussion Topics

1. Discuss with students where their drinking water supply comes from. Since water cycles (recycles) on Earth, what does that indicate about the water the students drank during breakfast or lunch?
2. Of what significance to aquatic life is the fact that ice floats? Why are some organisms able to live on the surface of aquatic environments?

3. Many students will be familiar with sport fishing and all of the interesting and often expensive tools associated with this hobby. Given that light varies with depth in aquatic environments, what implications does this have for all the brightly and variously colored lures that are bought by the many people who enjoy this sport?
4. Ask students if they think natural fish-kills (i.e., not resulting from pollution, etc.) are more common in lakes or rivers. Are there particular physical or biological reasons for any differences among the environments?
5. Is acid rain (deposition) still a problem in the United States and other countries? Is acid rain a useful term for describing this problem (i.e., What happens when CO_2 mixes with water?)?

CHAPTER 4 The Terrestrial Environment

Commentary

One of the largest evolutionary leaps was the transition from life in water to life on land, especially with the variety of constraints this change entailed (Section 4.1). Maintaining an appropriate water balance was particularly important for organisms during this transition. As discussed in Chapter 3, the composition of solar radiation changes as it interacts with water on the Earth's surface. However, unlike aquatic habitats where water is the greatest factor influencing solar radiation, the dominant factor influencing the vertical gradient of light in terrestrial environments is the absorption and reflection of solar radiation by plants (Section 4.2; see also Quantifying Ecology 4.1).

Soil is the foundation on which all terrestrial life depends (Section 4.3). The biggest challenge in teaching the concept of soils is that students' initial concepts of soils are very rudimentary. Most students have not thought about how soils might vary from place to place, what factors are responsible for this variation, and how this variation might influence living things. These concepts will help students better understand the abundance and distribution of organisms as well as the ongoing problem of soil erosion.

When introducing the concept of soils it is very helpful to give students experience with actual examples of soil profiles in their natural settings. You may be able to arrange a field trip with a soil scientist by contacting either the National Conservation Resource Service (formerly the Soil Conservation Service) or the Agronomy or Soil Science Department at a nearby land-grant university.

It is a useful exercise to work with students to find a definition of soil because they are asked to think about many of the biotic and abiotic characteristics of soils (Section 4.3). Understanding soil formation (Sections 4.4 and 4.5) has great value in understanding landscape-scale variation in soil characteristics. It is also important to emphasize that soil is formed by both biotic and abiotic factors, and the process can take thousands of years. Again, a field trip would be an excellent way to introduce students to these concepts. For example, students could dig soil pits and compare surface-horizon depth along a gradient from the foot of a slope to the top of the slope. Emphasize to students that the formation of soil is not simply a small-scale physical/chemical process (Section 4.4), but that it is strongly influenced by both local and regional variation in climate, vegetation, and other organisms (Sections 4.5 and 4.10). A field trip to a nearby road bank cut or excavation site would facilitate an introduction to the basic concept of horizontal layers in soil and their characteristics (Sections 4.6 and 4.7). These should be discussed in connection with soil forming factors, emphasizing the physical, chemical, and biological processes that produce horizontal layers and their traits.

Two important soil characteristics that students may be able to relate to human uses of soils are moisture-holding capacity (Section 4.8) and cation-exchange capacity (Section 4.9). An understanding of both of these properties is essential for relating spatial variation in soils to human uses of soils. For example, students should think about the characteristics of an ideal agricultural soil.

Furthermore, a detailed examination of these soil properties will facilitate a mechanistic understanding of soil properties since they depend on soil texture, topography, and soil chemistry.

Broad geographical differences in geology, climate, and vegetation give rise to different soils (Section 4.10). For example, the problem of land use and soil salinization, which generally occurs in arid environments, provides an opportunity for students to relate what they have learned about soils and water (Chapters 3 and 4) to an important issue for much of the human population.

Discussion Topics

1. What are some differences between living in water and living on land?
2. Discuss with students the major changes that were needed for the transition from living in water to living on land. What are some of the major constraints on organisms for making this transition?
3. Ask students what they think would be the effect on soils of removing the overlying vegetation. What if tallgrass prairie vegetation is replaced by forest due to fire suppression—how will the soils change in response?
4. A common misconception is that soil can be kept in a high state of productivity by adding commercial fertilizer to replace nutrients withdrawn from the soil. What is the fallacy of this attitude? How does fertilization affect organic matter and soil organisms, particularly plant-symbiotic microbes such as mycorrhizal fungi and Rhizobium bacteria?
5. How can soil salinization be reduced or eliminated? What are some of the consequences of soil salinization for non-agricultural organisms?
6. What are some ecological connections (linkages) between terrestrial and aquatic environments? What do your students believe may be important characteristics of terrestrial environments that influence biotic and abiotic factors in aquatic habitats? How might some human-caused land changes affect aquatic environments?

CHAPTER 5   Ecological Genetics: Adaptation and Natural Selection

Commentary

This chapter introduces the basics of adaptive evolution by natural selection. A real understanding of the process of natural selection will be essential to students in science and will allow them a better grasp of ecology. The most difficult and important concept to help students understand is that evolution by natural selection is the result of preexisting variation among individuals in a population (Sections 5.1 and 5.4). Evolution by natural selection does not create anything new. Instead, differences among individuals result in differences in survival and/or reproduction (Section 5.1; see Field Studies). This differential survival and/or reproduction is the process of natural selection. Do not underestimate the initial difficulty some students will have with this concept or the importance of them understanding it. It will be helpful to review the basic genetic concepts provided in Section 5.2 and 5.3, which discuss the basic ideas and language used to describe how traits are inherited (such as genes, genotypes, and phenotypes). Students should quickly grasp that in order for natural selection to work, the traits of importance (i.e., adaptations) must be passed from parent to offspring—they must be heritable (Section 5.2). Although adaptations are characteristics of individual organisms, ultimately, evolution is a population-level phenomenon (Section 5.4).

It may be useful when discussing the above material to introduce or review Darwin's understanding (or lack thereof) of genetics, as it provides an important context for the development of his theory of evolution. Darwin knew that for natural selection to work traits must be passed from parent to offspring, but he did not know exactly how inheritance happened. Unbeknownst to him, an Austrian monk named Gregor Mendel was making significant progress in understanding how traits are inherited. Hearing about the progression of our understanding of evolution through Darwin and Mendel may help students better appreciate the process of science—specifically, students should appreciate that science is the process of formulating and testing ideas and is not simply the collecting of facts.

The terminology provided in Sections 5.2 through 5.4 allows the introduction of a strict definition of evolution as a change in gene frequency in a population (Section 5.5). The example of the Galapagos finches studied by Peter and Rosemary Grant helps to illustrate both the concept of natural selection and the three types of natural selection: directional, stabilizing, and disruptive (Section 5.5).

At this point, students may be wondering how sufficient variation is generated for the process of adaptive evolution. Section 5.6 (see also Quantifying Ecology 5.1) discusses not only the importance of mutation but also the influence of mating system (sexual versus asexual) on the amount of variation maintained in a population.

Although students may comprehend how a single species changes through time, the idea of clines, ecotypes, and geographic isolates is more abstract, and an appreciation of geographic variation and its consequences for species formation is instructive (Section 5.7; see also Field Studies).

A discussion of the process of adaptation introduces the concepts of tradeoffs and constraints (Section 5.8). These will be important throughout the book and should be thoroughly introduced here. Students should understand that the characteristics that enable an individual organism to do well under one set of conditions may limit its performance under a different set of conditions. These constraints give rise to the idea that the characteristics of organisms make them more successful in certain environments than in others.

Finally, an important concept for ecologists is the idea that a genotype can give rise to a variety of different phenotypes (phenotypic plasticity) depending on environmental conditions (Section 5.9). This idea may help in designing ecological studies and/or in interpreting results when the environment changes with time, or when comparing populations over broad geographic areas.

Discussion Topics

1. An interesting way to demonstrate genetic change in a species is to play the "whisper game" during a lecture. Choose a phrase that is neither too complex nor overly familiar to the students (including your name in the phrase sometimes produces interesting results). Begin by whispering the phrase to a student in the front of the class. That student must then whisper the phrase to a person close by, who then whispers the phrase to another student. This continues until at least 8 to 10 students have heard the phrase. Students are only allowed to hear the phrase once and must immediately pass it along to the next student. Ask the last student to write down what he or she heard and then you can compare the original with this final phrase. It is important that students realize that the letters (or words) in the phrase represent genes being passed along in a population and that each student represents one (or several) generations.

2. An excellent exercise for helping students understand the process of natural selection is to ask them to describe an evolutionary scenario using the language of "evolutionary longhand." For example, ask a student to explain the observation that Moth Species A, which lives in the nearby forest, has wings that are colored almost exactly like the bark of the most dominant tree species. The student should systematically describe the evolution of the moth wing color by natural selection. This description should include the initial, genetically based variation for wing color that must have been present, a selective agent such as a visually oriented predator, and the differential success of moth individuals that were colored more like the bark of the tree.

3. Ask students to think about processes other than natural selection that could result in a change in gene frequency over time in a population, such as evolution. Introduce the idea of genetic drift and have students think about the way in which evolution in a local population might be affected by rates of immigration and emigration to and from that local population.

CHAPTER 6 Plant Adaptations to the Environment

Commentary

An important point for students of ecology to grasp is that because life is based on carbon, all life on Earth ultimately depends on the process of photosynthesis for structure and energy (Sections 6.1 and 6.7). We live in a solar-powered world: solar radiation provides the energy for photosynthesis (Section 6.2). Terrestrial plants must take up CO_2 from the atmosphere while facing the major challenge of minimizing the amount of water lost to the atmosphere in the process (Sections 6.3 and 6.4). Aquatic plants (most are secondarily adapted to the aquatic environment) have evolved different adaptations for carbon uptake and must contend with the problem of too much water (Section 6.5). Temperature is another main factor that affects the rates of photosynthesis and respiration (Section 6.6).

The remainder of Chapter 6 illustrates an important idea introduced in Chapter 5: trade-offs are ever-present for organisms, such that traits allowing success in one environment do not necessarily allow maximum success in other environments. These trade-offs result in adaptations—traits that allow organisms to be successful in a particular environment (Section 6.8). For example, plants can partition carbohydrates between growth of new leaves and growth of new roots (Section 6.7), and the best ratio of root growth to leaf growth may be different in different environments. For plants, a major variable that may differ among environments is the amount of light that is available for photosynthesis. As a result, some species are adapted to high light environments, while others are adapted to low light environments (Section 6.9; see also Field Studies). A major component of such adaptations is that photosynthesis must produce enough carbohydrates to compensate for those used in respiration (see Quantifying Ecology 6.1). Thus, plants that are adapted to low light will usually have a low rate of respiration, requiring only low light to compensate for respiration and therefore to grow.

As with light, terrestrial plants have evolved a range of adaptations in response to precipitation and soil moisture variations, and water demand by plants is especially linked to temperature (Section 6.10). As mentioned in Sections 6.3 and 6.4, plants face a major challenge of minimizing the amount of water lost to the atmosphere during photosynthesis. This challenge is especially great in arid environments, where the gradient in moisture between the interior of the leaf and the atmosphere is very steep and temperatures can be very high. Many plants in these environments use alternative photosynthetic pathways that allow either spatial (C_4 pathway) or temporal (CAM pathway) separation of the sites of CO_2 uptake and the sites of carbon fixation by the enzyme rubisco (Section 6.10). Both of these alternative pathways allow higher water-use efficiency by the plants that are employing them.

In addition to light, other environmental variables may provide selection pressure for adaptations in plants (Sections 6.11 and 6.12). Habitats may differ in average temperature and levels of various soil nutrients. Plants have adapted to these varied conditions with a myriad of strategies, and it is important to note that the adaptations to these differing environmental factors are not independent. For example, temperature and relative humidity are often directly linked. As a result, we see many correlations in the adaptations of plants to variation in these two environmental variables.

Nutrients are another major abiotic variable required by both plants and animals to function and reproduce. Students should understand that there are some 30 chemicals that are essential for the life of most organisms—some in large quantities (macronutrients) and others in only trace amounts (micronutrients) (Section 6.12). Of the macronutrients, carbon, hydrogen, and oxygen form the majority of plant tissues.

Wetlands provide ecologists with interesting areas to study plant adaptations for dealing with saturated soils and especially gas exchange (Section 6.13). Comparisons of plant adaptations in habitats with too little (arid) and too much water may be useful for the students' understanding of trade-offs and constraints.

Discussion Topics

1. How are differences between aquatic and terrestrial environments reflected in plant structure and function?
2. How do the shape and size of plant leaves function in maintaining a thermal balance in plants?
3. Collect leaves growing in shade and other leaves growing in direct sunlight from the same plant species. Have students study the differences in morphology and discuss how these differences may represent adaptations to different light regimes.
4. In a deciduous forest, what is the relative ranking in shade tolerance of forest trees, forest shrubs, early spring wildflowers, and late summer wildflowers?
5. Inform students that plants in African deserts are only distantly related evolutionarily to plants in American deserts and that their common ancestor did not live in a desert. Do they expect the two groups of plants to share common characteristics? Why or why not?
6. Ask students to think of a case when adaptation to one environmental problem may be in conflict with adaptation to a different environmental problem. What about the opposite case—are there situations in which a single trait gives an organism an advantage with respect to multiple environmental challenges?
7. What major changes may happen to plant communities if global climate change continues as predicted? Are all changes potentially bad, or could there be some benefits to global warming

CHAPTER 7   Animal Adaptations to the Environment

Commentary

The adaptation of animals to their environment is a complex topic because animals can obtain food by consuming any number of the many plants and animals on Earth. Students should think about this difference between plants and animals: all plants require the same few food resources (Chapter 6). However, a number of key processes are shared by all animals and form the basis for this chapter. When examining these processes, it must be emphasized that animal size is an important (and mostly predictable) factor to consider because it plays a major role in constraining morphological and physiological adaptations (Section 7.1). A primary process that must be carried out by all animals is the acquisition of energy from carbon compounds, and animals perform this task in a wide variety of ways (Section 7.2). One classification of animals is based on the manner by which they obtain their carbon for energy: herbivores feed on plant tissues, carnivores consume animal tissue, omnivores consume both, and detritivores feed on dead plant and animal matter. Each of these strategies involves specific adaptations that increase an animal's efficiency as a means of obtaining energy.

In addition to consuming carbon compounds for energy, animals must also satisfy a variety of nutritional needs (Section 7.3; see also Field Studies). How successfully these needs are satisfied can have strong effects on an animal's rate of growth and reproduction (Section 7.4). The nature of nutrient acquisition challenges facing animals varies both seasonally and among environments and can, thus, have a strong effect on the distribution and abundance of species. The work by Martin Wikelski and his colleagues (Field Studies) provides an excellent example of body size, environmental changes, and food supply acting in concert to affect animal populations.

Another major process shared by all animals is the breakdown of organic compounds through aerobic respiration (Section 7.5). This process requires oxygen and results in the release of energy that can be used by the animal. Evolution has resulted in a wide variety of adaptations that allow animals to obtain oxygen for respiration, including lungs in terrestrial animals and gills in many aquatic organisms.

A fairly constant environment is required by the wide variety of chemical and physical processes taking place inside an animal. Since the external environment is quite variable, animals have many adaptations that allow them to maintain a fairly consistent internal environment. This maintenance of the internal environment, referred to as homeostasis, is another process that unifies all animals (Section 7.6). One major component of homeostasis is the regulation of internal temperature. This regulation involves a significant exchange of energy with the external environment (Section 7.7; see also Quantifying Ecology 7.1). Some adaptations of animals to this process are facilitated by their mobility. For example, some animals can move to seek out heat or cold. Likewise, the body shape of animals has a strong effect on the rate of exchange of energy with the external environment. The variety of means by which animals regulate their temperature allows classification of animals into three groups (Section 7.8). Poikilotherms (ectotherms) depend on gaining heat from the environment and are subject to a variable body temperature (Section 7.9), while homeotherms (endotherms) maintain a relatively constant internal temperature by generating heat metabolically (Section 7.10). An examination of alternative strategies for obtaining heat provides an excellent illustration of the principle of tradeoffs—an important theme throughout the text (Section 7.11; see also Quantifying Ecology 7.1). Heterotherms (Section 7.12) vary in their heat acquisition by sometimes generating heat metabolically and at other times depending on heat from the environment. Torpor and hibernation are important adaptations that allow energy conservation in some animals (Section 7.13). Each strategy for obtaining or conserving heat involves advantages and disadvantages such that no single strategy is best in all environments. These types of trade-offs are the driving force behind adaptations of animals to their environments.

Many animals use evaporative cooling or other unique physiological processes for temperature balance (Section 7.14). One of these, countercurrent circulation, has evolved independently many times in a diverse array of animals.

Because of the nature of animal metabolism, animals face a more complicated challenge than plants in maintaining appropriate water content in their tissues (Section 7.15). This problem can be particularly acute in arid environments, where adaptations are necessary for conserving water. A related challenge is faced by animals in saline environments—these animals must have special processes to maintain proper osmotic balance in the face of a strongly hyperosmotic environment (Section 7.16). Animals living in freshwater have the opposite problem to those living in saline environments, as they must maintain osmotic balance in the face of a strongly hypoosmotic environment. Various methods for staying afloat have evolved in aquatic animals, thereby reducing energy costs (Section 7.17).

Not only do the challenges of energy, nutrient, and osmotic balance influence the activities of animals, but so do daily and seasonal cycles of light and dark (Section 7.18). Just as in plants (Chapter 6), animals seem to be operating according to an internal biological clock that allows organisms to efficiently respond to changes in environmental conditions. For example, many animals change their activity in anticipation of seasonal environmental changes by responding to critical day lengths (Section 7.19). In aquatic environments, the activities of many animals are influenced by the tides (Section 7.20).

Discussion Topics

1. Ask students to think about the many ways in which plants are different from animals. What are the implications of these differences? When is it useful to focus on these differences, and when should we seek commonalities?
2. Environmentally related nutrient deficiencies often affect human populations. What are some of these nutrient deficiencies, where do they occur, what are the deficiency symptoms, and how are they corrected?
3. The largest animals on Earth were some of the dinosaurs. A current debate concerns whether these large animals were homeotherms or poikilotherms. Have students discuss both viewpoints.
4. Ask students to think of a trade-off faced by an animal when coping with an environmental challenge, such as water balance or heat regulation. What are the choices faced by the animal, and why do the same traits not confer an advantage for both strategies?
5. Discuss the diurnal cycle and humans. What implications are there for humans who work at night, especially those involved in complex, dangerous, or life-saving jobs?

CHAPTER 8 Life History Patterns

Commentary

Variation among and within species with respect to life history patterns is tremendous. This variation in the ways that organisms grow and reproduce provides endless puzzles and possibilities for scientific exploration. For example, a debate persists to this day about the relative merits of sexual versus asexual reproductive strategies (Section 8.1). Comparing and contrasting these two major forms of reproduction provides students with an interesting introduction to life history strategies. Many plants and animals that are familiar to students can be used as examples to illustrate the wide variety of forms that sexual reproduction can take, from dioecy to a sequential hermaphroditic strategy (Section 8.2). The topics of mating strategies (Section 8.3), sexual selection (Section 8.4; see also Field Studies), and female choice of mates based on resources (Section 8.5) will be easily related to students because of the obvious parallels with and relevance to human mating behavior. Ask students to think about how typical human behaviors can be classified and understood in the context of the concepts being learned.

How organisms allocate their time and energy to reproduction (Section 8.6) and the actual timing of reproductive effort (Section 8.7) are some of the most active and fruitful areas of research in the ecology and evolution of life history patterns. The most important concept for students to grasp is the variety of allocation options that are available to an organism and the trade-offs that are inherent in choosing one strategy over another (see Quantifying Ecology 8.1). This principle is well illustrated in the question of whether an organism should produce many small or few large offspring (Section 8.8). Students should obtain a broad understanding of the many biotic and abiotic factors that impact not only the evolution of these life history traits but also the behavioral choices that organisms make on a short time scale (Sections 8.9–8.11). An important point to make is that the importance of allocation strategies is not restricted to animals. Plants also exhibit a wide range of strategies, from annual grasses to long-lived trees. Habitat selection is another life history trait that presents organisms with a wide variety of choices that are impacted by many factors (Section 8.12). Again, students should think about how these concepts relate to plants rather than just animals. Building such threads among topics throughout a course will allow students to obtain a broad perspective.

The concept of *r*-selection and *K*-selection is associated with fitness and life history patterns (Section 8.13). This concept is somewhat controversial and it has its weaknesses, the biggest being that it can be interpreted in many different ways. However, it has proved to be very useful in stimulating research since R. H. MacArthur introduced it in 1967 ("Some generalized theorems of natural selection," *Proc. Nat. Acad. Sci. USA* 48:1893–1897). Grime's model of life history variation, which was originally developed for plants (but now with wider use), provides a conceptual framework similar to the idea of *r*- and *K*-selection.

Discussion Topics

1. What are the potential pitfalls of attempting to associate life history traits with *r*- and *K*-selection?
2. Compare and contrast *r*- and *K*-selection with Grime's model of life history variation.
3. Consider the white-tailed deer of North America. By life history traits, it could be considered a *K*-selected species, yet in parts of its range it has reached the status of a pest, exhibiting the life history traits of an *r*-selected species. Discuss *r*- and *K*-selection in light of this fact.
4. Many of the concepts introduced in this chapter are applicable to human populations, but their application can be highly controversial. Consider, for example, the allocation of energy to reproduction. How is it relevant to teenage pregnancy and the age and experience of the mother? How does the allocation of energy (measured in energy, time, and money) apply to large versus small families? Does this have any effect on fitness, as measured in rearing and educating the young? What is the relationship between reproductive effort and the single parent?
5. Does the principle of mate selection in animals apply to the manner in which humans choose a mate? What are the similarities and differences? (Refer to Buss, 1994, and references therein listed in Further Readings, p. 191 of the textbook.) Are there differences among cultures?
6. Why is mate choice primarily a female choice, even in humans?

CHAPTER 9   Properties of Populations

Commentary

The next four chapters discuss one of the primary conceptual/organizing units in ecology: the population. Since ecologists define a population as a group of individuals of the same species, it becomes important to decide what, exactly, an individual is (Section 9.1). Students should see that this is much more easily done for some types of organisms than for others, and that this disparity has led to different scientific approaches to the ecology of different kinds of species.

It has been said that ecology is the study of the abundance and distribution of species. Both abundance and distribution are properties of populations, and Section 9.2 discusses how they are influenced by environmental variation. Here we are introduced to the concept of geographic range, which is the area that includes the entire population of a species. Understanding the relationship between the distribution of a population and environmental variation leads to the important idea of a metapopulaton—a population divided into local subpopulations (explored further in Chapter 12). Combining abundance and distribution allows us to calculate the density of a population, which is the number of individuals per unit of space (Section 9.3). Density can have strong effects on the individuals in a population both negatively through competition for resources and positively through a variety of subtle mechanisms. Given the potential importance of density, we need to understand the factors that influence it. As discussed in Section 9.3, the proportion of space that is appropriate for an organism should be taken into account when calculating density, since habitats are generally patchy and are not wholly appropriate for a species. Density is further affected by the nature of dispersion of organisms across a habitat; that is, whether they are distributed randomly, uniformly, or in clumps. For example, when individuals are clumped, the local density experienced by individuals may be higher than the average density calculated across the entire habitat. The concept of a metapopulation is especially useful when discussing populations of clumped individuals (Section 9.2 and Chapter 12). The most common spatial distribution is clumped and is maintained by the distribution of resources across the habitat or specific patterns of dispersal (see also Section 9.7), among other factors (Section 9.3). Ecologists have devoted much thought and energy to finding appropriate methods to measure the densities and patterns of dispersion of organisms in nature (Section 9.4).

A concept that should not be difficult for students to grasp is that not all individuals in a population are alike (Sections 9.5 and 9.6). For example, individuals of different ages may have very different characteristics (Sections 9.5). While information about the ages of organisms may be difficult to obtain, these data are valuable in projecting the future behavior of a population, such as how fast it will grow or decline. These types of changes in the size of populations are the focus of the next chapter.

Individuals in most populations are mobile during at least some part of their life history (Section 9.7). This dispersal is important in order to understand many aspects of a population, including spatial distribution and population dynamics (Section 9.8; see also Chapter 10). Humans have increasingly facilitated the dispersal of organisms around the world, usually beyond an organism's natural geographic range. These human-assisted dispersals often have deleterious effects on native species and ecosystems (see Ecological Issues).

Discussion Topics

1. Have students determine the pattern of human population distribution in your area. What is the degree of clumping? What landscape features influence population distribution?
2. Do human populations exhibit age structure? What traits vary with age?
3. What are some ways to reduce accidental human-assisted dispersal? Are these strategies cost effective? Is it important to reduce this type of dispersal or should humans be considered a natural dispersal mechanism for other organisms?
4. As a preview for the next few chapters, have students discuss how population density affects individuals. How are individual humans affected when population density becomes greatly elevated? What about when density is extremely low.

CHAPTER 10 Population Growth

Commentary

Population growth and the forces regulating it is one of the fundamental processes that ecologists strive to understand. This chapter explores population growth in a closed population (i.e., where no immigration or emigration occurs) using only birth and death rates (Section 10.1). Exponential growth is common in all populations given the correct conditions and forms the basis for a more complete understanding of population growth (Section 10.1; see also Quantifying Ecology 10.1 and 10.2). Although exponential growth is relatively simple, some students will have difficulty with the mathematical statements. It is wise to thoroughly explain the model because it forms the basis for more complex representations of population growth. Because mortality (and survivorship) is usually age-specific, it is helpful to use a life table (Section 10.2; see also Quantifying Ecology 10.3) to systematically keep track of mortality and to make related calculations. Constructing a life table can be an instructive exercise for students, giving them more of an intuitive feel for the various parameters describing population growth. One interesting way to obtain data for such an exercise is to take a field trip to a local cemetery. Have students collect survivorship data from gravestones and use these data to construct a life table.

It is useful to show students how concepts of population growth apply to both animals and plants. One difference is that life tables are generally more difficult to construct for plants, for various reasons. For example, it is often difficult to distinguish one individual from another in a plant population.

A useful product of life tables is the graphical depictions of population parameters that one can obtain (Section 10.4). Survivorship curves (and mortality curves) give a visual snapshot of the age-specific survivorship of a population at a given time and can be useful for comparing among different times, places, or sexes. Students should think about the traits of populations that produce survivorship curves of different shape, including characteristics of human populations.

Because birth rates are usually age-specific (Section 10.5), we can also construct, using an age-specific schedule of births, a fecundity table for a population (Section 10.6). These data can be used to determine the net reproductive rate of a population and, when combined with mortality rates from the life table, to project population growth into the future (Section 10.7). Specifically, these data can be used to calculate a population's finite multiplication rate, or lambda (λ). Students should become familiar with the relationship between lambda and r—the instantaneous rate of population increase (Section 10.7). A discussion of the conversion between lambda and r and of the equations using these parameters for population projection will reveal why populations are expected to grow exponentially when not limited by competition or other factors.

The models of population growth discussed in this chapter assume that birth and death rates are constant. However, stochastic (random) changes in birth and death rates and random variations in the environment leading to changes in these rates can influence population dynamics. Models have been developed to allow for this variation (Section 10.8). Sections 10.9 and 10.10 concern extinction—when deaths exceed births and r is negative. Rarely does extinction occur simultaneously over a species range; rather, it begins as local extinctions that proceed to a point at which a population becomes fragmented, isolated, and small (Section 10.10). At this point, each local subpopulation may encounter the problems of demographic and environmental stochasticity and restricted gene flow and genetic drift with consequent loss of fitness. Some species may be more extinction-prone than others, but the only known cause of the extinction of species in historical times is habitat alteration or destruction by humans.

Discussion Topics

1. Exponential growth can easily be visualized graphically, but it is often better to give students a different perspective to reinforce exactly what this type of growth entails. One way to do this is to mentally and/or visually create "bacteria world." Explain that a test tube represents bacteria world, with no inhabitants. You, as ruler of the universe, will be adding one bacterium to this world to begin its population. This bacterium (and all subsequent bacteria) will reproduce every minute (thus, at time 0 there is 1 individual, at 1 minute 2 individuals, at 2 minutes 4 individuals, etc.). Further explain that at 60 minutes the world will be full (it has reached carrying capacity). At this point it is instructive to ask students when they think this world would be half full. Any number of stories can be developed, but ultimately indicate that around 55 minutes a few bacteria are noticing that the world is getting crowded and over the next few minutes the clever bacterial engineers create 3 new worlds to alleviate the problem. The inhabitants of bacteria world rejoice—of course, at 60 minutes the original world fills, at 61 minutes world 2 is full, and at 62 minutes worlds 3 and 4 are filled.

2. Compare the mortality, survivorship, natality, and fecundity of a plant population with an animal population. Where do the differences lie?

3. Ask students to apply the concept of exponential population growth to humans. Are humans capable of exponential growth? Is the human population now growing exponentially? Do populations continue to always grow exponentially? Will our explosive population growth mean the extinction of most wild species?

4. What are some practical applications of life tables and fecundity tables in wildlife management? Have students think about how age-specific birth and death data might be useful in managing rare or endangered species.

CHAPTER 11 Intraspecific Population Regulation

Commentary

The idea that populations cannot grow forever, that they will always be limited at some point by the amount of resources in the environment, is one of the most important concepts in ecology (Section 11.1). This principle is described mathematically by the carrying capacity, or K, which is incorporated in the logistic model of population growth (see Quantifying Ecology 11.1)—an extension of the exponential growth model (Chapter 10). Students should see K as a theoretical construct that describes a population size, to which a given population tends to return, although fluctuations around it may be significant. The concept of carrying capacity has implications not only for our basic ecological understanding of population growth but also for our understanding of the process of evolution and the problem of human impacts on the Earth's resources (see Ecological Issues). That resources are limited, which produces competition for these resources, is one of the basic components of Charles Darwin's theory of evolution by natural selection. Furthermore, a lack of understanding of the concept of carrying capacity, it could be argued, is one major reason that the growth of the human population on Earth will continue to be one of the biggest problems that humans face in the near future.

An important concept in this chapter is that populations are regulated—that is, pushed toward an equilibrium size—by density-dependent processes (Section 11.2). As a population changes size, rates of birth and death change, thereby influencing the rate of subsequent population growth. The most commonly studied form of density-dependent population regulation results from increasing intraspecific competition as densities increase and per capita resource levels decline (Sections 11.3 and 11.4). When population densities increase, both individual growth and survival can decline (Section 11.5). This may lead to the process of self-thinning, which occurs as population densities progressively decline as a result of density-dependent regulation and more resources are made available to surviving persons, allowing them to increase their growth.

Students should understand that competition can occur through many different mechanisms (also see Chapter 13) and that the impact of competition on a population can occur at many different life stages (Section 11.6). The impact of intraspecific competition on per capita growth can be easily experienced by students using laboratory experiments in which a plant or animal species is maintained at a range of densities. Some animals also experience stressful conditions when population densities are too high, which leads to behavioral or physiological responses that further regulate population growth (Section 11.7).

Another potential response to increased population density is an increase in the rate of dispersal of individuals away from the population (Section 11.8). This section, oriented from an animal perspective, discusses the various reasons why dispersal might be beneficial. A valuable idea related to dispersal that will be explored in Chapter 12 is that of sources and sinks, as in habitats or patches of habitat in which reproduction exceeds or does not exceed mortality. This concept will be important when students are attempting to understand the effects of space on populations and interspecific interactions.

Sections 11.9 through 11.11 are also oriented from an animal perspective and discuss numerous ways that social behavior can influence and respond to changes in population density. There is some evidence that social behavior can contribute to population regulation in a density-dependent manner (Section 11.9). For example, social dominance can provide density-dependent population regulation in large mammals such as wolves that live in groups (Section 11.9). Students should be able to easily relate to the concepts of home ranges and territoriality (Section 11.10) when familiar organisms, such as mammals and birds, are used as examples. In Section 11.11, students have a chance to apply to plants some of the concepts they have just learned in the context of animal behavior.

This chapter focuses on density-dependent forces that influence populations. Indeed, only density-dependent mechanisms can truly regulate populations, since regulation necessarily involves feedback. However, students should be aware that factors independent of population density can have significant effects on birth rates and death rates, sometimes strongly limiting population growth (Section 11.12).

Discussion Topics

1. Do most populations reach a level at which intrinsic population regulatory mechanisms intervene, or are populations usually held at some lower level by extrinsic mechanisms?
2. Assume that tree cavities are very limited in a given area. Would a local population of secondary cavity-nesting birds (those that cannot excavate their own nesting places) be limited by density-dependent intraspecific competition or density-independent environmental deficiency by the lack of cavities? What if you provided more nesting sites by erecting suitable nest boxes?
3. In our very early history, humans were subject to the same regulatory mechanisms that affect other animal populations. Have humans completely escaped natural regulatory mechanisms? What problems do we face trying to impose our own cultural regulatory mechanisms?
4. Do humans exhibit the behavioral traits of social dominance and territoriality? Give examples at the individual, group, regional, and national levels. Are nationalism and the wars over national boundaries forms of territoriality?
5. Are humans exceeding the carrying capacity of Earth? What is human carrying capacity? What implications may our explosive population growth have for populations of other species?
6. What difficulties might one encounter as a scientist attempting to detect density-dependence in natural populations? Carrying capacity, K, in most population work refers to the average upper limit that a population experiences over time. But carrying capacity has other shades of meaning and is used in different contexts in population management. Consult R. F. Dasmann, 1964 (or later editions), *Wildlife Biology,* New York, NY: Wiley; Shaw (1985); and J. Macnab, 1985, "Carrying capacity and related shibboleths," *Wildl. Soc. Bull.* 11:397–401. Then discuss the various ways in which the term *carrying capacity* is and has been used. Is a different interpretation useful in different situations?

CHAPTER 12 Metapopulations

Commentary

Chapters 9 through 11 presented the idea of a population as a spatially contiguous unit that shares the same environment. Over the geographic distribution of a species, however, the environment is usually not uniformly favorable but rather consists of a mosaic of differentially suitable patches. The idea of a metapopulation—a group of spatially discrete subpopulations—has grown out of this understanding of the landscape and has given us a different view of populations and has enhanced our understanding of (among other things) wildlife management.

Ilkka Hanski has provided one definition of a metapopulation, which includes an understanding that even the largest subpopulations face a risk of extinction, that habitat patches are not too isolated, and that the local population dynamics are not synchronized (Section 12.1). A broader definition is also in use that suggests a metapopulation basically consists of a large core population that function as the main source of emigrants to smaller satellite populations.

Metapopulations exist when there is a dynamic balance between extinctions of local populations (subpopulations) and recolonization of habitat patches (Section 12.2). Metapopulation growth is analogous to population growth, as outlined in Chapter 10, where rates of colonization and extinction (metapopulation dynamics) are similar to birth and death rates (see also Quantifying Ecology 12.1). It should be emphasized that in this simple form of metapopulation dynamics, all habitat patches are considered equal, which is usually not the case in nature. Patch quality, size, and location can be very important (Section 12.3; see also Ecological Issues). For example, larger patches generally have more environmental heterogeneity than smaller ones, which increases the likelihood that a local population can persist (Section 12.4). This is especially true when environmental conditions change such that smaller patches become unfavorable for a species.

Some of the work on metapopulations has borrowed ideas from island biogeography theory (see also Section 19.4). For example, some "mainland" patches can function as primary emigrant sources for smaller "island" patches (sinks), greatly reducing the risk of local extinctions (Section 12.5). The greater the number of immigrants to a patch, the less likely a population will experience local extinction. This rescue effect occurs when there is high dispersal from source populations in a high-quality habitat to sink populations in poorer habitat, allowing local populations to persist in a habitat with suboptimum conditions.

Another factor that allows the persistence of a metapopulation is asynchronous dynamics of the local populations (Section 12.6). This is a good ecological example of "putting all your eggs in one basket," as the chance of extinction increases when local population dynamics are correlated. The idea that the physical environment influences the rates of extinction and colonization of a habitat within a metapopulation has been emphasized so far in this chapter. Species characteristics must also be considered when understanding metapopulations, especially the ability to disperse (Section 12.7). A review of life history characteristics (e.g., *r*- and *K*-selected species; see Chapter 8), which include rates of dispersal and the factors influencing those rates, will emphasize to students the connections of several ecological concepts.

In Chapter 1 we examined how the science of ecology can be viewed as a hierarchy (individuals to landscapes). The idea of a population can also be viewed in a similar manner and gives us a more thorough definition of a population than that provided in Chapters 9 through 11 (Section 12.8). Four levels of spatial aggregation provide a useful framework for defining the role of a population in various ecological processes: the local population (demography), the metapopulation (movement), the subspecies (evolution), and the large-scale species distribution (geography). With this framework in mind, ecologists can gain a better understanding of the processes driving population dynamics.

Discussion Topics

1. In many places, especially in urban and agricultural areas, it should be obvious to students that distinct habitat patches occur across the landscape (e.g., patches of forest in agricultural fields). Ask students to discuss how this human-created environment has influenced populations and what it might mean for the local (or total) extinction of some species.
2. How might the metapopulation concept (especially the rescue effect and source and sink populations) give us a better understanding of wildlife management? Do wildlife managers in your area take advantage of this knowledge? How could the introduction of game animals be improved using metapopulation ideas?

3. How could the design of nature reserves (or parks) be improved using metapopulation ecology concepts?

CHAPTER 13 Interspecific Competition

Commentary

It should be impressed on students that competition is one of the most fundamental processes in ecology and evolution. It is crucial to Darwin's theory of evolution by natural selection and is thought to be one of the driving forces behind the ecology and evolution of many species. Despite, or perhaps because of its importance, competition has provided much difficulty and controversy within the field of ecology.

In this chapter, the focus is on interspecific competition, or competition among two or more species (Section 13.1). When interspecific competition was first mathematically formulated by Alfred Lotka and Vittora Volterra, it became clear that there are essentially four possible outcomes of competition between two species (Section 13.2; see also Quantifying Ecology 13.1), three of which involve one species driving the other to extinction. The graphical depiction of this mathematical approach to competition may help students see the reasons for these outcomes and the differences between species that contribute to competitive superiority. A variety of laboratory experiments (Section 13.3) have provided examples of competitive exclusion, suggesting a general concept referred to as the "competitive exclusion principle" (Section 13.4). While very simplistic, this concept has been useful as a null model suggesting what should happen in the absence of complicating factors. One such complicating factor is that many physical characteristics of the environment besides the level of the limiting resource can influence the competitive ability of species (Section 13.5; see also Field Studies). Thus, changes in the physical conditions of a community over time can change the relative competitive abilities of the different species in a community (Section 13.6).

An oversimplification of interspecific competition that often is not true is that species are only competing for one resource (Section 13.7). In fact, species are often competing for multiple resources, and there are trade-offs with respect to competitive ability for one resource versus another. These trade-offs can lead to coexistence of species in the same community since the species that is best at competing for one resource is not the species that is best at competing for another resource. Competition for one resource also frequently influences access to other resources (Section 13.7). Another factor that must be taken into account in competition studies is that competitive abilities of different species change along environmental gradients over space (Section 13.8; see also Quantifying Ecology 13.2).

Often, the niche that a species occupies is actually a subset of the niche that it is physically capable of occupying because of the pressure of competition from other species (Section 13.9). Coexistence of species is further facilitated by niche partitioning among species (Section 13.10), by which species use different resources at different times and places, thereby avoiding competition. When organisms are able to reduce or avoid competition, their fitness generally increases (Section 13.11). One of the major difficulties in studying competition is that it can often be difficult to detect even when it has a strong history of importance in a particular community because it involves a variety of environmental factors that vary spatially and temporally (Section 13.12).

Discussion Topics

1. In light of Schoener's classification of competition into six different types, can you see any potential problems or limitations with the Lotka–Volterra models of competition?

2. Based on what we have learned about natural selection, why do you think competition was such an essential part of Darwin's original theory of natural selection?
3. What types of data are needed to determine if competition is occurring between two species (e.g., degree of intraspecific competition, measurement of resource levels)?
4. How could disturbance affect the outcome between two or more competing species?

CHAPTER 14 Predation

Commentary

Predation, in all its many forms (Section 14.1), can have an important impact on community structure. It can also serve as a major agent of natural selection that influences the evolution of both predator and prey. Most students will have a narrow view of predation and will see it as including only complete consumption of one animal by another (carnivory). However, a broad definition of predation includes less obvious forms, such as parasitoidism, parasitism, and herbivory. Ecologists now generally reserve the term predator (true predator) for species that basically kill their prey upon capture.

As with competition, predation was first mathematically formulated by Alfred Lotka and Vittora Volterra (Section 14.2). Using a similar graphical approach to that used for competition in Chapter 13, students can see how the Lotka–Volterra models predict the possible outcomes of predation. Specifically, they show how predator and prey can regulate each other's population sizes (Section 14.3). Students should realize that while these models are overly simplistic representations of nature they do serve to stimulate more careful research into the dynamics of predator–prey interactions. One of the more important aspects of realism that can be added to these models is the degree to which predators consume more prey and increase their growth rate in response to an increase in prey population size (Sections 14.4 and 14.5). Depending on the nature of these "functional and numerical responses," the predictions of models for the outcome of predator–prey interactions can vary greatly. This material presents an opportunity to impress on students the strong impact that the assumptions of a model can have on its predictions.

One of the areas of research in predator–prey relationships is the study of optimal foraging by predators (Sections 14.6–14.8; see also Quantifying Ecology 14.1). This research has spawned a large body of theory (e.g., marginal value theorem, Section 14.7) and many field studies attempting to determine the strategies that predators employ when searching for prey. This material provides another opportunity for students to study the concept of trade-offs, since much of optimal foraging theory is an exploration of the trade-offs between possible strategies. For example, extensive movement through a habitat during the daytime may be best for finding prey but may carry a risk of being preyed upon.

Another area of predator–prey research that continues to flourish today is the investigation of possible coevolution between predator and prey (Section 14.9). Coevolution is potentially an important process in many interspecific interactions; this predator–prey material provides an opportunity for students to become familiar with the general concepts of coevolution. In general, the process involves evolution of predator evasion or defense by prey species (Section 14.10; see also Field Studies) followed by the evolution in the predator of increased ability to attack the prey (Section 14.11). This process of predator–prey coevolution has led to the appearance of a wide variety of strategies for success in both predator and prey species.

Although students probably think of predation as the consumption of one animal by another, they should realize that herbivory is also a form of predation (Section 14.12). The consumption of plant tissue by insects is one of the most studied interactions in ecology and may be important in most communities. The study of herbivory has been complicated by the fact that plant reactions to being eaten are often not straightforward. For example, many plants can tolerate high levels of tissue loss to herbivores before suffering a reduction in reproductive success. Other plants have evolved complicated defenses against herbivores, such as chemical compounds that are produced by the plant immediately in response to herbivory (Section 14.13).

The concept of a food chain—a graphical depiction of the feeding relationships among different species in a community—will likely be familiar to most students (although a review of the idea is usually welcome; see Section 16.4). A fascinating phenomenon emerges from examination of food chains involving plants, herbivores, and the predators of the herbivores (Section 14.14). In these multitrophic interactions, the top predator not only affects its prey (the herbivore), but it can also influence the population dynamics and evolution of the plant indirectly through its influence on the herbivore. In this and many other ways (for example, see Section 14.15 for nonlethal effects on prey), predation has been shown to have a significant impact on prey populations and community structure, both through laboratory and field investigations.

Discussion Topics

1. Ask students to think about the possible implications of different types of functional responses of predators to their prey. For example, what are the implications of functional response for the control of an herbivore pest in a crop by a natural enemy of the herbivore, such as a parasitoid? What types of functional response will be conducive to such control?
2. Discuss the concept of trade-offs in the context of the optimal foraging theory. Have students think about different strategies that are possible for a predator to find prey and the advantages and disadvantages of each strategy.
3. The Lotka–Volterra model and some research suggest that predator and prey populations oscillate through time. In fact, predation is a classic explanation for why populations fluctuate. However, some research has shown that when a predator is removed from an area, the prey population continues to oscillate. What are some possible reasons for this observation?
4. Why do we need to add pesticides to most agricultural fields when many plants are capable of producing their own chemical defenses? Why wouldn't agricultural crops have these defenses, even if the original stock does (e.g., How much energy, which could be used for reproduction, does it take to produce chemicals?)?

CHAPTER 15 Parasitism and Mutualism

Commentary

At first glance, mutualism and parasitism may seem to be very different interactions—one is antagonistic and the other is not. The reason, however, that they are discussed in the same chapter is that the line between mutualism and parasitism is often very fine. In fact, some interactions can change between mutualism and parasitism in response to a change in environmental conditions, and many mutualisms are thought to have evolved from interactions that were originally parasitic. Thus, discussing them together may allow students to obtain a more realistic and dynamic view of these fascinating interspecific interactions.

One notable feature of parasitic interactions (and not, incidentally, many mutualisms) is that individuals of one species take resources from individuals of other species (Section 15.1). In the case of parasitism, the parasite takes resources from its host. These resources vary widely, as hosts provide a diverse habitat for parasites (Section 15.2). For example, parasites live on the skin, underneath the skin, in the bloodstream, in the brain, in nasal tracts, and in most other parts of animal bodies.

To understand any interspecific interaction we must recognize the challenges that are faced by the participants and the strategies that they have evolved in order to deal with those challenges. One of the major challenges to a parasite is the necessity of finding new hosts once the original host is dead (Section 15.2). Parasites have evolved a plethora of strategies for insuring transmission between hosts. For example, many parasites are transmitted directly from host to host, using only air, soil, or water as a medium for movement (Section 15.3). Other parasites have evolved elaborate means of transporting from host to host by using an intermediate vector organism (Section 15.4). In fact, some parasite life cycles are extremely complex, requiring multiple intermediate hosts to come to completion (Section 15.5).

Not only have parasites evolved elaborate mechanisms to more efficiently infect and parasitize their hosts, but hosts also have many different strategies for defense against parasites (Section 15.6). For example, plants respond to bacterial and fungal invasion of roots by forming cysts and scabs—cutting off contact between the parasite and healthy plant tissue. Despite the wide variety of defense mechanisms employed by hosts of parasites, their survival and reproduction is often negatively impacted by parasites (Section 15.7). As a result of the never-ending cycle of adaptation of hosts to parasites and of parasites to hosts, many host–parasite interactions coevolve to a point at which neither participant goes extinct. In some specific cases, parasites may even function as regulatory agents of the host population size (Section 15.8; see also Ecological Issues).

As mentioned above, one connection between mutualism and parasitism is that one can evolve from the other (Section 15.9). For example, if a host genotype arose that was able to exploit a parasite or derive a by-product benefit from the presence of the parasite then the interaction could quickly become beneficial to both species—a mutualism. Many ecologists have devoted their careers to understanding some aspect of how these relationships evolve and what factors affect the transition back and forth between mutualism and parasitism.

Interactions that we call mutualisms are very diverse (Section 15.10; see also Field Studies) but many of them involve the exchange of essential resources such as nutrients (Section 15.11). Students may notice that more often than not one of the partners in a mutualism is a photosynthesizer—a plant or an alga that trades the products of photosynthesis to another species for some other essential resource. For example, most plants form mutualisms with mycorrhizal fungi. The plant provides carbohydrates to the fungus and, in turn, the fungus provides the plant with increased access to soil nutrients such as nitrogen or phosphorus. Students can easily observe these fungi in the laboratory—the fungi form swollen coatings on the root tips of, for example, most conifer plants. These can be observed by rinsing the soil from the root system of a field-collected pine seedling. Another good example of a mutualistic relationship between an animal and a photosynthesizer is seen in coral reefs. Students will be familiar with coral reefs but they may not know about the vital mutualism that produces them.

Students should understand that the types of benefits exchanged between mutualisms are diverse—not all mutualisms involve the simple exchange of essential resources. For example, a number of mutualisms exist in which a species provides defense to a plant against herbivores (Section 15.12) in exchange for the products of photosynthesis. Many ants participate in such defensive mutualisms with plants. Furthermore, many mutualisms are not symbiotic. They do not involve one species living intimately on or inside the other. For example, many insects and other animals engage in a pollination mutualism with plants (Section 15.13) in which the plant provides, as usual, photosynthetic products, and the pollinator moves pollen from one plant to another. Many plants also depend on mobile animals to disperse their seeds (Section 15.14).

It is not difficult to see how such interactions (and mutualisms in general) can have broad effects on population dynamics and community structure (Section 15.15; see also Quantifying Ecology 15.1). Most species are involved in some type of mutualism, and thus most communities are intimately linked by these ubiquitous interactions.

Discussion Topics

1. Ask students to think about the difference between parasites and mutualists. What kinds of parasitism and mutualism are most alike? By what mechanisms could a mutualism change during the course of a year into a parasitism and vice versa?
2. Discuss possible experiments or field observations that you could design to detect possible impacts of parasitism and mutualism on community structure.
3. How common is it for a parasite to kill its host? It would seem that a parasite killing its host would be an evolutionary dead end. Under what circumstances would this strategy be beneficial to the parasite?
4. Most students will be familiar with coral reefs, but they will probably not realize that these structures are mostly the product of a mutualistic interaction. An interesting discussion can revolve around the bleaching of corals and the potential causes and implications of this phenomenon.

CHAPTER 16 Community Structure

Commentary

The concept of a community is intuitive but becomes more complex as it is examined more closely. This complexity should not be ignored as students are introduced to the concept of a community. For example, students should think about how it may be difficult to distinguish the transition between one community and another through time and space.

Among the various characteristics that we can use to define communities, the number (richness) and relative abundances of the species that are present may be most important (Section 16.1). In certain communities, the most abundant species may be very influential on the other species in the community, in which case they are referred to as dominants (Section 16.2). On the other hand, the concept of dominance is not as simple as this. The relative abundances of species in a community (evenness), combined with the number of species in that community, determine what ecologists refer to as the *diversity* of a community (Section 16.1). Because of the popularity of the term *biodiversity,* it is important to emphasize to students what diversity means to scientists. Characteristics of communities, such as diversity, contribute to what ecologists call a community's *structure.*

Dominance or relative abundance, however, is only one measure of a species contribution to a community. In some cases, less abundant organisms can play a crucial role in community dynamics. These keystone species, through their activities (e.g., habitat modification), affect a community disproportionately to their abundance (Section 16.3).

One popular method that ecologists use to depict and model the interactions in a community is the food web diagram (Section 16.4), which focuses on trophic interactions among species. The interspecific interactions covered in previous chapters all deal with acquisition of food resources. Using trophic levels to group species provides one way to simplify the study of communities. Another approach is to subdivide trophic levels into guilds, which are species that use a common resource in a similar way (Section 16.5).

It is important to note that not only do communities have biological structure, but they are also characterized by having physical structure (Section 16.6). An example to which students should relate easily is the structure that is created by different plant growth forms such as shrubs and trees on land and kelp or seagrasses in the ocean. Many communities, such as forests, have vertical physical structure, which, in turn, contributes to the biological structure of the community since different species live in different vertical zones. The vertical structure in the open portions of most lakes and oceans is largely determined by light penetration.

One of the complexities of the community concept is that within a community the species composition may change over space (Section 16.7). These patterns of zonation can make it difficult to determine the boundaries of a community (Section 16.8). Ecologists have met with varying success using a wide variety of methods in an attempt to define these boundaries (see Quantifying Ecology 16.1). One complicating factor in defining a community is that many attributes of communities are different, depending on the scale at which they are examined.

Students should find the topic of interspecific interactions to be complex and fascinating. There is a rich history in ecology of attempts to understand the rules that govern these interactions, and it should be impressed on students that this research continues to thrive today. A classic example of this rich history and its legacy is the debate about whether communities are linked as integrated units (the organismal concept of communities) or whether species are individualistic in their distributions (the individualistic or continuum concept) (Section 16.9).

Discussion Topics

1. Ask students to express their understanding of a community, and then ask them to think about and discuss what problems there might be with this concept. What observations about nature suggest that it is difficult to define a community?
2. After introducing the debate about whether species are distributed independently or whether they are parts of integrated communities (Section 16.9), ask students to propose observations or experiments that might distinguish between these hypotheses.
3. Ask students whether they know of any keystone species in their area (the beaver is a good example). What are the implications for a community if the population of this species declines or goes extinct? Are there examples in which humans have caused the decline of keystone species, leading to major community changes?
4. If students were asked to determine the impact of a pollutant on a community, what differences might they see if they measured this impact using species richness, functional groups, or a diversity index?

CHAPTER 17 Factors Influencing the Structure of Communities

Commentary

This chapter attempts to synthesize material from previous chapters about adaptations of organisms to their environment (Chapters 6–8) and interspecific interactions (Chapters 13–15) to explore the most important processes that control community structure. The first principle behind community structure is that species differ in their ability to utilize various environmental conditions (as in their fundamental niche), and these environmental conditions change over space and time. Thus, the distribution of species' fundamental niches over the landscape serves as a primary constraint on community structure (Section 17.1; see also Field Studies). This view serves as a starting point for understanding the composition of communities. Other processes, such as interspecific interactions, that may influence community structure will change communities with respect to the baseline structure predicated by the fundamental niches of the species themselves.

As mentioned in previous chapters, students should be aware that it can be very difficult to detect the importance of a given factor, such as interspecific interactions, for community structure. One reason that the importance of interspecific interactions may be difficult to determine is that these interactions are often diffuse, involving many species at a time (Section 17.2; see also Quantifying Ecology 17.1). Furthermore, many important interactions in communities are indirect, whereby they are mediated by an intermediate species (Section 17.3). One species affects a second species directly, the second species affects a third directly, and, thus, the first species affects the third species indirectly. Such indirect effects are quite common in natural communities, can be difficult to detect, and may contribute to the difficulty of understanding the impact of interspecific interactions on community structure. Food webs provide a means of analyzing communities and detecting the potential importance of both direct and indirect interactions among species (Sections 17.3 and 17.4; see also Quantifying Ecology 17.1). Indeed, food web analyses have led to some of the most stimulating ideas in ecology, such as the "world is green" hypothesis (Hairston, Smith, and Slobodkin) and whether all species are necessary for a community to function properly.

As mentioned above, the fundamental niches of species vary over space. Furthermore, as discussed in previous chapters, interspecific interactions change over space. For example, the outcome of competition between two species may be different in two different environments. Changes in the abilities of species to tolerate environmental conditions, combined with changes in the outcomes of interspecific interactions such as competition, provide powerful predictions about how community structure changes along environmental gradients (Section 17.5). These ideas have been applied successfully to the analysis of plant community structure. For example, in salt marsh plant communities, species-relative abundances seem to be determined to some extent by a trade-off between competitive ability and the ability to tolerate the stresses of salinity and low oxygen inherent to parts of the marsh habitat.

This chapter emphasizes that environmental conditions are not homogeneous within a community. This environmental heterogeneity, especially at small scales, can have a great influence on community diversity (Section 17.6). For example, gaps can form in a forest when a tree dies, and the resulting increased light to the forest floor allows shade-intolerant species to flourish. Another well-studied example of the influence of environmental heterogeneity on diversity is the link between vegetation structure and bird species diversity.

In general, there is a positive relationship between nutrient availability and factors such as plant growth and density (see Chapter 6). Interestingly, however, many studies have shown a negative relationship between nutrient availability and the diversity of plants in communities (Section 17.7). Huston suggests that higher diversity may result from reduced competitive displacement when nutrient availability is low. At higher nutrient availability, species that could dominate cannot realize their potential growth rates and thus are unable to displace less competitive species. Although some studies have corroborated Huston's hypothesis, much work needs to be done. Regardless, the inverse relationship between nutrient availability and diversity has important implications for human application of fertilizers to communities.

Discussion Topics

1. What kinds of studies are needed in ecology to understand how community structure is controlled in general?
2. This chapter makes an attempt to formulate general principles about factors controlling community structure. Why is it difficult to formulate principles in ecology?
3. Would species diversity be high or low in nutrient-rich environments such as eutrophic lakes? What are the implications of applying fertilizers to lawns? Can ecological research on nutrient availability provide any insight into human applications of fertilizer on lawns or agricultural systems? If high nutrient availability often leads to lower community diversity, why are herbicides still needed on agricultural fields?

4. Ask students to comment on the rivet versus redundancy models of species diversity. Do they think that these two extreme views are the only possible answers to the importance of diversity in communities? Even if there is species redundancy in a system, are there other reasons to protect species?

CHAPTER 18 Community Dynamics

Commentary

In the previous chapter, the processes that interact to influence community structure were emphasized. An observation that has been made throughout the history of ecology is that communities also change with time (Section 18.1; see also Ecological Issues). This temporal change in community structure is called "succession" and it seems to be common to most habitats and types of organisms. Succession may occur by a variety of mechanisms. For example, we can distinguish between primary succession, which occurs on a previously unoccupied site (Section 18.2), and secondary succession, which occurs in response to disturbance of an already present community (Section 18.3).

The study of succession (mostly in plant communities) has been an integral part of ecological research for over a century, and several hypotheses have been developed for explaining the processes that drive this phenomenon (Section 18.4). Clements proposed the *monoclimax hypothesis* that suggests succession is a gradual and progressive development of a plant community that leads to an ultimate or climax stage (see also Section 16.9). In the *initial floristic composition hypothesis,* the first colonizers inhibit establishment of other species. When they die, other species can become established. As opposed to Clements' idea, the *initial floristic composition hypothesis* is individualistic and depends on which species first colonize the site and in what order. Connell and Slayter (1977) proposed three models of succession. In their *facilitation model,* early colonizers modify the environment such that later arriving species can grow. The *inhibition model* suggests that the first species to arrive make a site less suitable for other species. The initial species only relinquish a site when they are damaged or die. In the *tolerance model,* later successional species are not influenced by early arrivers and can invade a newly opened area because they tolerate lower levels of resources. The search for a general model of plant succession continues today and is focused on how a species' adaptations and life history traits influence species interactions under changing environmental conditions.

Although there is no consensus on the proposed explanations for succession, as outlined above, some general principles have emerged that may help us understand the influences of succession on community structure in general (Section 18.5). For example, it seems that in all instances of plant succession, colonization by new plant species causes changes in the physical environment (autogenic environmental change) that have subsequent effects on the extinction and colonization by other species. These patterns of colonization and extinction drive patterns of succession, influencing not only species dominance but also species diversity over time (Section 18.6). Often, changes in plant communities through succession also drive corresponding successional changes in the heterotrophic component of communities (Section 18.7) that depend on the physical and biological structure of plant communities as a habitat.

This chapter mostly focuses on shifts in community structure that are caused by autogenic changes in the environment. However, abiotic environmental (allogenic) change over different time scales can also influence succession (Section 18.8). As such, the changes observed in communities over the course of succession are much different than the changes observed in communities over geologic time (Section 18.9). As introduced in Chapter 16, the same factors that vary over space and thereby influence community structure also vary over time, causing the temporal variation in community structure we refer to as succession.

Recall from Chapter 16 that two different views of the community have been proposed—Clements' organismal and Gleason's individualistic concept. These opposing views represent opposite ends of a thought continuum and likely the answer lies somewhere between them, especially since Gleason's view represents more of a population concept whereas the organismal view is a spatial concept (Section 18.10). These two ideas are different yet consistent. Each species has a continuous response along an environmental gradient, while the spatial distribution of environmental variables determines the composition of a community.

Discussion Topics

1. Ask students if there are good examples of primary and secondary succession that they are aware of or have seen. What factor(s) initiated the succession? What might be the end result (i.e., what might the community look like in a few years or decades)?
2. If a forest is cleared and an invasive plant species is among the initial colonizers, how might this affect the successional trajectory? If the invasive species becomes dominant, would they expect the forest to look similar to an adjacent forest that wasn't logged? How might any changes brought about by the invasive species influence the succession of heterotrophic species?
3. How has fire suppression in forests or prairies affected succession in these ecosystems?

CHAPTER 19 Landscape Ecology

Commentary

More and more in recent decades, ecologists have come to recognize the importance of processes happening at large spatial scales. This recognition has led to the development of a new subfield within ecology, landscape ecology, which is the study of the causes and ecological consequences of spatial patterns on the landscape scale. For the same reasons that landscape ecology did not develop until recently, students may find the concepts of landscape ecology less intuitive initially than those of, for example, community ecology.

The fundamental units of the landscape mosaic are patches—relatively homogeneous areas that differ from their surroundings and vary in size, shape, and degree of isolation from one another (Section 19.1). Both human and natural processes create these patches, and their characteristics may strongly affect the ecology and evolution of the species inhabiting them. Among the most important features of patches are the transition zones at their edges or borders (Section 19.2). These transition zones mark abrupt or gradual changes in physical or biological characteristics, and some groups of species are much more adapted to these transition zones than others. This is one reason that changes in patch size have such a strong impact on community structure (Section 19.3)—as patches become smaller, the ratio of edge to interior habitat greatly increases, favoring species that are adapted to edge habitats. Furthermore, large patches support a larger number of species simply because they typically encompass a larger variety of habitat types. The positive relationship between patch area and patch diversity is one of the most consistent observations in landscape ecology. Students should think about the critical link between this observation and the consistent fragmenting effect that human activities have on our landscape.

Some of the key elements of landscape ecology are not new. For example, a naturalist in the 18th century noted that larger islands support larger numbers of species than smaller islands. This simple but consistent observation led to the development of one of the most widely cited and utilized theories in ecology—the theory of island biogeography, which was first published by R. MacArthur and E. O. Wilson in 1963 (Section 19.4). The theory holds that the number of species on an island is a simple function of the balance between extinction of species on the island and immigration of new species from a nearby mainland. This theory is relevant to landscape ecology because any habitat patch that is relatively isolated from other patches by inhospitable terrain can be considered an island. Thus, the theory of island biogeography has been applied extensively to terrestrial "islands" or patches of habitat in a larger landscape. A unique dimension to this framework that has been added for terrestrial habitats is the idea of corridors—narrow strips of habitat that link one patch to another (Section 19.5; see also Field Studies). This concept is often quite important in human-dominated landscapes as we fragment a habitat, leaving only patches connected by narrow strips such as culverts, roadsides, field borders, and river edges. Metapopulation theory, which is a rich body of ecological theory, has developed by way of integrating some of the ideas from island biogeography with additional concepts from landscape ecology (Section 19.6). Metapopulation theory focuses on one or a small number of species, recognizing that their persistence at a landscape scale is a function of their population dynamics and extinction in individual patches and their dispersal among those patches (see also Field Studies).

Our discussion so far of landscape ecology has been relatively phenomenological. We evoked few specific mechanisms to explain the observed patterns of population dynamics and extinction within patches and dispersal among patches. One major variable that has a significant impact on the landscape-scale processes we have discussed so far is disturbance (Section 19.7). We define disturbance as a process, such as fire, wind, or flooding, that damages or disrupts community structure and function. Such disturbances can lead to extinction of some or all species within a habitat patch, can cause increased or decreased rates of dispersal away from a patch, or can change the size and shape of a patch. In these ways, disturbance can play a large role in generating the landscape-scale patterns and processes that we have discussed so far in this chapter. Students should recognize that disturbances, while having both natural (Section 19.8) and human causes (Section 19.9), are often essential features of many ecosystems to which many species are adapted. Disturbance combined with the varying responses of species to disturbance causes a shifting mosaic of habitat patches that never reaches a final stable state (Section 19.10). The challenge of landscape ecology is to predict and understand the trajectory of this shifting mosaic.

Discussion Topics

1. What human activities are causing a change in the degree to which habitats are fragmented into small patches? Based on what we have learned in this chapter, what are the consequences of these changes for the species in those habitats? Will all species respond the same?
2. Based on our knowledge of landscape ecology, should humans encourage fire or discourage it? What are the complicating factors behind this decision? How can we know what the "natural" frequency of fire is in a habitat?
3. It should be interesting at this point to revisit the question about design of nature reserves given the melding of metapopulation and landscape ecology ideas. For example, how does the edge effect alter our view of some current ways of designing parks or reserves? What are some advantages and disadvantages of incorporating corridors in these designs? Given the idea of a shifting mosaic of communities in a landscape, how much (or by what techniques) should reserves be "managed"?

CHAPTER 20 Ecosystem Energetics

Commentary

So far, we have discussed abiotic and biotic (physical and biological) factors as being separate, distinct entities. However, a more realistic view acknowledges that they are inseparable—organisms are not simply affected by their physical environment; rather, they also influence it and even create it. Recognition of the intrinsic link between the physical and the biological led to the formulation of the idea of the ecosystem. In this chapter, we explore ecosystems and their properties in greater depth, with a focus on productivity—the generation of biological matter through the harnessing of solar energy.

All ecological processes are a result of the transfer of energy, and ecosystems are no different than physical systems in that they are subject to the same physical laws (Section 20.1). We think of an ecosystem as the combination of the species in an area and their physical environment. We can further separate these species into two major groups based on their importance for ecosystem processes: the producers, or autotrophs, which use the energy of the sun for photosynthesis; and the consumers, or heterotrophs, which use the energy as their food source that the organic compounds produced by autotrophs. One of the main interests in the study of ecology at the scale of ecosystems is to understand the flow of energy from the sun, into the autotrophs, and subsequently through the many and varied paths of the food chain (Section 20.2). This is one area of ecology in which the science of physics is useful, since we expect the flow of energy to be governed by the laws of physics. Perhaps the most important and fundamental biological process on Earth is photosynthesis; it should be emphasized to students that without photosynthesis, life on Earth could not exist.

Perhaps the two most significant environmental variables in terrestrial ecosystems with respect to ecosystem properties and the distribution and abundance of species are temperature and moisture (Section 20.3). For energy flow through ecosystems, these two variables primarily affect rates of photosynthesis: where temperature and moisture availability are both relatively high, rates of photosynthesis are also high, leading to maximum primary production of plant biomass. This principle leads to the obvious global pattern of productivity in which we see that the most productive ecosystems are the warm, wet forests of the tropics. Obviously, temperature and moisture vary with time as well, producing seasonal, year-to-year, and longer time-scale patterns in primary production. In aquatic ecosystems light (and the depth to which light penetrates) and nutrients are the major limitations for primary production (Section 20.4).

How much energy is captured by different plant species, how they allocate that energy for their own growth (Section 20.5), and how efficiently that energy is passed on to consumers will determine many of the important characteristics of ecosystems. In addition, primary production varies across various temporal scales (e.g., seasonally, year-to-year) and with the age of individuals in an ecosystem (Section 20.6).

Because consumers are completely dependent on primary producers for energy, processes that limit primary production will also limit the amount of energy available for consumers (Section 20.7; see also Field Studies and Ecological Issues). Thus, the structure of food chains will always be heavily influenced by the rate of primary production. Another major influence, however, will be variation in the efficiency with which consumers transform the energy obtained by consuming primary producers (Section 20.8). Some types of consumer organisms are more efficient than others at transforming their food into their own biomass.

Ecologists have found it useful to group the species in food chains into trophic levels and to quantify the flow of energy from one trophic level to another (Sections 20.9 and 20.10). When we do this, we see that there are links between the detrital and grazing food chains. It may surprise students to learn that of the two main food chains—the grazing food chain and the detrital food chain—far more energy flows from primary producers to the detrital food chain than to the grazing food chain. Moreover, in terrestrial ecosystems, not only is a majority of the detrital food chain belowground but a large portion of grazing also occurs belowground. Of course, these patterns vary among ecosystems (Section 20.11). A universal pattern that ecologists have observed is that there is a net loss of energy with each successive trophic level (Section 20.12). Energy transfer from one trophic level to the next is not completely efficient, and thus, lower trophic levels will always contain a higher amount of energy than upper trophic levels. Pyramid diagrams are a useful means of depicting this pattern. This general pattern of energy distribution among trophic levels may contribute to many patterns that we see in the abundances and biomass of organisms at different trophic levels.

Discussion Topics

1. Do you agree that photosynthesis is the most important biological process on Earth? Why or why not? Can you think of any other biochemical processes that are equally or almost as important?
2. Why are species at lower trophic levels generally more abundant and diverse than species at higher trophic levels?
3. Given the ecological efficiency of the various organisms in a food chain, how many links or levels are theoretically possible? Why?
4. Could the introduction of an alien species to an ecosystem—for example, the introduction of earthworms to North American forests—have an influence on the food chains in that system?

CHAPTER 21   Decomposition and Nutrient Cycling

Commentary

In the previous chapter we discussed one of the primary processes of ecosystems—the flow of energy. In fact, the other most important ecosystem process, nutrient cycling (Section 21.1), is intimately linked with energy flow: one does not happen without the other. While life on Earth could not exist without photosynthesis (the process that turns CO_2 into the carbon building blocks of life) students should understand that another process—decomposition—is equally important. Decomposition completes the carbon cycle, releasing carbon dioxide and nutrients from dead plant and animal tissue. Being a composite of many processes, decomposition requires a variety of organisms to be completed (Section 21.2). For example, invertebrate animals are responsible for much of the primary fragmentation of organic matter into smaller pieces. Microbes (or microflora), bacteria, and fungi are responsible for the further chemical breakdown of organic matter and for the final stages of nutrient mineralization. Students may not be aware of the complex food web that is supported by decomposers, including the microbivores that eat bacteria and the fungi and predators that eat the microbivores. One common method by which scientists study the process of decomposition uses litterbags to follow the decay of dead plant tissues (litter) through time (Section 21.3; see also Quantifying Ecology 21.1).

A variety of factors influence the rate of decomposition of organic matter (Section 21.4; see also Field Studies). It is important for students to understand that the factors that govern decomposition rate vary strongly among ecosystems and lead to considerably different conditions for the species in those ecosystems. Furthermore, an understanding of how global climate change will affect ecosystems requires a thorough understanding of the carbon cycle and the factors that affect the rates of its primary processes, such as decomposition. Section 21.5 describes how plant tissues can vary in their quality as food sources for decomposer organisms, thus influencing the rate of decomposition of plant material. For example, nitrogen content varies in dead leaves; the higher the nitrogen levels, the higher the nutrient value for decomposers. Over relatively short time periods, decomposition transforms nutrients into a form that is usable by organisms. Microbial decomposers, while immobilizing some nutrients into their own tissues for growth, also release many nutrients into the soil in the process called "mineralization." Nutrients that have been thus mineralized are then available for uptake by plants and other photosynthesizing organisms. Often, changes in nutrient value during decomposition are examined concurrently with changes in mass and carbon content through using litterbag experiments (see Section 21.3). As decomposition continues over longer periods, there is often a reduction in soil organic matter quality (Section 21.6). This occurs because more easily broken down matter is decomposed first, leaving more recalcitrant material (both plant and animal) in the soil. A very important area of the soil is the rhizosphere, where plant roots function (Section 21.7). In addition to being a vital region for the plants themselves, roots contribute a large amount of secreted carbon to the rhizoshpere that greatly enhances microbial decomposition. This enhanced decomposition, along with microbivores feeding on bacteria and fungi, ultimately provides more nutrients for plants and constitutes the soil microbial loop.

Decomposition proceeds in much the same manner in aquatic systems as in terrestrial systems, with a few major differences (Section 21.8). Primarily, the processes of photosynthesis, immobilization, and decomposition are distributed much more broadly along a vertical or downstream gradient in aquatic systems.

Primary productivity, by affecting nutrient transfer and decomposition, is a major factor that influences nutrient cycling within ecosystems (Section 21.9). For example, nitrogen availability in soil or aquatic sediments directly influences primary productivity through its influence on photosynthesis and carbon uptake (see also Ecological Issues). More nitrogen equals more (and higher quality) material for decomposers. Thus, nutrient cycling is a vital feature of all ecosystems and represents a direct link between primary productivity and decomposition. This link varies among ecosystems, especially between terrestrial and aquatic ecosystems (Section 21.10). A comparison of nutrient cycling between terrestrial and aquatic systems serves to highlight some of the essential features of nutrient cycling and some of the most unique features of terrestrial and aquatic environments. One of the major differences is that the zones of decomposition and photosynthesis are physically separated in most parts of aquatic systems such that nutrients must be transported from where they become available to where they are needed by primary producers.

Although differences exist between ecosystems in their nutrient-cycling properties, it is interesting to note the degree to which adjacent ecosystems influence each other's nutrient cycling. For example, nutrient cycling in streams and rivers is known to be strongly affected by inputs from adjacent terrestrial habitats (Section 21.11), after which the internal cycling of those nutrients is largely determined by water flow. Thus, in stream ecosystems, a spiral rather than a cycle best describes the travel of nutrients. Similarly, coastal ecosystems are heavily influenced in their nutrient cycling by both oceanic and mainland ecosystems (Section 21.12). In fact, the entire identity of nutrient cycling in coastal estuaries is shaped by inputs from terrestrial and oceanic ecosystems. The transport of nutrients from deeper to surface ocean layers, as a result of surface currents, is especially important for understanding nutrient cycling and productivity in some coastal areas (Section 21.13).

Discussion Topics

1. Ask students to discuss why decomposition is an important process. What would happen if decomposition stopped completely?
2. Why is an understanding of decomposition necessary for predicting how the Earth's ecosystems will respond to elevated atmospheric CO_2? What ccosystem traits will tend to buffer them against elevated CO_2?
3. Why do we add fertilizers, especially nitrogen, to agricultural land? How does this activity affect adjacent ecosystems (e.g., rivers or forests)?

4. How are rivers and coastal ecosystems similar in their nutrient-cycling properties? How are they different?
5. Nutrient upwelling in certain coastal ecosystems has produced some of the most productive areas in the world. How might large-scale phenomena, such as El Niño or human-induced climate change, influence these ecosystems?

CHAPTER 22 Biogeochemical Cycles

Commentary

The previous chapter presented a general model for nutrient cycling in ecosystems. Here we concentrate on the cycling of specific nutrients, focusing on exchanges of nutrients among ecosystems. Hopefully, understanding these cycles will provide students with some perspective on how ecosystems function and on the origins and fates of essential resources on which humans and other species depend. Nutrient cycling is considered an ecosystem process because nutrients pass through both components of the ecosystem— the living and the non-living—during the course of their flow. Depending on whether the cycle is primarily gaseous or sedimentary, nutrients begin their cycling through ecosystems from the atmosphere or from the weathering of rocks (Sections 22.1 and 22.2) and are lost from ecosystems through many processes (Section 22.3). After nutrients have been incorporated into the biological portion of an ecosystem, it is possible for them to be recycled many times within that ecosystem when organisms, or parts of organisms, die. In addition to this internal cycling, often the output from one ecosystem equals the input into another (Section 22.4). Understanding larger-scale chemical cycling is especially important when the potential human interference in the cycle is great (e.g., carbon).

In the previous chapter, we introduced the idea that energy cycling and nutrient cycling are intimately tied together. This is most true for carbon because the basic currency of energy in organisms consists of carbon compounds (Section 22.5). Carbon is removed from its atmospheric pool through the process of photosynthesis and is returned to its pool through the process of respiration. Because the rate of photosynthesis in an ecosystem follows daily and seasonal cycles so does the carbon cycle (Section 22.6). A large fraction of the active global carbon pool is in the oceans, while the majority of Earth's carbon is buried in sedimentary rocks (Section 22.7). A thorough understanding of the carbon cycle will serve students well, since one of the most high profile and controversial environmental issues of the 21st century is global climate change in response to elevated atmospheric CO_2.

Nitrogen, unlike carbon, has its largest pool in the atmosphere (Section 22.8; see also Ecological Issues). As for carbon, however, the essential process in its cycle is the fixation of the gaseous form into a form that can be used by organisms. Called nitrogen fixation, this process is performed both by organisms and through physical chemical pathways. The nitrogen cycle is important to humans for a number of reasons. We depend heavily on nitrogen for agriculture because nitrogen is the most limiting element for plant growth in most ecosystems. In addition, as a result of agricultural practices and the use of motorized vehicles, nitrogen pollution is becoming a major problem in many parts of the world. An understanding of the essential components of the nitrogen cycle will allow us to effectively address these issues.

Unlike carbon and nitrogen, phosphorus is rare in the atmosphere (Section 22.9)—the main reservoir for phosphorus is in rocks and minerals. For this reason, after being washed from land into the sea, phosphorus is not easily cycled back into terrestrial and aquatic systems. This fact leads to a scarcity of phosphorus in many terrestrial and freshwater aquatic systems. Mycorrhizal fungi are essential for plants to acquire adequate phosphorus for growth and reproduction, especially in more basic soils. A comprehension of the phosphorus cycle is particularly important for understanding the causes of cultural eutrophication in lakes and streams.

The global cycle of sulfur, which includes a gaseous phase and a sedimentary phase (Section 22.10), is poorly understood (Section 22.11). One thing we do know, however, is that human inputs into the sulfur cycle are quite important, as opposed to the global oxygen cycle, on which humans generally seem to have little impact (Section 22.12). Because oxygen is so reactive, it is contained in many biologically important molecules and has an extremely complex cycle. In fact, the oxygen cycle illustrates well the idea of the last section of this chapter—the various biogeochemical cycles are not independent of each other (Section 22.13). For example, the oxygen atom is contained in CO_2, which is an essential part of the carbon cycle; NO_x, which is an important part of the nitrogen cycle; and SO_2, which is an important part of the sulfur cycle. Furthermore, because essential biological processes such as photosynthesis require many different nutrients, if one is in limited supply then the rates of cycling of the others can be affected.

Discussion Topics

1. Is there one biogeochemical cycle that is most important for all the others? What about for humans?
2. Where did the nutrients consumed yesterday by each student come from? Make a list of foods, their point of origin, and nutrient contents. How are these nutrients replaced?
3. How might human interference in a biogeochemical cycle differ depending on whether the cycle has primarily gaseous or sedimentary inputs?
4. Consider an agricultural ecosystem such as a cornfield. What are the major inputs to this system? What are the major outputs? For example, phosphorus is added to increase primary production. Where does most of the phosphorus go, especially after harvest?
5. How is ozone formed? Why is it an important compound? If ozone is a valuable substance, why are there unhealthy air alerts in some cities that often implicate ozone?

CHAPTER 23 Terrestrial Ecosystems

Commentary

One of the most important observations made by a number of scientists independently was that similar vegetation structure seems to result from similar climatic conditions. In fact, data for the worldwide distribution of vegetation at one point were more complete than for climate, which lead some scientists to use vegetation maps to infer worldwide climate patterns. Eventually, biogeographers in the early 20th century used both vegetation and climate data to produce a system that classifies the world's animal and plant life into units called "biomes," which is still in use today. This chapter describes how terrestrial ecosystems can be classified into biomes based on their predominant plants and associated animals. This broad-scale scheme generally reflects the relative contribution of three plant life forms—trees, shrubs, and grasses—and the dominant vegetation form represents adaptation to specific climatic factors (Section 23.1; see also Quantifying Ecology 23.1). Each of these plant life forms represents a diverse range of species, and they especially characterize different patterns of carbon allocation and morphology. Temperature and moisture variability are primary factors that affect the geographic distribution of terrestrial biomes, and students should begin noticing a trend: temperature and moisture are two very important abiotic variables for ecology at many different scales.

Near the equator is a climate that is characterized by constant warmth and almost daily precipitation, resulting in tropical rainforests where evergreen broadleaf trees predominate (Section 23.2). Tropical rainforests receive more publicity than many ecosystem types, largely due to their exceptionally high diversity and the rapid rate at which we are losing them. Many students, therefore, may be curious about *why* tropical rainforests support such high diversity. One reason is that the tree community provides a habitat of exceptional biological and physical structure (Section 23.2). Thousands of other plant and animal species have evolved to take advantage of the niches created by this structure. For example, a great diversity of plants has adapted to live in the crowns of the rainforest trees. These plants, called epiphytes, make their living by using trees as support to grow near the canopy where they can access sunlight. Many other plant species are adapted to take advantage of gaps created by the death of large trees, a process that is ongoing in all forests. Similarly, thousands of animal species utilize different spaces in the vertical structure of the forest. For example, many insectivorous birds and bats live above the canopy, while the forest floor is occupied by large herbivorous mammals.

Tropical savannas, which are associated with areas that have a high interannual variation in precipitation, form the transition from forest to grassland (Section 23.3). These savannas cover much of central and southern Africa, northern Australia, and large areas of northern South America. Unlike the closed-canopy forests discussed above, savannas are characterized by a lack of vertical structure. Instead, a patchwork of trees, open spaces, bunches of grass, and marshy areas create a varied horizontal structure that supports a diversity of herbivorous animals. Although we typically think of Africa when discussing savannas, there are a number of excellent examples in North America—the pinon-juniper woodland of the American Southwest and the oak woodland of the California Central Valley.

As we move into temperate regions, grasslands dominate areas of lower moisture availability (Section 23.4). Most temperate grasslands are characterized by an abundance of grazing mammals and periodic fires; grasses have adaptations to both of these forces. One point to emphasize to students is that under the global heading of "grasslands" are many habitats ranging from the tallgrass prairies of North America to the pampas of South America. This wide variety of grassland types is driven by fluctuation in both climate and regional geography, and, as in most ecosystems, the productivity of these grasslands is directly related to moisture availability. Contrary to what one might expect, grasslands are characterized by significant vertical physical structure. The root layer is especially well developed in grasslands and is an extensive belowground allocation of carbon by plants and a strong presence of burrowing animals that combine to produce a deep, well-mixed organic layer full of roots and a wide variety of grazing and decomposing organisms. The physical structure and diversity of plant life in grasslands support a wide diversity of animals ranging from a high diversity of invertebrates to some very conspicuous large grazing mammals. Many of the large mammals of grasslands are among the most well-known animals in the world.

At the extreme end of the moisture availability gradient are deserts, which are regions where evaporation exceeds rainfall (Section 23.5). Many ecosystems are classified as deserts. All deserts, however, are characterized by low rainfall, high evaporation, and a wide daily range in temperature. Productivity in deserts is universally limited by moisture availability. Deserts often have a relatively simple physical structure that is created by widely spaced drought-tolerant shrubs. Surprisingly, many types of animals have adapted to the arid conditions of the desert and use opportunistic strategies to take advantage of short-term favorable conditions such as the lower temperatures during the night.

Another major ecosystem that occurs in arid and semiarid regions of the world is the shrublands (Section 23.6). Many ecosystems are considered to be shrublands but all are dominated by woody plants of small stature. One climatic situation that promotes shrubland formation worldwide is a regime of hot, dry summers and cool, rainy winters—a Mediterranean climate. What all of these habitats have in common is a dominance of drought-tolerant shrubs, often a history of fire, and a very patchy spatial structure. For all of these reasons, shrublands support a unique animal community.

Temperate deciduous forests, which may be more familiar to students (Section 23.7), are characterized by significant vertical structure (like tropical rainforests) that influences the diversity of life found there. These forests are found in moist, midlatitude regions that are characterized by strong seasonal variation in temperature and moisture. Although the vertical stratification in these forests is not as extreme as in tropical rainforests, many animal species are adapted to live in the various layers. For example, the beautiful scarlet tanager lives in the upper canopy while the wood pewee occupies the lower canopy.

Temperate evergreen forests are wide-ranging and diverse (Section 23.7) but generally occupy drier habitats than temperate deciduous forests. The vertical structure of coniferous forests is relatively simple. Consequently, while there are many plant and animal species found associated with coniferous forests, they support a lower diversity of plant and animal species than forests with more complex physical structure.

It may surprise students to know that boreal forests are the most widespread vegetation type on Earth (Section 23.8). These habitats are characterized by cold temperatures and extreme seasonality, and they have short, moist summers and prolonged winters. The vegetation that results from this climate is relatively simple, with a relatively open canopy of conifers dominating most areas. Despite the simple physical structure of boreal forests, they have a unique animal community that includes the lynx, hare, and red squirrels (made famous by the work of ecologist Charles Krebs on predator–prey dynamics). One might expect to find the equivalent of boreal forests at high altitude in southern mountain ranges, and to some extent this is what we find. However, high winds at high altitudes often create harsher conditions than are found farther north at low altitudes, causing stunted tree growth.

The final ecosystem type in this chapter, tundra, is the coolest of all the moisture-limited ecosystems we have discussed (Section 23.9). Tundra occurs at both high latitudes and at high elevations. Productivity is not only limited by moisture availability but also by low temperature. The growing season is extremely short and relatively cool, and thus total productivity in tundra ecosystems is very low. The vegetation that results from these conditions is simple and of relatively low diversity. As a result, the animal community, well adapted to the low temperature, is also not very diverse.

Discussion Topics

1. A common theme in this chapter is that low moisture availability limits productivity in these ecosystems. What are the differences between sites that have produced such a wide variety of ecosystems?
2. Which of the main ecosystems we discuss in this chapter is under the most threat from human development? What differences among these ecosystems created differences in the degree of threat? Is there a correlation between the diversity of the ecosystem and the amount of pressure from humans? If not, then what explains variation in human pressure on these ecosystems?
3. What are the tree-dominated ecosystems near you? What are the climatic conditions that led to their development? To what degree does vertical structure provide habitat for additional plant and animal species?
4. Are there other ways to classify terrestrial ecosystems besides using the biome system? Are there specific advantages of classifying terrestrial ecosystems by biomes?
5. What biome do you live in, and what are the distinguishing characteristics? How far would you have to travel to enter a different biome?

CHAPTER 24 Aquatic Ecosystems

Commentary

In this chapter, we turn to aquatic ecosystems—lakes, rivers, coastal estuaries, and oceans. We will discuss how the factors limiting and influencing productivity and nutrient cycling are often different in these systems than in terrestrial ecosystems. This is reflected by the fact that aquatic ecosystems are generally classified by physical factors.

We begin with lakes and ponds, which are inland depressions that contain standing water. These have many origins, including glacial abrasion, movement of the earth's crust, and erosion associated with streams and rivers (Section 24.1). Unlike many ecosystems, ponds and lakes have well-defined boundaries and, while conditions vary from one pond or lake to another, most are influenced by the same physical factors (Section 24.2). Rather than productivity being limited by moisture, as is the case in many of the terrestrial ecosystems we have discussed, other physical factors are more important: light, temperature, and oxygen availability. All three factors vary seasonally and with depth, and all have an influence on community structure, productivity, and nutrient cycling (Section 24.3). For example, the shallow water around the edge, referred to as the littoral zone, typically supports the most life since it receives the most consistent light and plenty of oxygen and has plants that are able to root in the bottom. Similarly, the shallow portion of the open water, termed the "limnetic zone," contains plenty of light and oxygen, and it supports a rich planktonic community. Below the limnetic zone, life is often limited by a lack or low amounts of oxygen and light. On the bottom, in the deepest regions of the benthic zone, anaerobic bacteria dominate, taking advantage of the large amount of organic matter that comes from the limnetic and littoral zones. In shallower benthic areas, various factors, including water action and plant growth, modify the environment to produce a much richer aquatic assemblage than that found in the deeper areas.

In addition to these within-site variations in conditions, ponds and lakes can also differ significantly from one another, depending on the terrestrial ecosystems that surround them (Section 24.4). For example, farmland often provides high nutrient input into a lake, which encourages algal growth and consequently reduces light penetration. In contrast, when lakes are surrounded by coniferous forest with thin acidic soils they are usually low in nutrients, especially phosphorus. These lakes have high light penetration and abundant oxygen and are not dominated by algal growth.

Some of the factors that influence rivers and streams are different than those that influence ponds and lakes. For example, flow especially has a strong impact on the characteristics of a river, with faster-flowing water able to carry more sediment (Section 24.5; see also Quantifying Ecology 24.1). Within a flowing body of water, a variety of habitats result from the horizontal flow, with a horizontal zonation of primary production and decomposition. Quiet pools are the sites of decomposition, while faster-moving, structure-laden riffles are the sites of primary production. Many organisms are particularly adapted to life in a flowing medium (Section 24.6). Furthermore, this biological community changes as the characteristics of the body of water change—along a gradient from the headwaters to the downstream regions (Section 24.7). These flow conditions change with the seasons as well, and the biological community is adapted to these fluctuating flow conditions. For these reasons dams, which can severely alter the flow characteristics of a river or stream, can negatively impact the biological community (see Ecological Issues).

A unique ecosystem results where rivers empty their contents into oceans—the estuary (Section 24.8). At these junctions, freshwater mixes with saltwater and both physical and biological properties are influenced by the river, its terrestrial watershed, and the ocean itself. Organisms living in estuaries must be adapted to a complex set of conditions, including freshwater and saltwater, tides and the downstream flow of the river, and nutrients from the river and the ocean. From these complexities, the plants and animals of the estuaries create extremely productive ecosystems.

Marine ecosystems, while similar to freshwater systems in some fundamental ways, also have unique characteristics. They share with freshwater ecosystems some of the issues related to vertical stratification: the attenuation of light penetration with depth and a physical separation between the sites of decomposition and the sites of photosynthesis (Section 24.9). The most productive marine systems are those that have significant upwelling currents that supply nutrients to the sites of photosynthesis at the surface. However, many characteristics are unique to marine systems: the salinity of marine systems creates water availability problems for many organisms; oceans are extremely large such that the volume of sunlit water is small compared to their total volume; and marine systems are influenced by unique currents, tides, and significant waves. What should be emphasized to students is the spatial and temporal variation in physical conditions that leads to unique ecosystems. Vertical and horizontal variations in all the variables discussed above create many ecological regions within the oceans, ranging from biologically rich upwelling communities off the coast of California to the shallow, nutrient-rich shelf ecosystems of the North Atlantic.

As in freshwater lakes and ponds, the surface waters are the sites of photosynthesis; light penetration supports a large phytoplankton community (Section 24.10). A complex food web is based on these primary producers, with zooplankton making up the bulk of the first level of herbivorous consumers. The higher trophic levels are occupied by the nekton, swimming organisms such as fish that prey on zooplankton and on each other.

The organic matter that drops out of the complex surface community serves to support a diverse, and largely separate, ocean bottom–inhabiting (benthic) community (Section 24.11). Entirely dependent on organic matter, these communities are heterotrophic and extremely diverse. One hypothesis suggests that such diversity has been able to evolve due to the extreme stability of the benthic system—the ocean bottom is largely unaffected by storms and the temperature is nearly constant. An exception to these generalizations about benthic communities is the unique ecosystem associated with hydrothermal vents. The food web in these vent habitats is based on autotrophic primary producers—chemosynthetic bacteria that derive energy by oxidizing sulfur compounds. A complex and diverse food web is supported by these unique autotrophs.

Coral reefs will be familiar to most students (Section 24.12). These diverse and complex ecosystems form in the warm, shallow waters around tropical islands and continental landmasses. What many students will be surprised to learn is that these often-massive ecosystems are primarily built by small animals and their endosymbiotic algae. The mutualism between the coral animal and their symbiotic algal partners creates a physical structure of great productivity that supports a complex associated food web. Contrary to the pattern found on land, primary productivity in the oceans generally increases with latitude (Section 24.13). One reason for this pattern is that in the tropics, upwelling currents that bring nutrients to the surface are basically absent. Thus, the oceans in tropical regions are less productive than in northern areas where upwelling currents are more prevalent. The exceptions to this pattern of productivity are tropical coral reefs, which are among the most productive ecosystems on earth (Section 24.12).

Discussion Topics

1. How does shoreline development affect the ecology of lakes or ponds? Does development destroy the very features that attracted people to lakeshores?
2. List the effects of dams on the river continuum. What effect do dams have on fish distribution? What are the ecological characteristics of impoundments relative to vertical stratification? What effects does regulated flow have on downstream aquatic life?
3. What threatened or endangered species of fish or other flowing water inhabitants, such as freshwater mussels, are found in your region? What are the causes for their decline? What efforts are in place to protect them?
4. A topic not discussed in this chapter is the phenomenon of convergent evolution. Do you expect that the worldwide currents in oceans are sufficient to swamp convergent evolution such that oceans are

taxonomically well mixed? If not, then in what marine habitats would you expect to find convergent evolution?

5. What characteristics of coral reefs make them susceptible to and slow to recover from human disturbance?

CHAPTER 25 Coastal and Wetland Systems

Commentary

In previous chapters, we explored both terrestrial and aquatic ecosystems. Chapter 25 discusses ecosystems that occur at the interface between terrestrial and aquatic systems. Transition zones between land and water have produced a diverse array of ecosystems that are often greatly threatened by human actions. Intertidal zones (Section 25.1), which are alternately exposed and submerged by ocean tides, have been extensively studied by ecologists. For example, Robert Paine's research on intertidal areas led to some key concepts of food web dynamics, particularly the idea of a keystone predator. Shoreline marine habitats exhibit great variation especially due to differences among sites in the substrate on which they are built (Sections 25.2 and 25.3). The unifying feature, however, is that all shoreline ecosystems are heavily influenced by tides and waves. All rocky shores have three basic zones, and each zone is characterized by predominant organisms (Section 25.2). Because of the fluctuations in water level caused by tides and waves, shoreline organisms are subject to extremely variable conditions. Light levels, temperature, salinity, and the risk of desiccation all fluctuate dramatically over the course of a day. Organisms living in these habitats must have adaptations to accommodate these extremes. The most challenging shoreline marine communities are those where the substrate is largely comprised of sand or mud rather than rock (Section 25.3). Because life on the surface of sand is nearly impossible, the biological community is largely hidden, burrowing into the substrate to escape the harsh conditions at the surface. The food base for these communities is organic matter that accumulates and percolates between sand grains.

Salt marshes occur along many temperate coastal areas and are greatly influenced by tides and salinity (Section 25.4). The interplay of tides and salinity variation creates distinct plant communities from the sea to high land. The species inhabiting coastal wetlands must be adapted to the daily fluctuations in physical conditions associated with tides. In tropical regions, salt marshes are replaced by mangrove forests, which develop where wave action is absent and sediments accumulate (Section 25.5). Mangrove forests are home to a diverse fauna that contains a unique mix of terrestrial and aquatic species.

Freshwater wetlands are transitional zones between land and freshwater (Section 25.6). Although it can be difficult sometimes to delineate the borders of a wetland, they are generally defined as areas that have saturated soil and that support water-loving plants during some portion of the year. Some plant species are good indicators of wetlands while others use plasticity or local adaptation to span a gradient from wetland to upland. Not surprisingly, many habitats around the world are classified as wetlands. Often, a major variable for classifying wetlands into different types is the nature of the water flow in and out of the wetland: saltwater versus freshwater, constant unidirectional flow versus bidirectional flow, vertical versus horizontal flow. Not coincidentally, the nature of water flow, or *hydrology,* is also the major factor in determining the structure of a wetland (Section 25.7).

Despite the fact that wetlands have the potential to provide many beneficial services to human populations, we have had a very negative historical relationship with wetlands (see Ecological Issues). To make room for cities and agriculture and to rid our environment of organisms that are thought to be harmful to ourselves and our crops, humans have drained millions of acres of wetlands during our history. In many places, the loss of wetlands continues at a rapid rate. There is a growing awareness, however, of the ecological and economic value of wetlands. They act as flood buffers, water filtration systems, sites for hunting and fishing, and as havens of high biodiversity (Section 25.8). These benefits are often out of proportion with the size of the wetlands, which makes each decision to preserve wetlands potentially quite important.

Discussion Topics

1. What characteristics of rocky shores make them so vulnerable to oil pollution?
2. If possible, visit a local wetland. Note the abundance and variety of plant and animal life, and discuss the unique physical factors that contribute to its structure. What is the nature of the dominant hydrology, and what features of the wetland result?
3. Why does development to the very edge of a wetland have the potential to destroy the wetland?
4. Ask students to list the benefits and drawbacks of coastal and freshwater wetlands. Do the benefits outweigh the negative aspects? You may want to introduce some ecological economics at this point. For example, what does it cost to treat surface drinking water versus the cost of not developing wetlands?

CHAPTER 26 Large-Scale Patterns of Biological Diversity

Commentary

The study of biodiversity is an important endeavor that has become a particularly heated scientific and political issue. It is unclear how many species exist on Earth, but estimates range from 5 to 10 million or more. No matter what the actual number is, it is clear that the patterns of global diversity change over geologic time (Section 26.1). For example, among most groups of organisms the number of species has generally been increasing during the past 600 million years. This pattern has been counterbalanced by relatively brief periods of declining diversity (extinctions), some of which were especially large (Section 26.2).

During the course of classifying the world's organisms into biomes (Chapter 23), scientists have found some striking patterns of species diversity at the geographic scale (Section 26.3). The most prevalent pattern is that diversity is highest closer to the equator for many types of organisms. Ecologists have been trying to explain this pattern for more than a century, and to date no consensus has been reached. Indeed, we are still adding new hypotheses to the list of possible explanations. One hypothesis is that diversity in terrestrial ecosystems is highest where productivity is highest—a pattern that is seen for many groups of terrestrial species, especially plants, at some spatial scales (Section 26.4). Animal diversity is usually linked to plant diversity because plants provide both food and habitat for animals. This pattern does not hold for diversity in marine environments, however, where productivity is highest at higher latitudes and diversity is lowest (Section 26.5). Further complicating matters is the fact that patterns of diversity are not the same at all spatial scales (Section 26.6; see also Quantifying Ecology 26.1). In reality, no single hypothesis will be able to explain all patterns of diversity that we observe. The challenge is to devise means of collecting data that will help to eliminate one or more of the competing hypotheses.

Discussion Topics

1. Why do you think it has been so difficult for ecologists to determine why there are more species in the tropics than at higher latitudes?
2. Besides productivity, what other factors are related to diversity? Would you expect the diversity in freshwater ecosystems to decrease from the equator as it does for most groups of terrestrial and marine organisms?
3. Are there differences in the factors that affect diversity at local, regional, and global scales?

CHAPTER 27 Population Growth, Resource Use, and Sustainability

Commentary

Although all organisms are able to modify their environment, humans have perhaps had a greater impact than any organism on the Earth's environments at local to global scales. The final chapters in the text explore the relationship of our species with the environment and other species. These relationships focus on the expanding human population and its increasing need for resources, especially energy.

The emphasis of this chapter is on environmental sustainability as it relates to agriculture, forestry, and fisheries. Sustainability is not an easy idea to define (Section 27.1). At its simplest, sustainability refers to using resources at a slower rate than they are produced. The use of water in the Aral Sea watershed provides an excellent (and devastating) example where the rate of harvest (water removal) greatly exceeds the rate of supply. This example can be contrasted with the sustainable harvest of forests. Students need to realize that in both of these examples the resources are renewable. By definition, use of non-renewable resources is not sustainable.

A timely and important topic raised in this chapter is that of ecosystem services, which are processes performed by ecosystems that benefit humans, such as cleaning water and air (Section 27.2). Sustainable resource use is tied to ecosystem services when these services are negatively impacted by poor resource use, leading to overall degradation of resource production. Water use around the Aral Sea provides an excellent example of this linkage and how often we forget the lessons from nature—sustainability is a normal function of natural ecosystems and we should learn from their example (Section 27.3).

Humans have impacted natural ecosystems through practices such as agriculture that greatly favor some species over others. Students may be surprised to learn how precarious our agricultural system is, since we rely on only a few species to produce most of our food (Section 27.4). Because of agriculture, a small subset of plants (crops) has flourished while many others (those formerly living in habitat now converted to agriculture) have been negatively affected (see also Chapter 28).

Growing crops in the tropics often relies on shifting cultivation or swidden agriculture (Section 27.5; see also Field Studies). This method, sometimes referred to as "slash and burn" agriculture, ultimately leads to a decline in productivity and the abandoning of fields. With time, the land may return to a productive state and can be used again for agriculture. Although this represents a sustainable form of cultivation, the increasing human population requires more land, and it is becoming progressively more difficult to allow enough recovery time for the land. In contrast to agricultural techniques in the tropics, most agriculture in the temperate zone (i.e., industrialized countries) is dependent on large inputs of energy from non-renewable fossil fuels (Section 27.6). This is a good example of non-sustainable resource use and is an especially good example of ignoring the lessons from natural ecosystems. The big difference in the two types of agriculture listed above is one of energy input and output. Agriculture in industrial countries consumes much more energy than is harvested in food, but the overall harvest is much larger (Section 27.7; see also Ecological Issues). We are largely dependent on industrialized agriculture because of the growing human population, although there is an increasing interest in sustainable agricultural methods (Section 27.8).

One major way that humans have had and continue to have major direct impact on other species is through exploitation of organisms such as trees and fish for human use and consumption (Sections 27.9–27.11). In fact, humans have had such a massive impact in some cases that specific management efforts have to be made to assure that we do not drive species extinct. Specifically, these management efforts have led to the development of mathematical methods for predicting the amount of harvest that can be sustained from year to year without driving species extinct. The discussion of "sustainable yield" gives students a chance to apply what they learned about population growth in Chapter 10.

While the concept of sustainable yield has been quite useful, it is sometimes very difficult to apply to natural populations, especially in the case of animals such as fish. Besides the inherent difficulties of accurately assessing parameters of population growth of fish populations, economic pressures can make the application of sustainable yield principles very difficult. This conflict between short-term economic gain and long-term sustainability of an industry is typical of human conflicts over the use of natural resources, and thus provides students with an introduction to the complexities of environmental issues and also economics (Section 27.12). With respect to accurately assessing the parameters of population growth, the application of sustainable yield to forestry is easier than in the case of fisheries. Unfortunately, the same economic pressures that make sustainable yield difficult to practice in fisheries also affect its application in forestry. Furthermore, in both fisheries and forestry, the application of sustainable yield principles ignores the community context of the population of interest. As a result, we manage for populations of trees rather than for an entire forest ecosystem, and a great deal of biodiversity is disregarded or lost.

Discussion Topics

1. It is instructive to examine the energy cost to produce a typical food or beverage in North America. Pick a food or beverage that students are familiar with (e.g., can of beer, diet soda, pizza)—you should have the energy calculations done before this exercise. Ask them to list all the ingredients and the processes that are needed to make those ingredients (some will be obvious, but transportation, storage, veterinarian services, and so on are often forgotten) and then have them estimate how much energy each step takes and how much energy they receive. A can of diet soda is particularly interesting (don't forget the energy to produce the aluminum can—about 2100 kcal) since the energy gain for the student is about 1 kcal.
2. Given the increasing human population, could "sustainable agriculture" ever be viable?
3. How is forestry similar to growing agricultural crops such as corn? How are they different?
4. For a hypothetical fish species, make a list of the various groups of people that are interested in the fate of that fish species. How might the interests of those groups conflict and make implementation of sustainable harvest techniques difficult?

CHAPTER 28 Habitat Loss, Biodiversity, and Conservation

Commentary

This chapter should be useful to the instructor as a means of showing students how humans have a great influence on biodiversity in both negative and positive ways. In addition to our direct impact on species through the harvesting of natural populations as discussed in Chapter 27, humans have also strongly impacted natural communities through land transformation, especially agriculture (Section 28.1). Although much attention is focused on the loss of tropical habitats and the concomitant loss of species, students should be aware that large changes in land use have also occurred in North America.

Students may be surprised to learn that many of the common plant and animal species they see every day are recent immigrants from other parts of the world and that humans are often the vehicle of their movement (Section 28.2). Not only can these invasive or "alien" species often have significant negative effects on local native communities of species but they also may have effects on community and ecosystem properties that humans value greatly. Efforts to eradicate unwanted species, whether native or non-native, have met with mixed success. Natural populations often behave in ways we cannot predict and, for example, can adapt to resist chemical pesticides.

Determining the susceptibility of a species to extinction is not easy because variation in life history characteristics, among other factors, differentially influence their vulnerability to human and natural disturbances (Section 28.3; see also Ecological Issues). Nonetheless, identifying those species that are most threatened by extinction is an important part of conservation efforts (Section 28.4). One way that species conservation has progressed with limited economic resources is to identify areas of high species diversity ("hotspots") and to concentrate efforts in those regions (Section 28.5).

Often, endangered species are concentrated in one or a few populations, and it has become apparent that protecting these populations is vital for the preservation of the species (Section 28.6). Specifically, the question of survival relates to the minimum viable population (MVP), or how many individuals of a species are necessary to ensure the survival of that species in the face of demographic variation, environmental changes, and genetic drift (see also Quantifying Ecology 28.1). It is also important to consider the necessary amount of suitable habitat for maintaining the MVP. Even with an understanding of these factors, in some cases a reintroduction of individuals into an area is needed to protect the species (Section 28.7). Students will likely be familiar with some of these efforts, particularly the reestablishment of wolf, California condor, and whooping crane populations. Condors and cranes are examples in which individuals were reestablished from captive-bred populations.

A great deal of effort has focused on saving species, but probably the most important way to preserve biodiversity comes from the protection of habitats or whole ecosystems (Sections 28.8 and 28.9). This approach requires a community-level understanding of the relationship between diversity and landscape features, such as the positive correlation between area and species richness. However, as logical as this idea seems, it is not without controversy. For example, whether it is better to preserve a few large areas or many small ones is open to debate.

Humans clearly have a negative impact on biological communities in many ways: non-sustainable harvesting practices, the introduction of invasive species, widespread habitat destruction for activities such as real estate development and agriculture, and the spraying of chemical pesticides that harm many species besides the target pest. Recently, we are making efforts to undo some of this damage by restoring natural communities (Section 28.10). These restoration activities vary in both their scope and their level of success. While restoration efforts can sometimes be successful, students should recognize that successful habitat restoration is not easily attained. For example, invasive species can be extremely difficult to eradicate. Furthermore, successful restoration often requires extensive monitoring after the project has been initiated, and funding is often not available for sufficient monitoring.

Whichever methods we use to protect or restore biodiversity, there are important reasons to maintain this diversity (Section 28.11), including economic, evolutionary, and ethical considerations.

Discussion Topics

1. What is the difference between a native and a non-native species? How would you classify a species that has been a member of a community for 150 years? Is the distinction between native and non-native species always clear?

2. Are students aware of any invasive species in their area? Have these species caused any impacts on native flora or fauna? Are there any invasive species that are not a problem?

3. The concentration of species conservation efforts in "hotspots" has its benefits. What are some drawbacks to this approach?

4. There are numerous areas that are open for discussion regarding the preservation of species. For example, a large amount of time, effort, and money has gone into protecting a few "charismatic megafauna." Is this a sound ecological idea? Are all species necessary for a properly functioning ecosystem?

5. What are the benefits and problems associated with creating several small or a few large nature preserves? (The metapopulation concept can be revisited here; see Chapter 12.)

6. How can ecologists restore an ecosystem if they do not know what the ecosystem was like before human disturbance? Are there other measures that could help ecologists determine whether restoration efforts were successful?

CHAPTER 29 Global Climate Change

Commentary

While the environment of our planet is constantly changing and has been since Earth's formation, in this chapter we focus on a small subset of these changes that is due to recent human activities. In particular, we focus on changes in the chemistry of our atmosphere brought about by the impact of human industry. Some of these changes have the potential to severely impact ecosystems at many different scales. This chapter offers students a chance to integrate what they have learned so far in attempting to understand the potential consequences of a major ecosystem perturbation.

Carbon dioxide, along with water vapor and ozone, are the major compounds involved in the Earth's energy balance and climate (Section 29.1). However, the amount of CO_2 (and other compounds) in our atmosphere has dramatically increased since the Industrial Revolution in the mid-1800s (Section 29.2). By using a variety of techniques, scientists have determined that the burning of fossil fuels, combined with deforestation, has been the major cause of this change. The degree to which ecosystems can act as sinks for carbon, providing a buffer for excess CO_2 emissions, is not yet fully understood (Section 29.3). Oceans, in particular, have the potential to absorb a great deal of excess CO_2 (Section 29.4). It is clear, however, that the buffering capacity of ecosystems, including oceans, is not nearly complete—some sustained increase in atmospheric CO_2 levels is occurring and will continue to do so if current conditions persist.

The ecological impacts of elevated atmospheric CO_2 are potentially widespread, although they are difficult to predict in some instances. For example, plants use CO_2 in photosynthesis and we might predict that photosynthetic rates would respond positively to elevated CO_2 (Section 29.5; see also Field Studies)—this is what happens at a coarse level of resolution. Long-term responses of plants to elevated CO_2 are not so simple, however. Complicated feedbacks that involve nutrient limitations, for example, may act to limit long-term increases in primary productivity. Another complicating factor not addressed by most experimental research to date is that increases in CO_2 concentrations are expected to increase global average temperatures and levels of precipitation, which could affect plant responses in surprising ways (Section 29.6; see also Ecological Issues). Our ability to predict the effects of rising temperatures has been limited so far to mathematical models of global climate change, the sophistication of which is constantly evolving.

As mentioned above, global climate change is expected to have ecological effects at many scales (Section 29.7). Individual behavior, population dynamics, community structure, nutrient cycling, primary productivity, and geographical distributions of species could all be affected. One expected effect, however, that is predicted by many different models of global climate change is that climate change will alter the spatial distribution of many ecosystems (Section 29.8). Such changes could have severe consequences not only for the species that make up the natural communities involved but also for human populations that are dependent on the services provided by local ecosystems. For example, global climate change is expected to raise sea levels in many places, which would have significant impacts on coastal environments (Section

29.9). Consider, for example, that 13 of the world's 20 largest cities are located in coastal regions. Other major potential impacts of climate change include a significant alteration in the agricultural properties of regions around the world (Section 29.10) as well as direct and indirect effects on human health (Section 29.11). Understanding these extremely complicated effects requires an ecological perspective that is global in scale, seeing the ecosystems of Earth as a single, integrated system (Section 29.12).

Discussion Topics

1. At an international conference in Japan on global warming there was a great deal of dissension among nations over the steps to take to reduce inputs of greenhouse gases into the atmosphere. Developed nations (especially the United States), the largest producers of greenhouse gases, were reluctant to take the strong steps necessary to reduce emissions. Developing nations were reluctant to cap their growing greenhouse gas emissions. Some argued that there was no strong scientific proof that global climate change was taking place, and therefore saw no need for action. Although some agreement was reached, many observers feel the steps proposed were not strong enough. Why, in the face of scientific evidence and a general consensus among world scientists that the threat of global climate change exists, should there be such reluctance to take necessary steps to reduce the threat? Once global climate change occurs, can it be reversed under crisis management? What are the complex social factors that make a global consensus on response to global climate change difficult to achieve?

2. If CO_2 is essential to photosynthesis, shouldn't elevated CO_2 levels in the atmosphere increase plant production? Isn't this a good thing? What complications might this argument be ignoring?

3. Encourage students to explore the potential effects of global climate change on food production. What effect might global climate change have on the major food-producing regions of the world? Will it be easy for human society to adapt to these changes?

4. What are some of the potential changes to the geographical distributions of human diseases that result from global climate change?

5. If scientists disagree about an issue, does that mean the issue is not a problem? How certain must scientists be before a conclusion can be made about a scientific hypothesis? How much and what types of data are necessary for providing strong support for a hypothesis?

Test Bank

Chapter 1 The Nature of Ecology

Short Answer Questions

1) _____ is the scientific study of the relationship between organisms and their environment.

Answer: Ecology
Topic: Section 1.1

2) The biotic and abiotic components of the environment interacting together are referred to as a(n)

_____.

Answer: ecosystem
Topic: Section 1.2

3) At the _____ level, communities and ecosystems are linked through processes such as dispersal of organisms.

Answer: landscape
Topic: Section 1.3

4) The highest level of organization of ecological systems is the _____.

Answer: biosphere
Topic: Section 1.3

5) All populations of different species living and interacting within an ecosystem are referred to as a(n)

_____.

Answer: community
Topic: Section 1.3

6) At the _____ level, an ecologist might focus on the factors that affect the relative abundance of various populations in the area.

Answer: community
Topic: Section 1.4

7) An "educated guess" that a scientist poses to explain an observed phenomenon is referred to as a(n)

_____.

Answer: hypothesis
Topic: Section 1.5

8) An ecologist who adds different amounts of nitrogen to specific plots of grasses uses a(n) _____ to answer her research question.

Answer: field experiment
Topic: Section 1.5

9) Bird wingspan would be considered _____ data.

Answer: numerical
Topic: Quantifying Ecology 1.1

10) An abstract, simplified representation of a real system is referred to as a(n) _____.

Answer: model
Topic: Section 1.6

11) If an ecologist wanted to illustrate whether a relationship exists between body length and body weight, he would probably produce a(n) _____.

Answer: scatterplot
Topic: Quantifying Ecology 1.2

12) The _____ forms the basic unit in ecology.

Answer: individual organism
Topic: Section 1.9

Multiple-Choice Questions

1) The term "ecology" is defined as the study of the
    A) environment.
    B) relationships between organisms.
    C) relationships between organisms and their environment.
    D) impact of humans on the environment.

Answer: C
Topic: Section 1.1

2) Ambient temperature and concentration of carbon dioxide
    A) are parts of an organism's environment.
    B) have no effect on the physiology of an organism.
    C) are biological conditions that impact an organism's survival.
    D) do not vary in the environment.

Answer: A
Topic: Section 1.1

3) A biotic community and its abiotic environment is referred to as a(n)
    A) biosphere.
    B) ecosystem.
    C) population.
    D) biome.

Answer: B
Topic: Section 1.2

4) Which of the following is considered a biotic component of the ecosystem?
    A) climate
    B) microbes
    C) soil
    D) water

Answer: B
Topic: Section 1.2

5) The biosphere is
    A) the thin layer surrounding the Earth that supports all life.
    B) all the populations of different species living and interacting within an ecosystem.
    C) a broad-scale region dominated by similar types of ecosystems.
    D) an area of land or water composed of a patchwork of communities and ecosystems.

Answer: A
Topic: Section 1.3

6) A group of individuals of the same species occupying a given area is referred to as a(n)
    A) community.
    B) biome.
    C) population.
    D) ecosystem.

Answer: C
Topic: Section 1.3

7) Which of the following is the correct ecological hierarchy (from smallest unit to largest unit) of a daisy?
    A) landscape, community, population, individual organism
    B) individual organism, community, population, landscape
    C) individual organism, population, community, landscape
    D) landscape, population, community, individual organism

Answer: C
Topic: Section 1.4

8) Which of the following questions is most appropriate to investigate at the population level?
    A) What is the effect of diminished resources on an individual's life span?
    B) What is the relationship between resource availability and birth rate?
    C) What factors influence the distribution of tropical forests?
    D) How long does it take for carbon to be cycled from the atmosphere into living tissue?

Answer: B
Topic: Section 1.4

9) An ecologist who focuses on the individual would study all of the following, except:
    A) morphology.
    B) physiology.
    C) behavior.
    D) death rate.

Answer: D
Topic: Section 1.4

10) A hypothesis refers to a(n)
    A) phenomenon that is observed but is not yet understood.
    B) testable explanation for an observed phenomenon.
    C) untestable explanation for an observed phenomenon.
    D) falsified explanation for an observed phenomenon.

Answer: B
Topic: Section 1.5

11) A field study
    A) generally takes place within a greenhouse environment.
    B) requires the ecologist to vary the level of an independent variable.
    C) is the most controlled of research approaches.
    D) utilizes sites in which the independent variable fluctuates naturally.

Answer: D
Topic: Section 1.5

12) An ecologist conducts a greenhouse experiment to study the effect of nitrogen concentration on the productivity of *Eucalyptus* seedlings. What is the dependent variable in this experiment?
   A) *Eucalyptus* productivity
   B) nitrogen concentration
   C) the number of *Eucalyptus* seedlings planted
   D) the amount of water given to each seedling each day

Answer: A
Topic: Section 1.5

13) Which of the following is an example of categorical data that an ecologist might record for a bird?
   A) beak length
   B) feather color
   C) wingspan
   D) feather number

Answer: B
Topic: Quantifying Ecology 1.1

14) A model is used by ecologists to
   A) prove how nature works by demonstrating cause and effect relationships.
   B) analyze data that have been collected during an experiment.
   C) make predictions about how nature works using a set of explicit assumptions.
   D) observe how nature works in an experimental setting.

Answer: C
Topic: Section 1.6

15) The real goal of hypothesis testing is to
   A) eliminate incorrect ideas.
   B) form a theory.
   C) fully explain observations.
   D) understand why science never changes.

Answer: A
Topic: Section 1.7

16) If *x* and *y* have a positive relationship as shown by a scatterplot, then the value of *y* will
   A) increase as the value of *x* decreases.
   B) increase as the value of *x* increases.
   C) decrease as the value of *x* increases.
   D) stay the same as the value of *x* decreases.

Answer: B
Topic: Quantifying Ecology 1.2

17) Because ecology relies on many different branches of science (e.g., geology) it is considered
   A) hypothetical.
   B) uncertain.
   C) permanent.
   D) interdisciplinary.

Answer: D
Topic: Section 1.8

18) The basic unit in ecology is the
   A) ecosystem.
   B) gene.
   C) individual organism.
   D) Earth.

Answer: C
Topic: Section 1.9

True/False Questions

1) Ecology is the same as environmentalism.

Answer: FALSE
Topic: Section 1.1

2) An ecosystem includes both living and nonliving components.

Answer: TRUE
Topic: Section 1.2

3) Light intensity is considered a biotic factor.

Answer: FALSE
Topic: Section 1.2

4) A population refers to all the individuals of the same species that occupy a given area.

Answer: TRUE
Topic: Section 1.3

5) The community of a pine forest would include all living organisms and nonliving components.

Answer: FALSE
Topic: Section 1.3

6) The number of seeds produced by a single flower affects the birth rate of that population of flowers.

Answer: TRUE
Topic: Section 1.4

7) Ecology is an interdisciplinary science that relies heavily on many different branches of science.

Answer: TRUE
Topic: Section 1.4

8) To be valid a hypothesis must be testable.

Answer: TRUE
Topic: Section 1.5

9) A hypothesis is an integrated set of theories.

Answer: FALSE
Topic: Section 1.5

10) An experiment is a test under controlled conditions performed to examine the validity of a hypothesis.

Answer: TRUE
Topic: Section 1.5

11) When data are categorical, any value within an interval is possible.

Answer: FALSE
Topic: Quantifying Ecology 1.1

12) Ecological models can be mathematical or they can be verbally descriptive.

Answer: TRUE
Topic: Section 1.6

13) Science is a process of testing and correcting concepts in order to explain the world around us.

Answer: TRUE
Topic: Section 1.7

14) There is generally only one valid explanation for an observation.

Answer: FALSE
Topic: Section 1.7

15) The most common method for displaying a single data set is to construct a frequency distribution.

Answer: TRUE
Topic: Quantifying Ecology 1.2

16) In a histogram, the *x*-axis represents the number of individuals with a particular characteristic while the *y*-axis represents the category intervals.

Answer: FALSE
Topic: Quantifying Ecology 1.2

17) Ecology only examines the impact of natural processes and ignores the influence of human activity on the environment.

Answer: FALSE
Topic: Ecological Issues: The Human Factor

Essay Questions

1) Explain the distinction between ecology and environmentalism.

Topic: Section 1.1

2) Using a real example, illustrate how an organism can both respond to and modify the abiotic conditions of its ecosystem.

Topic: Section 1.2

3) Explain why animal and plant populations are dependent on one another at the ecosystem level.

Topic: Section 1.3

4) Explain why ecology is inherently an interdisciplinary science. Give two examples of the ties between ecology and other branches of science.

Topic: Section 1.4

5) Describe a field experiment that you might use to test the hypothesis that water availability affects plant growth. Suggest one set of possible results and the implications of those results for the hypothesis.

Topic: Section 1.5

6) Define five types of data that can be used for quantitative analyses and give an example of each.

Topic: Quantifying Ecology 1.1

7) Explain why it is difficult for ecologists to give definitive answers.

Topic: Section 1.7

8) Explain why human population growth, biological diversity, sustainability, and global climate change are considered crucial environmental problems facing humans.

Topic: Section 1.8

9) Explain why current and past human activity is now considered part of the "natural world" by many ecologists. How might this change the field of ecology?

Topic: Ecological Issues: The Human Factor

Chapter 2 Climate

Short Answer Questions

1) The ability of the physical environment to support life is known as its _____.

   Answer: habitability
   Topic: Introduction to Chapter 2

2) The temperature, humidity, precipitation, wind, cloudiness, and other atmospheric conditions that occur at a specific place and time is referred to as _____.

   Answer: weather
   Topic: Introduction to Chapter 2

3) The average pattern of local, regional, or global weather conditions over a long period of time is _____.

   Answer: climate
   Topic: Introduction to Chapter 2

4) _____ and water vapor are the major gases in the atmosphere that absorb energy from the sun.

   Answer: Carbon dioxide
   Topic: Section 2.1

5) The absorption and reradiation of infrared radiation by gases in the atmosphere is called the _____.

   Answer: greenhouse effect
   Topic: Section 2.1

6) _____ is the portion of the electromagnetic spectrum that is used by plants to power photosynthesis.

   Answer: Visible light or Photosynthetically active radiation (PAR)
   Topic: Section 2.1

7) In the Northern Hemisphere, the summer _____ occurs when solar rays fall directly on the Tropic of Capricorn.

   Answer: solstice
   Topic: Section 2.2

8) Radiation at higher latitudes is spread out over a larger area because of the angle of incidence and the _____.

   Answer: air depth or distance it must travel through the atmosphere
   Topic: Section 2.2

9) The amount of force exerted over a given area of surface is called atmospheric _____.

   Answer: pressure
   Topic: Section 2.3

10) As altitude above sea level increases, both air pressure and density _____.

   Answer: decrease
   Topic: Section 2.3

11) The deflection of air masses to the right in the Northern Hemisphere and to the left in the Southern Hemisphere is called the _____.

Answer: Coriolis effect
Topic: Section 2.4

12) The _____ are formed by the air that reaches Earth's poles, slowly sinks to the surface, and flows southward is deflected by the Coriolis effect.

Answer: polar easterlies
Topic: Section 2.4

13) In the Northern Hemisphere, oceanic gyres circulate in a _____ direction.

Answer: clockwise
Topic: Section 2.5

14) _____ is the amount of water vapor in the air expressed as a percentage of the saturation vapor pressure.

Answer: Relative humidity
Topic: Section 2.6

15) The amount of energy lost or gained per gram during a change of state is known as _____.

Answer: latent heat
Topic: Section 2.6

16) The _____ is the temperature at which atmospheric water condenses.

Answer: dew point
Topic: Section 2.6

17) The narrow region near the Equator where trade winds meet is referred to as the _____.

Answer: intertropical convergence zone
Topic: Section 2.7

18) Air loses most of its water content as it moves up and over a mountain range and causes a _____ to form on the leeward side of the same range.

Answer: rain shadow
Topic: Section 2.8

19) An east-west oscillation in weather patterns across the Pacific Ocean is referred to as the _____-Southern Oscillation.

Answer: El Niño
Topic: Section 2.9

20) During an El Niño event, the waters of the eastern Pacific Ocean are unusually _____.

Answer: warm
Topic: Section 2.9

21) Most organisms live in habitats that provide specific conditions or a _____ that may be very different than regional weather patterns.

Answer: microclimate
Topic: Section 2.10

22) The _____ effect can raise temperatures from 6°C to 8°C above those in the surrounding countryside.

Answer: urban heat, or heat island
Topic: Ecological Issues: Urban Microclimates

Multiple-Choice Questions

1) Habitability
   A) is the ability of an organism to survive in a particular habitat.
   B) is the ability of the physical environment to support life.
   C) is the ability of the organism to take in resources.
   D) is the ability of the physical environment to change.

Answer: B
Topic: Introduction to Chapter 2

2) Water vapor and _____ are the two major atmospheric gases that absorb energy from the sun.
   A) oxygen
   B) nitrogen
   C) hydrogen
   D) carbon dioxide

Answer: D
Topic: Section 2.1

3) Without the greenhouse effect, the Earth would
   A) be much warmer than it currently is.
   B) be much colder than it currently is.
   C) have uniform temperatures and would lack seasons.
   D) have constant sunlight.

Answer: B
Topic: Section 2.1

4) What percentage of incoming solar radiation actually reaches Earth's surface?
   A) 100 percent
   B) 51 percent
   C) 15 percent
   D) 3 percent

Answer: B
Topic: Section 2.1

5) Of the 51 units of solar radiation that reach Earth's surface _____ units are lost to the evaporation of water.
   A) 51
   B) 30
   C) 23
   D) 7

Answer: D
Topic: Section 2.1

6) Photosynthetically active radiation (PAR)
    A) is the longwave radiation emitted from the Earth's surface.
    B) includes wavelengths that are shorter than ultraviolet (UV) light.
    C) includes only the solar energy with wavelengths of 400-700 nm.
    D) is the energy that is absorbed by Earth's atmosphere.

Answer: C
Topic: Section 2.1

7) In which of the following areas is the solar radiation the greatest in June?
    A) at the equator
    B) at the Tropic of Cancer
    C) at 90° in the southern hemisphere
    D) at 90° in the northern hemisphere

Answer: D
Topic: Section 2.2

8) Seasonal variation in temperature and daylength is due to the
    A) tilt of the Earth's axis.
    B) greenhouse effect.
    C) spinning of the Earth on its axis.
    D) latitudinal variation in solar radiation striking the Earth's surface.

Answer: A
Topic: Section 2.2

9) All the following could be used to describe or define "environmental lapse rate," except:
    A) This rate ignores the affect of moving air.
    B) This is the rate at which air temperature decreases with increasing altitude.
    C) This rate takes into account the influence of moisture on air temperature.
    D) This rate is influenced by air pressure.

Answer: C
Topic: Section 2.3

10) The rate of adiabatic cooling depends on the
    A) amount of moisture in the air.
    B) temperature of the air.
    C) latitude.
    D) season.

Answer: A
Topic: Section 2.3

11) The atmospheric region that is furthest from the Earth's surface is called the
    A) mesosphere.
    B) stratosphere.
    C) thermosphere.
    D) troposphere.

Answer: C
Topic: Section 2.3

12) Of the following areas on Earth's surface, which area moves fastest and has the greatest linear velocity?
    A) the North Pole (90° north)

    B) Barcelona, Spain (41° north)

    C) the Tropic of Capricorn (23.5° south)

    D) the Equator (0°)

Answer: D
Topic: Section 2.4

13) Between 30-60° north latitude, wind currents typically
    A) blow from west to east and are deflected toward the left.
    B) blow from east to west and are deflected toward the left.
    C) blow from west to east and are deflected toward the right.
    D) blow from east to west and are deflected toward the right.

Answer: C
Topic: Section 2.4

14) Which of the following is an incorrect match?
    A) equatorial low: rising air heated in the equatorial zone

    B) subtropical high: semipermanent high-pressure belt of air at 30° north and south of the equator
    C) Coriolis effect: deflection in the pattern of wind flow
    D) subpolar low: right-deflected, southward-flowing stream of air

Answer: D
Topic: Section 2.4

15) Surface currents in the ocean typically
    A) flow most strongly from west to east in equatorial regions.
    B) are colder on the western side of continents.
    C) flow counterclockwise in gyres in the Northern Hemisphere.
    D) flow unimpeded from east to west just north of Antarctica.

Answer: B
Topic: Section 2.5

16) The systematic patterns of water movement are known as
    A) circulations.
    B) currents.
    C) gyres.
    D) trade winds.

Answer: B
Topic: Section 2.5

17) Relative humidity is the
    A) amount of pressure at a given temperature at which water transforms from a liquid to a gaseous state.
    B) amount of pressure that water vapor exerts independent of the pressure of dry air.
    C) temperature at which saturation vapor pressure is achieved.
    D) amount of water vapor in the air relative to the saturation vapor pressure.

Answer: D
Topic: Section 2.6

18) The transformation of water vapor to a liquid state is known as
    A) condensation.
    B) evaporation.
    C) saturation.
    D) solidification.

Answer: A
Topic: Section 2.6

19) In the vicinity of the Equator, air typically
    A) rises, cools, and precipitates.
    B) descends, warms, and precipitates.
    C) rises, cools, and is dry.
    D) descends, warms, and is dry.

Answer: A
Topic: Section 2.7

20) During winter in the Southern Hemisphere, the intertropical convergence zone (ITCZ)
    A) sits directly over the equator.
    B) is shifted into the northern latitudes.
    C) is shifted into the southern latitudes.
    D) does not exist.

Answer: B
Topic: Section 2.7

21) Precipitation is generally greater
    A) in the Northern Hemisphere than in the Southern Hemisphere.
    B) in coastal areas than in interior areas.
    C) at horse latitudes (approximately 30⁰ of latitude) than at equatorial latitudes.
    D) on the leeward side of mountains than on the windward side.

Answer: B
Topic: Sections 2.7 and 2.8

22) Air loses moisture as it rises over a mountain for all the following reasons, except:
    A) As air cools it loses its ability to hold moisture.
    B) Air has a lower saturation water vapor at higher altitudes.
    C) Air that encounters a mountain is too heavy to rise up and over unless it loses excess water vapor.
    D) Water converts from a gaseous to liquid state.

Answer: C
Topic: Sections 2.3, 2.6, 2.8

23) Some variation in the solar radiation striking the Earth's surface is linked to _____ activity.
    A) sunspot
    B) El Niño
    C) La Niña
    D) glacial

Answer: A
Topic: Section 2.9

24) During El Niño conditions
    A) surface water temperatures are warmer in the eastern Pacific Ocean.
    B) less rainfall occurs in the eastern Pacific Ocean.
    C) trade winds across the Pacific Ocean are strong.
    D) increased upwelling of nutrient-rich water occurs in the eastern Pacific Ocean.

Answer: D
Topic: Section 2.9

25) _____ is considered a primary influence on local climate.
    A) Aspect
    B) Soil temperature
    C) Rainfall
    D) Vegetation

Answer: A
Topic: Section 2.10

26) Habitats in the Northern Hemisphere that are positioned on north-facing slopes generally _____ than those habitats situated on south-facing slopes.
    A) have a higher rate of evaporation
    B) have a greater soil moisture
    C) experience higher air temperatures
    D) experience greater fluxes in weather conditions

Answer: B
Topic: Section 2.10

27) Densely populated urban areas tend to have
    A) higher relative humidity than rural areas.
    B) higher temperatures than rural areas.
    C) higher wind speeds than rural areas.
    D) less fog than rural areas.

Answer: B
Topic: Ecological Issues: Urban Microclimates

True/False Questions

1) The physical environment influences organisms on a generational timescale.

Answer: TRUE
Topic: Introduction to Chapter 2

2) Weather is the long-term average of local, regional, or global conditions.

Answer: FALSE
Topic: Introduction to Chapter 2

3) Most of the energy from the sun that strikes Earth is used to power living systems.

Answer: FALSE
Topic: Section 2.1

4) A hotter object emits higher energy wavelengths than a cooler object.

Answer: TRUE
Topic: Section 2.1

5) Solar radiation is more direct in tropical latitudes than in temperate latitudes.

Answer: TRUE
Topic: Section 2.2

6) Mean global temperatures change with latitude and season.

Answer: TRUE
Topic: Section 2.2

7) Atmospheric temperature increases with an increase in altitude.

Answer: FALSE
Topic: Section 2.3

8) Cooler air is more dense than warmer air.

Answer: TRUE
Topic: Section 2.3

9) Masses of air and water are deflected to the left in the Northern Hemisphere and to the right in the Southern Hemisphere.

Answer: FALSE
Topic: Section 2.4

10) The complicated circulation of air in Earth's atmosphere is due to both the Earth's rotation and irregular land masses on Earth's surface.

Answer: TRUE
Topic: Section 2.4

11) Trade winds are instrumental in forming the oceanic currents that originate at the Equator.

Answer: TRUE
Topic: Section 2.5

12) The water vapor capacity of air cannot be exceeded.

Answer: TRUE
Topic: Section 2.6

13) Cold air can hold more water than warm air.

Answer: FALSE
Topic: Section 2.6

14) Rainfall in the Southern Hemisphere is greater than rainfall in the Northern Hemisphere because the oceans cover a greater proportion of the Southern Hemisphere.

Answer: TRUE
Topic: Section 2.7

15) Precipitation is highest in polar regions.

Answer: FALSE
Topic: Section 2.7

16) The intertropical convergence zone (ITCZ) tends to migrate toward regions of the globe with the warmest surface temperature.

Answer: TRUE
Topic: Section 2.7

17) Vegetation is usually more dense and vigorous on the leeward side of mountains than on the windward side.

Answer: FALSE
Topic: Section 2.8

18) Surface temperatures in the eastern Pacific Ocean are cooler during El Niño conditions than during La Niña conditions.

Answer: FALSE
Topic: Section 2.9

19) In temperate regions of the Northern Hemisphere, north-facing slopes are more humid than south-facing slopes.

Answer: TRUE
Topic: Section 2.10

20) The average temperature in a city is greater than in the surrounding open countryside.

Answer: TRUE
Topic: Ecological Issues: Urban Microclimates

Essay Questions

1) Explain the differences between weather, climate, and microclimate. Which is most important for individual organisms? Give an example.

Topic: Introduction to Chapter 2 and Section 2.10

2) Explain how or why the Earth's surface emits more energy than it receives from the sun.

Topic: Section 2.1

3) Explain why seasonality occurs and why it is more pronounced at temperate and polar latitudes.

Topic: Section 2.2

4) Explain why air temperature decreases as one moves further from Earth's surface into higher altitudes.

Topic: Section 2.3

5) Explain how the trade winds develop and why these were so important to 17th century merchant sailors.

Topic: Section 2.4

6) Explain why the saturation vapor pressure increases with air temperature. How does relative humidity change in response to air warming or cooling?

Topic: Section 2.6

7) Why is it that, in general, more rain falls in the Southern Hemisphere than in the Northern Hemisphere?

Topic: Section 2.7

8) Why do the amount of rainfall and the composition of vegetation differ greatly on the opposite sides of a mountain range?

Topic: Section 2.8

9) Compare the causes and effects of the El Niño and La Niña events.

Topic: Section 2.9

10) You study two neighboring plant populations growing at 200 meters above sea level (asl). One population is situated on a north-facing slope while the other population grows on a south-facing slope. Compare the environmental conditions and microclimates that each population experiences.

Topic: Section 2.10

11) Why does the climate of urban areas differ from that of the surrounding countryside?

Topic: Ecological Issues: Urban Microclimates

Chapter 3 The Aquatic Environment

Short Answer Questions

1) Aquatic ecosystems are divided into two major categories: freshwater and _____.

Answer: salt water, or marine
Topic: Introduction to Chapter 3

2) Precipitation that reaches the soil moves into the ground by _____.

Answer: infiltration
Topic: Section 3.1

3) The total amount of evaporating water from the surfaces of the ground and vegetation is called

_____.

Answer: evapotranspiration
Topic: Section 3.1

4) An underground layer of permeable, water-bearing substrate is known as a/an _____.

Answer: aquifer
Topic: Ecological Issues: Groundwater Resources

5) Individual water molecules are joined together by _____ bonds.

Answer: hydrogen
Topic: Section 3.2

6) The _____ of water is the amount of heat that is required to raise the temperature of water one degree Celsius.

Answer: specific heat
Topic: Section 3.2

7) _____ is the source of frictional resistance to objects moving through water.

Answer: Viscosity
Topic: Section 3.2

8) As sunlight passes through water, only _____ wavelengths are able to penetrate into deeper water.

Answer: blue
Topic: Section 3.3

9) The upper layer of warm, low-density water of an open body of water is called the _____.

Answer: epilimnion
Topic: Section 3.4

10) Water is a(n) _____ molecule.

Answer: polar
Topic: Section 3.2, 3.5

11) Compounds that consist of electrically charged atoms or groups of atoms are called _____.

Answer: ions
Topic: Section 3.5

12) The movement of molecules from an area of high concentration to an area of low concentration is called
_____.

Answer: diffusion
Topic: Section 3.6

13) The solubility of oxygen _____ as water warms.

Answer: decreases
Topic: Section 3.6

14) The solubility of gases in water is a function of pressure, salinity, and _____.

Answer: temperature
Topic: Section 3.6

15) _____ solutions are those that have a higher concentration of OH^- (hydroxyl ions) than H^+ ions.

Answer: Alkaline
Topic: Section 3.7

16) _____ is highly toxic to many species of aquatic life and thus may lead to a decline in aquatic populations.

Answer: Aluminum
Topic: Section 3.7

17) The abundance of hydrogen ions in solution is a measure of _____.

Answer: acidity
Topic: Section 3.7

18) A region of _____ occurs where deep waters of the ocean move upward to the surface.

Answer: upwelling
Topic: Section 3.8

19) The physical movements of water caused by the gravitational pull of the Sun and the Moon are called
_____.

Answer: tides
Topic: Section 3.9

20) The place where freshwater streams and rivers meet the sea and mix with saltwater is called a(n)
_____.

Answer: estuary
Topic: Section 3.10

21) Biological diversity in an estuary is generally _____ in spite of high productivity.

Answer: low
Topic: Section 3.10

Multiple–Choice Questions

1) Water is the dominant environment on Earth and covers _____ of the Earth's surface.
   A) 25 percent
   B) 50 percent
   C) 75 percent
   D) 95 percent

   Answer: C
   Topic: Introduction to Chapter 3

2) The evaporation of water from internal surfaces of leaves, stems, and other living parts of a plant is called
   A) osmosis.
   B) transpiration.
   C) diffusion.
   D) infiltration.

   Answer: B
   Topic: Section 3.1

3) In the global water cycle, which of the following is considered a "flux"?
   A) atmosphere
   B) groundwater
   C) precipitation
   D) ocean

   Answer: C
   Topic: Section 3.1

4) Most of Earth's water resides in
   A) the oceans.
   B) the polar ice caps and glaciers.
   C) freshwater lakes, ponds, rivers, and streams.
   D) groundwater.

   Answer: A
   Topic: Section 3.1

5) An aquifer refers to
   A) an intermittent spring that flows during only part of the year.
   B) a layer of water-bearing permeable rock, sand, or gravel.
   C) any freshwater body of water.
   D) the cool, dense layer of water at the bottom of a body of water.

   Answer: B
   Topic: Ecological Issues: Groundwater Resources

6) The individual atoms of a water molecule are held together by
   A) covalent bonds.
   B) hydrogen bonds.
   C) ionic bonds.
   D) weak bonds.

   Answer: A
   Topic: Section 3.2

7) Large bodies of water maintain a relatively constant temperature compared with smaller bodies of water because of water's high
    A) specific heat.
    B) viscosity.
    C) surface tension.
    D) density.

Answer: A
Topic: Section 3.2

8) The ability of water striders to glide across the surface of water is due to
    A) specific heat.
    B) buoyancy.
    C) surface tension.
    D) viscosity.

Answer: C
Topic: Section 3.2

9) Water is at its most dense state at
    A) -4°C.
    B) 0°C.
    C) 4°C.
    D) 100°C.

Answer: C
Topic: Section 3.2

10) Aquatic organisms are usually more streamlined than terrestrial organisms because of water's high
    A) buoyancy.
    B) viscosity.
    C) surface tension.
    D) density.

Answer: B
Topic: Section 3.2

11) Aquatic organisms generally require less structural support (e.g., skeletons) due to water's
    A) specific heat.
    B) buoyancy.
    C) surface tension.
    D) viscosity.

Answer: B
Topic: Section 3.2

12) As light enters water, the first wavelength/s absorbed are
    A) ultraviolet and infrared radiation.
    B) visible red light.
    C) visible blue light and ultraviolet radiation.
    D) visible red light and infrared radiation.

Answer: D
Topic: Section 3.3

13) An organism that lives in a deep marine environment may exhibit the following physical characteristics, except:
   A) large eyes.
   B) bioluminescence.
   C) colorful skin pigmentation.
   D) streamlined body.

Answer: C
Topic: Section 3.2, 3.3

14) The region of the vertical depth profile where water temperature declines most rapidly is the
   A) thermocline.
   B) hypolimnion.
   C) epilimnion.
   D) benthic zone.

Answer: A
Topic: Section 3.4

15) In temperate lakes, the thermocline is most pronounced during
   A) spring.
   B) summer.
   C) fall.
   D) winter.

Answer: B
Topic: Section 3.4

16) The depth of a thermocline is directly influenced by all the following factors, except:
   A) wind speed.
   B) wave action.
   C) input of solar radiation.
   D) influx of water.

Answer: D
Topic: Section 3.4

17) The water of the epilimnion is _____ than the water of the hypolimnion.
   A) warmer
   B) less dense
   C) cooler
   D) more oxygenated

Answer: C
Topic: Section 3.4, 3.6

18) In which form is water the most pure (contains the least solutes)?
   A) atmospheric water
   B) surface water
   C) groundwater
   D) precipitation

Answer: A
Topic: Section 3.5

19) Of the following list, which water body contains the most solutes (highest concentration)?
   A) Pacific Ocean
   B) Lake Superior
   C) Colorado River
   D) High Plains-Ogallala aquifer

Answer: A
Topic: Section 3.5

20) The primary ions that contribute to the salinity of ocean waters are
   A) calcium and sodium.
   B) sodium and chloride.
   C) sodium and carbonate.
   D) calcium and chloride.

Answer: B
Topic: Section 3.5

21) Molecules spontaneously move from an area of higher concentration to an area of lower concentration in a process known as
   A) conduction.
   B) solution.
   C) evaporation.
   D) diffusion.

Answer: D
Topic: Section 3.6

22) The primary sources of oxygen in a water body are the atmosphere and
   A) decomposition.
   B) evaporation.
   C) photosynthesis.
   D) respiration.

Answer: C
Topic: Section 3.6

23) A solution with a pH of 3
   A) is more alkaline than a solution with a pH of 2.
   B) has a higher concentration of OH^- than a solution with a pH of 4.
   C) is neutral.
   D) is more acidic than a solution with a pH of 3.5.

Answer: A
Topic: Section 3.7

24) The pH of aquatic environments
   A) remains the same regardless of the water source.
   B) may affect the solubility of toxic metals.
   C) has little influence on living organisms.
   D) is usually very acidic (pH < 3).

Answer: B
Topic: Section 3.7

25) The density of seawater increases when
    A) temperature and salinity decrease.
    B) temperature and salinity increase.
    C) temperature increases and salinity decreases.
    D) temperature decreases and salinity increases.

Answer: D
Topic: Section 3.8

26) Tides are strongest when the
    A) body of water is very large.
    B) sun is setting.
    C) Earth, Moon, and Sun are in line.
    D) Moon and Sun are at right angles to the Earth.

Answer: C
Topic: Section 3.9

27) The gravitational pull of the moon on Earth's oceans cause _____ to form on opposite sides of the Earth.
    A) intertidal zones
    B) estuaries
    C) fluctuations
    D) tidal bulges

Answer: D
Topic: Section 3.9

28) Daily and seasonal fluctuations in temperature, salinity, and dissolved gases are most extreme in
    A) the intertidal zone.
    B) sandy beaches.
    C) the estuary.
    D) the open ocean.

Answer: C
Topic: Sections 3.9 and 3.10

29) Tidal overmixing
    A) is influenced by density differences of salt and freshwater.
    B) rarely occurs in an estuary.
    C) is primarily influenced by freshwater input from upstream of the estuary.
    D) has minimal effect on the organisms living in an estuary.

Answer: A
Topic: Section 3.10

True/False Questions

1) Solar radiation is the driving force behind the water cycle.

Answer: TRUE
Topic: Section 3.1

2) The turnover rate of water in the atmosphere is nearly 3000 years.

Answer: FALSE
Topic: Section 3.1

3) Aquifers, like the High-Plains Ogallala aquifer, provide a limitless supply of water.

Answer: FALSE
Topic: Ecological Issues: Groundwater Resources

4) Individual water molecules are held together by covalent bonds.

Answer: FALSE
Topic: Section 3.2

5) Temperatures fluctuate less in aquatic habitats than in terrestrial habitats.

Answer: TRUE
Topic: Section 3.2

6) Under standard atmospheric conditions, the density of water is the same as the density of air.

Answer: FALSE
Topic: Section 3.2

7) Of the visible light spectrum, green wavelengths penetrate the deepest into water.

Answer: FALSE
Topic: Section 3.3

8) The position of the thermocline is a permanent feature in tropical waters.

Answer: TRUE
Topic: Section 3.4

9) In lakes and ponds of temperate latitudes, the upper and bottom layers of water usually turn over during fall.

Answer: TRUE
Topic: Section 3.4

10) Freshwater has a higher concentration of solutes than seawater.

Answer: FALSE
Topic: Section 3.5

11) Cold water can hold more oxygen than warm water can.

Answer: TRUE
Topic: Section 3.6

12) The diffusion of gases through water is slowed because of water's high density.

Answer: TRUE
Topic: Section 3.6

13) A high pH indicates a very acidic solution.

Answer: FALSE
Topic: Section 3.7

14) Aluminum is toxic to many aquatic species.

Answer: TRUE
Topic: Section 3.7

15) A wave is formed of particles of water that are transported long distances across a stretch of open water.

Answer: FALSE
Topic: Section 3.8

16) Major tides are influenced by only the moon, not the sun.

Answer: FALSE
Topic: Section 3.9

17) Tides are not entirely regular, nor are they the same all over the Earth.

Answer: TRUE
Topic: Section 3.9

18) The salinity in an estuary varies vertically and horizontally.

Answer: TRUE
Topic: Section 3.10

Essay Questions

1) Describe the water cycle and explain how it arrives at various reservoirs where it is stored.
Topic: Section 3.1

2) Discuss the importance of the High Plains-Ogallala aquifer to agriculture in the United States.
Topic: Ecological Issues: Groundwater Resources

3) Use examples to describe several physical and chemical properties of water that affect life on Earth.
Topic: Section 3.2

4) Describe several adaptations that organisms have developed in response to the minimal light environments in deep water.
Topic: Section 3.3

5) Compare the temperature profile of Lake Tahoe (on the border of California and Nevada) in each season and explain why the profiles change.
Topic: Section 3.4

6) Explain why water can dissolve more substances than any other liquid. Furthermore, explain the importance of this property to life on Earth.
Topic: Section 3.5

7) Explain how pH of an aquatic environment can influence the organisms that live in or around the water body.
Topic: Section 3.7

8) Describe how the action of water (e.g., waves) shapes the environments that it occurs in.
Topic: Section 3.8

9) How do tides form? Explain why tides are not always the same size and why tides vary from place to place.
Topic: Section 3.9

10) Define an estuary, and describe how gradients in salinity are maintained.
Topic: Section 3.10

Chapter 4 The Terrestrial Environment

Short Answer Questions

1) The _____ conditions within a region impose the primary constraints on plant and animal life.

Answer: physical
Topic: Introduction to Chapter 4

2) The aboveground parts (e.g., leaves) of most plants are coated with a waxy _____ that reduces water loss.

Answer: cuticle
Topic: Section 4.1

3) The two physical factors that vary most in terrestrial environments are _____ and _____.

Answer: temperature; precipitation
Topic: Section 4.1

4) _____ are the dominant factor that influence the vertical gradient of light in terrestrial environments.

Answer: Plants
Topic: Section 4.2

5) The wavelengths that make up the visible light spectrum are referred to as _____ radiation.

Answer: photosynthetically active
Topic: Section 4.2

6) Patches of light that penetrate the canopy of a forest and reach the forest floor are called _____.

Answer: sunflecks
Topic: Section 4.2

7) The vertical reduction or _____ of light through a stand can be estimated by leaf area index.

Answer: attenuation
Topic: Quantifying Ecology: Beer's Law and the Attenuation of Light

8) The layer of unconsolidated debris overlaying the layer of hard, unweathered rock is called the

_____.

Answer: regolith
Topic: Section 4.3

9) It is agreed that soil is teeming with life and is a three-dimensional unit, having length, _____, and depth.

Answer: width
Topic: Section 4.3

10) A rock that is broken into smaller fragments as a result of freezing and thawing has experienced _____ weathering.

Answer: mechanical
Topic: Section 4.4

11) The parent material of soils may originate from underlying bedrock or be deposited by glacial, eolian (wind), gravitational, or _____ processes.

Answer: fluvial
Topic: Section 4.5

12) The movement of solutes through the soil is known as _____.

Answer: leaching
Topic: Section 4.5

13) _____ particles control the water-holding capacity of soil and ion exchange.

Answer: Clay
Topic: Section 4.6

14) Although it can be used to determine important physical and chemical properties, _____ has little effect on soil function.

Answer: color
Topic: Section 4.6

15) _____ is a property of soils that is determined by the different sizes and types of particles in soils.

Answer: Soil texture
Topic: Section 4.6

16) _____-sized particles are between 0.002 and 0.05 mm in diameter.

Answer: Sand
Topic: Section 4.6

17) A collective sequence of horizontal layers in soil is a _____.

Answer: soil profile
Topic: Section 4.7

18) Distinct layers in the soil that are created by localized chemical and physical processes are called _____.

Answer: horizons
Topic: Section 4.7

19) _____ is the process of maximum leaching from the E horizon of a soil profile.

Answer: Eluviation
Topic: Section 4.7

20) When the amount of water in a soil exceeds what the pore space can hold, it is _____.

Answer: saturated
Topic: Section 4.8

21) The _____ point is the stage at which the moisture level in soil decreases to a level at which plants can no longer extract water.

Answer: wilting
Topic: Section 4.8

22) Particle size of the soil directly influences the _____ and the surface area onto which water adheres.

Answer: pore size
Topic: Section 4.8

23) _____ are negatively charged particles in the soil that attract cations.

Answer: Colloids or anions
Topic: Section 4.9

24) The _____ is a basic measure of soil quality and increases with higher clay and organic matter content.

Answer: cation exchange capacity (CEC)
Topic: Section 4.9

25) A measure of the degree of acidity or alkalinity of a soil is _____.

Answer: pH
Topic: Section 4.9

26) Regions that are subjected to heavy volcanic activity have dark soils called _____.

Answer: andisols
Topic: Section 4.10

27) _____ are soils that are low in organic matter and are found in arid and semiarid regions.

Answer: Aridisols
Topic: Section 4.10

28) In low-lying areas with poor drainage, _____ results in a black or bluish-gray soil with a high organic content.

Answer: gleization
Topic: Section 4.10

Multiple-Choice Questions

1) Perhaps the greatest constraint imposed on life in terrestrial environments is
    A) low nutrient availability.
    B) ultraviolet radiation.
    C) access to water.
    D) difficulty of dispersal.

Answer: C
Topic: Section 4.1

2) Organisms that live in aquatic systems experience limited temperature fluctuations due to water's
    A) high specific heat.
    B) high viscosity.
    C) high surface tension.
    D) covalent nature.

Answer: A
Topic: Section 4.1

3) Each of the following is a challenge faced by a terrestrial plant except:
    A) buoyancy.
    B) dessication.
    C) cells and tissues to maintain structure.
    D) variability in air temperature.

Answer: A
Topic: Section 4.1

4) Leaf area index (LAI)
    A) is calculated by counting the number of leaves in a forest canopy.
    B) is lowest for leaves held perpendicular to the sun's rays.
    C) is the primary influence on the attenuation of light in terrestrial environments.
    D) is the same regardless of season.

Answer: C
Topic: Section 4.2

5) Which wavelength of light penetrates through plant cover the furthest?
    A) violet (400 nm)
    B) far-red (730 nm)
    C) red (660 nm)
    D) green (500 nm)

Answer: B
Topic: Section 4.2

6) In which season would the leaf area index (LAI) of a temperate deciduous forest be lowest?
    A) fall
    B) spring
    C) summer
    D) winter

Answer: D
Topic: Section 4.2

7) In a temperate deciduous forest, photosynthetically active radiation (PAR) is greatest in _____.
    A) fall
    B) spring
    C) summer
    D) winter

Answer: C
Topic: Section 4.2 (Figure 4.6)

8) The general relationship between available light and leaf area index (LAI) is described by
    A) Bohr's law.
    B) Beer's law.
    C) Leibig's law.
    D) The Central Limit Theorem.

Answer: B
Topic: Quantifying Ecology: Beer's Law and the Attenuation of Light

9) All the following are factors that affect the attenuation of light in water, except:
    A) phytoplankton.
    B) water itself.
    C) intensity of light.
    D) dissolved substances.

Answer: D
Topic: Quantifying Ecology: Beer's Law and the Attenuation of Light

10) Which of the following is not considered an important function of soil?
    A) to provide a heat source to plants and animals
    B) to control the fate of water in terrestrial environments
    C) to break down and transform the waste products of plants and animals
    D) to provide habitat for a diversity of life

Answer: A
Topic: Section 4.3

11) The mechanical destruction and/or chemical modification of rock into smaller particles is called
    A) leaching.
    B) mineralization.
    C) percolation.
    D) weathering.

Answer: D
Topic: Section 4.4

12) The unconsolidated mass from which different types of soil can develop is called the
    A) mantle.
    B) parent material.
    C) lacustrine.
    D) till.

Answer: B
Topic: Section 4.5

13) Under which conditions are the processes of weathering, leaching, and input of organic material from plants into soil maximized?
    A) warm temperatures and abundant water
    B) cool temperatures and abundant water
    C) cool temperatures and scarce water
    D) warm temperatures and scarce water

Answer: A
Topic: Section 4.5

14) Which of the following statements is incorrect?
    A) Topography affects the erosion of parent material.
    B) Soil develops very rapidly, within several years.
    C) Plants move nutrients from deep in the soil to the surface.
    D) Plant roots stabilize the soil surface.

Answer: B
Topic: Section 4.5

15) Soil particles are classified based on
    A) age.
    B) color.
    C) water content.
    D) size.

Answer: D
Topic: Section 4.6

16) You examine a soil that is quite dark, even black. Because of this, you know that this soil has a high content of
    A) iron.
    B) calcium.
    C) humus.
    D) gypsum.

Answer: C
Topic: Section 4.6

17) Which of the following soil textures would have the largest pore spaces?
    A) clay
    B) gravel
    C) sand
    D) silt

Answer: C
Topic: Section 4.6

18) In general, the soils in or on _____ are the most shallow.
    A) steep slopes
    B) native grasslands
    C) valleys
    D) floodplains

Answer: A
Topic: Section 4.6

19) Organized layers of soil are known as
    A) profiles.
    B) tills.
    C) regoliths.
    D) horizons.

Answer: D
Topic: Section 4.7

20) The O horizon
    A) is the area of maximum deposition of nutrients as a result of illuviation.
    B) contains intact and decomposing organic material.
    C) is composed of very large soil particles.
    D) is often referred to as topsoil.

Answer: B
Topic: Section 4.7

21) Clay particles and salts tend to accumulate in the _____ horizon.
    A) A
    B) B
    C) C
    D) O

Answer: B
Topic: Section 4.7

22) The available water capacity is
   A) the water available for plant uptake.
   B) the same as the saturation point.
   C) equal to the difference between the saturation point and field capacity.
   D) unaffected by pore size.

Answer: A
Topic: Section 4.8

23) When the amount of water in soil exceeds what the pore space can hold, the soil is
   A) at field capacity.
   B) at the wilting point.
   C) saturated.
   D) dessicated.

Answer: C
Topic: Section 4.8

24) Which of the following soils holds the most water?
   A) a clay loam on a ridgetop
   B) a sandy loam in a valley
   C) a clay loam in a valley
   D) a sandy loam on a ridgetop

Answer: C
Topic: Section 4.8

25) When compared with sandy soils, clay soils have _____ wilting point.
   A) a lower
   B) a higher
   C) the same
   D) no

Answer: A
Topic: Section 4.8

26) Which of the following is a common soil anion?
   A) NH_4^+
   B) Ca^{2+}
   C) NO_3^-
   D) Mg^{2+}

Answer: C
Topic: Section 4.9

27) As soil acidity increases, the concentration of _____ is relatively unchanged.
   A) Ca^{2+}
   B) Al^{3+}
   C) Na^+
   D) SO_4^{2-}

Answer: D
Topic: Section 4.9

28) Generally, an ion with a _____ positive charge and _____ size will bind most strongly to a soil particle.
   A) greater, smaller
   B) smaller, larger
   C) smaller, smaller
   D) greater, larger

Answer: A
Topic: Section 4.9

29) Which of the following tends to displace cations from soil exchange sites as pH decreases?
   A) Ca^{2+}
   B) NH_4^+
   C) H^+
   D) SO_4^{2-}

Answer: C
Topic: Section 4.9

30) Which soil has a high, dark clay content and shows significant expansion and contraction due to wetting and drying?
   A) Mollisol
   B) Vertisol
   C) Spodosol
   D) Andisol

Answer: B
Topic: Section 4.10

31) Which of the following is an incorrect match between the soil-forming process and the resulting soil order?
   A) laterization-Ultisol
   B) podzolization-Spodosol
   C) gleization-Gelisol
   D) calcification-Aridisol

Answer: D
Topic: Section 4.10

32) Which of the following is an incorrect description of the given soil order?
   A) Inceptisols experience intense leaching and are generally found in humid, warm climates.
   B) Histosols are indicative of bogs and have a high content of organic matter.
   C) Oxisols are found in the tropics and subtropics and are highly weathered.
   D) The surface horizons of Mollisols are dark brown to black with a soft consistency.

Answer: A
Topic: Section 4.10

33) This process is a problem in agricultural areas where irrigation is prevalent.
   A) calcification
   B) gleization
   C) laterization
   D) salinization

Answer: D
Topic: Section 4.10

True/False Questions

1) The greatest limitation faced by terrestrial organisms is low nutrient availability.

Answer: FALSE
Topic: Section 4.1

2) Air is less dense than water and, as a result, decreases the effect of gravity on terrestrial organisms.

Answer: FALSE
Topic: Section 5.1

3) Aquatic environments are relatively stable because water requires a large amount of energy to change states.

Answer: TRUE
Topic: Section 4.1

4) In terrestrial environments, the dominant factor that influences the vertical gradient of light is the absorption and reflection of solar radiation by water vapor in the air.

Answer: FALSE
Topic: Section 4.2

5) The lower the leaf area index (LAI) above the forest floor, the lower the quantity of light reaching the forest floor.

Answer: FALSE
Topic: Section 4.2

6) In high-latitude habitats, forest canopies that have leaves displayed at an angle will absorb light more effectively.

Answer: TRUE
Topic: Section 4.2

7) Beer's law can be used to describe the attenuation of light in both aquatic and terrestrial environments.

Answer: TRUE
Topic: Quantifying Ecology: Beer's Law and the Attenuation of Light

8) The application of Beer's law to attenuation of light in aquatic environments is more complex than in terrestrial environments.

Answer: TRUE
Topic: Quantifying Ecology: Beer's Law and the Attenuation of Light

9) Soil is best described as an abiotic environment for plants.

Answer: FALSE
Topic: Section 4.3

10) Tree roots growing through rock and splitting the rock into smaller pieces is an example of mechanical weathering.

Answer: TRUE
Topic: Section 4.4

11) Heavy rainfall results in heavy soil leaching and rapid chemical weathering.

Answer: TRUE
Topic: Section 4.5

12) The formation of well-developed soils takes approximately 500 years.

Answer: FALSE
Topic: Section 4.5

13) More rainfall enters the soil on steep slopes than on level land.

Answer: FALSE
Topic: Section 4.5

14) Iron oxides give soil a purplish to black color.

Answer: FALSE
Topic: Section 4.6

15) In forests, most of the organic matter that enters the soil comes from plant roots.

Answer: FALSE
Topic: Section 4.6

16) The soil in a particular area is arranged in layers called horizons that will vary in texture, structure, and consistency from one another.

Answer: TRUE
Topic: Section 4.7

17) The E horizon in soils is characterized by an accumulation of mineral particles.

Answer: FALSE
Topic: Section 4.7

18) The bedrock lies above the C horizon.

Answer: FALSE
Topic: Section 4.7

19) Clay soils have smaller pores and hold considerably less water than sandy soils.

Answer: FALSE
Topic: Section 4.8

20) Soils on ridgetops are generally drier than valley soils.

Answer: TRUE
Topic: Section 4.8

21) Field water is the water held between soil particles by capillary forces.

Answer: FALSE
Topic: Section 4.8

22) Clay particles carry a negative charge and bind to cations in the soil solution.

Answer: TRUE
Topic: Section 4.9

23) The cation exchange capacity (CEC) of soils decreases with higher clay and organic matter content.

Answer: FALSE
Topic: Section 4.9

24) An increase in soil acidity is responsible for releasing soluble aluminum, which can be toxic to plant roots.

Answer: TRUE
Topic: Section 4.9

25) Gelisols are characteristic of the high latitudes in the Northern Hemisphere.

Answer: TRUE
Topic: Section 4.10

26) Vertisols are immature soils associated with recently deposited sediments.

Answer: FALSE
Topic: Section 4.10

27) Salinization results in the buildup of salts in the B horizon of soils.

Answer: FALSE
Topic: Section 4.10

28) Laterization is a soil-forming process that is typical of cool, moist climates at high latitudes.

Answer: FALSE
Topic: Section 4.10

Essay Questions

1) Describe three structural adaptations of terrestrial plants that allow them survive on land.
Topic: Section 4.1

2) Explain why leaves that are not parallel to the ground are beneficial to plants living in arid environments and high-latitude forests.
Topic: Section 4.2

3) Give several possible definitions of "soil." Why is it difficult to develop a good definition of soil, even for a pedologist?
Topic: Section 4.3

4) Explain and give examples of how mechanical and chemical weathering lead to the formation of soils.
Topic: Section 4.4

5) List and briefly describe the five interdependent factors that are crucial to soil formation.
Topic: Section 4.5

6) Define soil texture and describe two different ways that texture may influence the soil function.
Topic: Section 4.6

7) Draw a typical soil profile. Label and describe each of the four horizons.
Topic: Section 4.7

8) What factor largely determines the available water capacity (AWC) of soil? Why is this so? Name two additional factors that contribute to the AWC.
Topic: Section 4.8

9) Define soil fertility and explain why cation exchange capacity (CEC) is integral to the maintenance of soil fertility.

Topic: Section 4.9

10) Explain one example of the influence of climate and vegetation on the type of soil that develops in an area.

Topic: Section 4.10

Chapter 5 Ecological Genetics: Adaptation and Natural Selection

Short Answer Questions

1) An organism's structure and _____ reflect adaptations to its particular environment.

   Answer: function
   Topic: Introduction to Part 2

2) The acquisition of _____ is probably the most fundamental constraint to life.

   Answer: energy
   Topic: Introduction to Part 2

3) An organism that derives its energy from sunlight is a(n) _____.

   Answer: autotroph, or primary producer
   Topic: Introduction to Part 2

4) _____ is the differential success of individuals in a population in response to environmental conditions.

   Answer: Natural selection
   Topic: Section 5.1

5) The proportionate contribution that an individual makes to future generations is called its _____.

   Answer: fitness
   Topic: Section 5.1

6) The basic informational units of DNA are called _____.

   Answer: genes
   Topic: Section 5.2

7) A _____ individual has the same alleles at the same locus on homologous chromosomes.

   Answer: homozygous
   Topic: Section 5.2

8) The position occupied by a gene on the chromosome is called the _____.

   Answer: locus
   Topic: Section 5.2

9) If the physical expression of a heterozygous individual is intermediate between those of the homozygotes, the alleles are _____.

   Answer: codominant
   Topic: Section 5.3

10) The outward appearance of an organism for a given characteristic is called its _____.

   Answer: phenotype
   Topic: Section 5.3

11) Phenotypic characteristics that fall into a limited number of discrete categories are considered _____ traits.

   Answer: qualitative
   Topic: Section 5.3

12) When genetic variation occurs among subpopulations of the same species it is known as genetic
_____.
Answer: differentiation
Topic: Section 5.4

13) The total collection of alleles across all individuals in a population at any one time is called the
_____.
Answer: gene pool
Topic: Section 5.4

14) Phenotypic evolution is a change in _____ over time within a population.
Answer: allele frequencies
Topic: Section 5.5

15) The type of natural selection in which the mean value of a trait is shifted toward one extreme is called
_____ selection.
Answer: directional
Topic: Section 5.5

16) _____ are inheritable changes in a gene or chromosome.
Answer: Mutations
Topic: Section 5.6

17) _____ is the movement of individuals between local populations.
Answer: Migration
Topic: Section 5.6

18) _____ mating occurs when individuals choose mates nonrandomly.
Answer: Assortative
Topic: Section 5.6

19) The Hardy-Weinberg principle assumes _____ mating.
Answer: random
Topic: Quantifying Ecology 5.1: Hardy-Weinberg Principle

20) A(n) _____ is a measurable, gradual change over a geographic region in the average value of a trait.
Answer: cline
Topic: Section 5.7

21) A(n) _____ is a population that has adapted to its unique local environmental conditions.
Answer: ecotype
Topic: Section 5.7

22) The _____ of any phenotype is a function of the prevailing environmental conditions.
Answer: fitness
Topic: Section 5.8

23) The process by which one species gives rise to multiple species that exploit different features of the
environment is called _____.
Answer: adaptive radiation
Topic: Section 5.8

24) Researcher Beren Robinson has studied sticklebacks inhabiting two habitat types: benthic and

_____.

Answer: limnetic
Topic: Field Studies: Beren Robinson

25) The ability of a genotype to give rise to a variety of phenotypic expressions under different environmental conditions is called _____.

Answer: phenotypic plasticity
Topic: Field Studies: Beren Robinson, Section 5.9

26) Organisms can respond to both temporal and _____ changes in the environment.

Answer: spatial
Topic: Section 5.9

27) Bacteria may become resistant to an antibiotic via mutation, plasmid transfer, or _____.

Answer: transformation
Topic: Ecological Issues: The Ecology of Antibiotic Resistance

Multiple-Choice Questions

1) The mechanism of evolution proposed by Darwin is
   A) mutation.
   B) natural selection.
   C) inheritance.
   D) adaptation.

Answer: B
Topic: Introduction to Chapter 5

2) Natural selection is a function of
   A) reproduction.
   B) survival.
   C) survival and size.
   D) reproduction and survival.

Answer: D
Topic: Section 5.1

3) The specific traits of a particular organism in a given environment are called
   A) mutations.
   B) genes.
   C) adaptations.
   D) phenotypes.

Answer: C
Topic: Section 5.1

4) In relationship to natural selection and subsequent evolution, fitness
   A) represents the physical stamina of an organism.
   B) is inherited.
   C) increases with body size.
   D) is a measure of lifespan.

Answer: B
Topic: Section 5.1

5) The mechanism of evolution that Darwin presents in *The Origin of Species* is
   A) genetic drift.
   B) natural selection.
   C) plasticity.
   D) acclimatization.

Answer: B
Topic: Section 5.1

6) Evolution is a generational change in
   A) phenotypes.
   B) mutations.
   C) gene frequencies.
   D) heritability of characteristics.

Answer: C
Topic: Section 5.1

7) The identity of the alleles at a given locus is the
   A) genotype.
   B) phenotype.
   C) heterozygote.
   D) chromosome

Answer: A
Topic: Section 5.2

8) The alternate forms of a gene are called
   A) chromosomes.
   B) loci.
   C) alleles.
   D) genomes.

Answer: C
Topic: Section 5.2

9) An allele that completely masks the effect of another allele is considered
   A) codominant.
   B) dominant.
   C) ineffective.
   D) recessive.

Answer: B
Topic: Section 5.3

10) What color are the eyes of a bird heterozygous for eye color (A = yellow, a = blue)?
    A) blue
    B) green
    C) yellow
    D) white

Answer: C
Topic: Section 5.3

11) Which of the following characteristics is an example of a qualitative trait?
   A) flower color
   B) arm length
   C) body weight
   D) root length

Answer: A
Topic: Section 5.3

12) The sum of all alleles across all individuals in the population is called the
   A) phenotype frequency.
   B) gene pool.
   C) allele assemblage.
   D) genetic equilibration.

Answer: B
Topic: Section 5.4

13) Researchers Rosemary and Peter Grant have discovered that beak size frequency of Galapagos Island medium ground finch populations varies with all the following, except:
   A) rainfall.
   B) seed hardness.
   C) seed size.
   D) seed color.

Answer: D
Topic: Section 5.5

14) If birds with larger beaks are favored by the environment, it is likely that _____ selection will occur.
   A) directional
   B) disruptive
   C) stabilizing
   D) standardizing

Answer: A
Topic: Section 5.5

15) A bimodal distribution of a trait in a population is the result of
   A) stabilizing selection.
   B) natural selection.
   C) directional selection.
   D) disruptive selection.

Answer: D
Topic: Section 5.5

16) What is the primary *original* source of genetic variation in a population?
   A) mutation
   B) genetic drift
   C) blending inheritance
   D) cloning

Answer: A
Topic: Section 5.6

17) A change in allele frequency due to random chance is known as
    A) inbreeding.
    B) mutation.
    C) migration.
    D) genetic drift.

Answer: D
Topic: Section 5.6

18) Under which of the following conditions would genetic drift exert the greatest influence?
    A) a population with a large range
    B) a small population
    C) a very large population
    D) a population that has access to sufficient resources

Answer: B
Topic: Section 5.6

19) The effect of positive assortative mating is to
    A) increase the number of homozygotes in the population.
    B) increase the number of hetozygotes in the population.
    C) reduce the number of individuals with diseases in the population.
    D) increase the fertility of individuals in the population.

Answer: A
Topic: Section 5.6

20) According to the Hardy-Weinberg principle, the following must be true for gene frequencies in a population to remain the same.
    A) Mating is random.
    B) Mutations occur consistently.
    C) The population is small.
    D) Natural selection occurs.

Answer: A
Topic: Quantifying Ecology 5.1: Hardy-Weinberg Principle

21) In the Hardy-Weinberg equation $P + H + Q = 1$, what does "Q" represent?
    A) the total number of individuals in the population
    B) the frequency of heterozygotes
    C) the frequency of dominant homozygotes
    D) the frequency of recessive homozygotes

Answer: D
Topic: Quantifying Ecology 5.1: Hardy-Weinberg Principle

22) A population that is adapted to its unique local environmental conditions is called a(n)
    A) clinal population.
    B) subspecies.
    C) geographic isolate.
    D) ecotype.

Answer: D
Topic: Section 5.7

23) Geographic isolates of a particular species (e.g., *Plethodon* of the Appalachian highlands) are considered
   A) genetically stable.
   B) subspecies.
   C) an evolutionary "dead end."
   D) an ecotype.

Answer: B
Topic: Section 5.7

24) Individual beak size of individual finches of the Galapagos islands
   A) may change during a bird's lifetime.
   B) will always match the beak size useful for seed foraging.
   C) has nothing to do with overall population characteristics.
   D) will greatly influence individual survival.

Answer: D
Topic: Section 5.8

25) Adaptive radiation
   A) is the mechanism of evolution.
   B) results in new specialized species.
   C) reduces diversity.
   D) is the result of fixed environmental conditions.

Answer: B
Topic: Section 5.8

26) Researcher Beren Robinson has documented divergent natural selection in several populations of
   A) stickleback.
   B) salamander.
   C) finch.
   D) white-tailed deer.

Answer: A
Topic: Field Studies: Beren Robinson

27) The simplest response an individual organism can make to a change in environmental conditions is to
   A) remain still.
   B) move to a more suitable location.
   C) produce offspring that are better suited to the new conditions.
   D) reduce foraging activity.

Answer: B
Topic: Section 5.9

28) Reversible phenotypic changes of an individual organism in response to changing environmental conditions are referred to as
   A) acclimation.
   B) evolution.
   C) selection.
   D) norm of reaction.

Answer: A
Topic: Section 5.9

29) Bacteria may acquire genes that confer antibiotic resistance in all of the following ways except:
   A) mutation.
   B) transformation.
   C) plasmid transfer.
   D) recombination following sexual reproduction.

Answer: D
Topic: Ecological Issues: The Ecology of Antibiotic Resistance

True/False Questions

1) All living things assimilate energy, reproduce, and respond to stimuli.

Answer: TRUE
Topic: Introduction to Part 2

2) Charles Darwin advocated a theory of evolution by individuals acquiring useful characteristics during their lifetimes.

Answer: FALSE
Topic: Section 5.1

3) An individual evolves during its lifetime.

Answer: FALSE
Topic: Section 5.1

4) Heritability is not an essential feature of natural selection.

Answer: FALSE
Topic: Sections 5.1 and 5.2

5) Genes are arranged in threadlike bodies called chromosomes.

Answer: TRUE
Topic: Section 5.2

6) Genes are discrete subunits of chromosomes that form the informational units of the DNA molecule.

Answer: TRUE
Topic: Section 5.2

7) Most traits are influenced by only one locus.

Answer: FALSE
Topic: Section 5.3

8) Evolution is defined as a change in phenotypic frequencies over time in a population.

Answer: FALSE
Topic: Section 5.3

9) Species are generally limited to a single isolated population.

Answer: FALSE
Topic: Section 5.4

10) Peter and Rosemary Grant documented natural selection and evolution in a population of finches in the Galapagos Islands.

Answer: TRUE
Topic: Section 5.5

11) Disruptive selection favors individuals possessing traits near the mean value of a population.

Answer: FALSE
Topic: Section 5.5

12) Genetic variation is essential for natural selection.

Answer: TRUE
Topic: Section 5.6

13) Inbreeding is usually beneficial to a population because it increases genetic diversity.

Answer: FALSE
Topic: Section 5.6

14) In natural populations, the assumptions of the Hardy-Weinberg principle are usually met.

Answer: FALSE
Topic: Quantifying Ecology 5.1: Hardy-Weinberg Principle

15) Ecotypes are variants within a species that are adapted to local environmental conditions.

Answer: TRUE
Topic: Section 5.7

16) Gene flow is restricted for geographic isolates because of some extrinsic barrier.

Answer: TRUE
Topic: Section 5.7

17) Variation within and among species would increase dramatically if the environment were homogenous.

Answer: FALSE
Topic: Section 5.8

18) Often, characteristics that give an individual an advantage in one environment will be a disadvantage in other environments.

Answer: TRUE
Topic: Section 5.8

19) Phenotypic plasticity is the ability of a population to adapt to changing environmental conditions.

Answer: FALSE
Topic: Field Studies: Beren Robinson, Section 5.9

20) Some of the best examples of phenotypic plasticity occur among plants.

Answer: TRUE
Topic: Section 5.9

21) Changes due to developmental plasticity are reversible.

Answer: FALSE
Topic: Section 5.9

22) Humans have contributed to the prevalence of resistant bacteria by inappropriate use of antibiotics.

Answer: TRUE
Topic: Ecological Issues: The Ecology of Antibiotic Resistance

Essay Questions

1) Describe the general relationship between an autotroph and a heterotroph.

   Topic: Introduction to Part 2

2) Describe the two main conditions for evolution by natural selection as offered by Darwin in *The Origin of Species.*

   Topic: Section 5.1

3) Use an example to explain how and why the genotype and environment influence the phenotype of an organism.

   Topic: Section 5.3

4) Describe the differences between stabilizing, disruptive, and directional selection.

   Topic: Section 5.5

5) Explain how the effects of mutation, genetic drift, and gene flow influence the genetic variation of a population.

   Topic: Section 5.6

6) List the five conditions for a lack of evolution, according to the Hardy-Weinberg principle. Explain how these factors might contribute to population stasis.

   Topic: Quantifying Ecology 5.1: Hardy-Weinberg Principle

7) Explain the ecotype concept.

   Topic: Section 5.7

8) Explain the concept of a trade-off and suggest how this idea relates to the diversity of species we see among different habitats.

   Topic: Section 5.8, Field Studies: Beren Robinson

9) According to the research of Beren Robinson, how would you expect stickleback species to differ between two lakes, one of which supports two species of stickleback and the other has a single species?

   Topic: Field Studies: Beren Robinson

10) Explain the difference between phenotypic plasticity and adaptation, and suggest how you would collect data that would distinguish between them.

   Topic: Section 5.9

11) Explain how the phenomenon of antibiotic resistance in bacteria provides an excellent example of rapid evolution by natural selection.

   Topic: Ecological Issues: The Ecology of Antibiotic Resistance

Chapter 6 Plant Adaptations to the Environment

Short Answer Questions

1) All life is _____ based.

    Answer: carbon
    Topic: Introduction to Chapter 6

2) The stage of photosynthesis during which chlorophyll absorbs light energy is called the _____.

    Answer: light reactions
    Topic: Section 6.1

3) The enzyme that catalyzes carboxylation during photosynthesis is called _____.

    Answer: rubisco
    Topic: Section 6.1

4) The portion of sunlight that is available to plants for photosynthesis is called _____.

    Answer: photosynthetically active radiation (PAR)
    Topic: Section 6.2

5) The light level at which the rate of carbon uptake in photosynthesis equals the rate of carbon loss in respiration is the _____ point.

    Answer: light compensation
    Topic: Section 6.2

6) The process of photosynthesis in plants occurs in specialized cells within the leaf called _____ cells.

    Answer: mesophyll
    Topic: Section 6.3

7) _____ are openings in the leaves of terrestrial plants that allow for the uptake of CO_2.

    Answer: Stomata
    Topic: Section 6.3

8) The process of water loss by plants through stomata is called _____.

    Answer: transpiration
    Topic: Section 6.3

9) The force exerted outward on a plant cell wall by the water contained in the cell is called _____.

    Answer: turgor pressure
    Topic: Section 6.4

10) The tendency of a solution to attract water molecules from areas of high to low concentration is called its _____.

    Answer: osmotic potential
    Topic: Section 6.4

11) The ratio of carbon fixed (photosynthesis) per unit of water lost (transpiration) is called the _____.

    Answer: water-use efficiency
    Topic: Section 6.4

12) Once dissolved in water, the CO_2 molecule reacts with water to form _____.

Answer: bicarbonate (HCO_3^-)
Topic: Section 6.5

13) The diffusion of CO_2 in water is _____ than the diffusion of CO_2 in air.

Answer: slower
Topic: Section 6.5

14) Terrestrial plants exchange heat by convection and _____.

Answer: evaporation
Topic: Section 6.6

15) Leaf shape and size influences the thickness and dynamics of the _____ layer and therefore the ability of plants to exchange heat through _____.

Answer: boundary, convection
Topic: Section 6.6

16) Under ideal conditions, the allocation of carbon to the further production of _____ tissue will promote the fastest growth.

Answer: leaf
Topic: Section 6.7

17) _____ tissue provides vertical support to the plant and elevates leaves.

Answer: Stem
Topic: Section 6.7

18) To survive, grow, and reproduce, plants must maintain a _____ carbon balance.

Answer: positive
Topic: Sections 6.7 and 6.8

19) A plant growing in a sun is expected to have a _____ maximum photosynthetic rate than a plant growing in shade.

Answer: higher, or greater
Topic: Section 6.9

20) The ratio of surface area to weight for a leaf is called the _____.

Answer: specific leaf area (SLA)
Topic: Section 6.9 and Quantifying Ecology 6.1

21) _____ expresses the change in size of an individual during the observed period of time as a function of the size of the individual.

Answer: Relative growth rate (RGR)
Topic: Quantifying Ecology 6.1

22) _____ is the component of relative growth rate that represents the leaf area per unit of plant weight.

Answer: Leaf area ratio (LAR)
Topic: Quantifying Ecology 6.1

23) In studies of shade-tolerant and shade-intolerant tropical rain forest species, Kaoru Kitajima found that seed mass is negatively correlated with seedling _____ rates.

Answer: mortality
Topic: Field Studies: Kaoru Kitajima

24) Two contrasting functional forms of cotyledons found in tropical rain forest trees are storage and

_____ .

Answer: photosynthesis
Topic: Field Studies: Kaoru Kitajima

25) In tropical regions with distinct wet and dry seasons, plants that drop their leaves at the onset of the dry season are termed _____ .

Answer: drought deciduous
Topic: Section 6.10

26) C_4 plants use the enzyme _____ to fix CO_2.

Answer: PEP carboxylase
Topic: Section 6.10

27) Many plants adapted to arid environments utilize the _____ photosynthetic pathway to fix CO_2 during the night.

Answer: crassulacean acid metabolism (CAM)
Topic: Section 6.10

28) Some plants have the ability to tolerate extreme cold, known as _____ .

Answer: frost hardening
Topic: Section 6.11

29) Nutrients that are needed by plants in large amounts are called _____ .

Answer: macronutrients
Topic: Section 6.12

30) Much of the nitrogen taken in by a plant is used to synthesis the molecules rubisco and _____ .

Answer: chlorophyll
Topic: Section 6.12

31) Spongy passages, or _____ , allow for the transport of oxygen and other gases to submerged roots.

Answer: aerenchyma
Topic: Section 6.13

32) Plants adapted to saline habitats are called _____ .

Answer: halophytes
Topic: Section 6.13

Multiple-Choice Questions

1) The ultimate source of carbon from which life is constructed is derived from
    A) atmospheric carbon dioxide.
    B) respiration.
    C) decomposition.
    D) the consumption of other organisms.

Answer: A
Topic: Introduction to Chapter 6

2) Organisms that derive their energy from sunlight are referred to as
    A) heterotrophs.
    B) chemotrophs.
    C) autotrophs.
    D) None of the above

Answer: C
Topic: Introduction to Chapter 6

3) The process of converting CO_2 into organic molecules is called
    A) respiration.
    B) assimilation.
    C) photosynthesis.
    D) None of the above

Answer: C
Topic: Section 6.1

4) The pigment that absorbs light energy (photons) in photosynthesis is
    A) rubisco.
    B) chlorophyll.
    C) PEP.
    D) CAM.

Answer: B
Topic: Section 6.1

5) In the C_3 photosynthetic pathway, the enzyme rubisco catalyzes the reaction called
    A) chemosynthesis.
    B) carboxylation.
    C) photoreduction.
    D) None of the above

Answer: B
Topic: Section 6.1

6) The primary drawback of the C_3 photosynthetic pathway is that
    A) it requires large amounts of phosphorus and potassium.
    B) it requires a large amount of nitrogen.
    C) the enzyme rubisco can also act as an oxygenase.
    D) the enzyme rubisco is subject to damage by UV radiation.

Answer: C
Topic: Section 6.1

7) The value of PAR above which no further increase in photosynthesis occurs is referred to as the
_____ point.
   A) photoinhibition
   B) chlorophyll compensation
   C) light compensation point
   D) light saturation point

Answer: D
Topic: Section 6.2

8) Net CO_2 uptake by a plant is greatest
   A) when PAR equals zero.
   B) at the light compensation point.
   C) during photoinhibition.
   D) at the light saturation point.

Answer: D
Topic: Section 6.2

9) A CO_2 gradient between the inside and outside of a leaf is maintained during photosynthesis because
   A) energy is expended by the plant to maintain the CO_2 gradient.
   B) the CO_2 concentration outside of the leaf is always increasing.
   C) the CO_2 concentration in the mesophyll is constantly decreasing.
   D) the stomata close whenever more CO_2 is needed.

Answer: C
Topic: Section 6.3

10) Which of the following enters a plant via its stomata?
   A) CO_2
   B) H_2O
   C) phosphorus
   D) O_2

Answer: A
Topic: Section 6.3

11) Overall, water movement from the soil, through plant tissues, and finally to the atmosphere through transpiration is driven by a gradient of
   A) water potential.
   B) osmotic pressure.
   C) water temperature.
   D) specific leaf area.

Answer: A
Topic: Section 6.4

12) The effect of solute concentration on the state of water loss from plant cells is called
   A) water potential.
   B) matric potential.
   C) osmotic potential.
   D) osmotic pressure.

Answer: C
Topic: Section 6.4

13) Which of the following conditions is required for a continued movement of water from the soil into and through a plant via transpiration?
    A) $\psi_{atm} < \psi_{root} < \psi_{leaf} < \psi_{soil}$
    B) $\psi_{atm} < \psi_{leaf} < \psi_{root} < \psi_{soil}$
    C) $\psi_{soil} < \psi_{root} < \psi_{leaf} < \psi_{atm}$
    D) $\psi_{soil} < \psi_{atm} < \psi_{root} < \psi_{leaf}$

Answer: B
Topic: Section 6.4

14) Compared with terrestrial plants, submerged aquatic plants lack
    A) leaves.
    B) chlorophyll.
    C) stomata.
    D) stems.

Answer: C
Topic: Section 6.5

15) Submerged aquatic plants can take up CO_2 from the water in all of the following ways, except:
    A) diffusion through stomata.
    B) direct diffusion of ambient CO_2 from water across cell membranes.
    C) active transport of bicarbonate into the leaf followed by conversion to CO_2.
    D) excretion of carbonic anhydrase into the water, followed by uptake of the resulting CO_2.

Answer: A
Topic: Section 6.5

16) Some aquatic plants can utilize HCO_3^- as a carbon source but must first convert it into CO_2 by using the enzyme
    A) carboxylase.
    B) rubisco.
    C) oxygenase.
    D) carbonic anhydrase.

Answer: D
Topic: Section 6.5

17) _____ temperature controls the rates of photosynthesis and respiration.
    A) Soil
    B) Air
    C) Leaf
    D) Root

Answer: C
Topic: Section 6.6

18) As temperatures continue to rise, the photosynthetic rate reaches a maximum related to
    A) the temperature response of rubisco.
    B) the thickness of the boundary layer.
    C) soil temperature.
    D) oxygen availability.

Answer: A
Topic: Section 6.6

19) Carbon balance focuses on the balance between
   A) uptake of CO_2 in photosynthesis and loss of heat via evapotranspiration.
   B) loss of CO_2 through respiration and gain of nutrients.
   C) loss of H_2O balanced with the gain of CO_2 via transpiration.
   D) uptake of CO_2 in photosynthesis balanced with the loss of CO_2 during respiration.

Answer: D
Topic: Section 6.7

20) Net carbon uptake per unit time by a plant is directly related to
   A) the difference between photosynthetic rate and respiration rate.
   B) photosynthetic rate.
   C) respiration rate.
   D) the difference between photosynthetic rate and decomposition rate.

Answer: A
Topic: Section 6.7

21) When resources are plentiful, plants will allocate the most carbon to the production of
   A) roots.
   B) stems.
   C) leaves.
   D) flowers.

Answer: C
Topic: Section 6.7

22) A plant adapted to a dry, sunny environment might be expected to have
   A) thin, flexible leaves.
   B) large leaves.
   C) a minimal root system.
   D) small leaves.

Answer: D
Topic: Sections 6.8 and 6.9

23) Compared with plants growing in high light, plants growing in shaded environments tend to produce
   _____ rubisco.
   A) equal amounts of
   B) more
   C) less
   D) a different type of

Answer: B
Topic: Section 6.9

24) Compared with a shade-intolerant plant, a shade-tolerant plant
   A) has a greater SLA.
   B) grows faster.
   C) requires a higher intake of CO_2 to balance losses of CO_2 from respiration.
   D) allocates very little carbon to leaf tissue.

Answer: A
Topic: Section 6.9

25) Which of the following is an incorrect statement?
  A) A large leaf will maximizes light interception.
  B) A deeply lobed leaf will minimize heat exchange with the atmosphere.
  C) A thick leaf will reduce loss of water via transpiration
  D) A leaf with a high SLA will generally be thin and flexible.

Answer: B
Topic: Section 6.9

26) An *Acacia* seedling grown in shade (50% full sun) is expected to have a _____ net assimilation rate (NAR) and _____ leaf area ratio (LAR) than an *Acacia* seedling grown in full sun.
  A) higher; higher
  B) lower; lower
  C) lower; higher
  D) higher; lower

Answer: C
Topic: Quantifying Ecology 6.1

27) Leaf area ratio (LAR) is the product of specific leaf area (SLA) and
  A) net assimilation rate (NAR).
  B) relative growth rate (RGR).
  C) maximum net photosynthesis.
  D) leaf weight ratio (LWR).

Answer: D
Topic: Quantifying Ecology 6.1

28) According to research done by Kaoru Kitajima, shade-tolerant seedlings growing in a tropical rain forest
  A) utilize seed reserves over longer periods of time than do shade-intolerant seedlings.
  B) develop more rapidly than do shade-intolerant seedlings.
  C) initially allocate most of their energy to the production of leaves.
  D) generally grow from very small seeds.

Answer: A
Topic: Field Studies: Kaoru Kitajima

29) Which of the following statements is false?
  A) PEP carboxylase has a low affinity for oxygen.
  B) CO_2 is initially fixed into oxaloacetate (OAA) in the mesophyll cell.
  C) C_4 plants have a lower water use efficiency than C_3 plants.
  D) C_4 plants are mostly grasses.

Answer: C
Topic: Section 6.10

30) CAM plants fix CO_2
  A) into oxaloacetate (OAA).
  B) at night.
  C) in mesophyll cells.
  D) only when it is raining.

Answer: B
Topic: Section 6.10

31) The C$_4$ photosynthetic pathway is most common among plants inhabiting _____ habitats.
    A) cool
    B) high-latitude
    C) high-altitude
    D) hot

Answer: D
Topic: Section 6.10

32) Plants can reduce water loss by
    A) closing their stomata.
    B) growing larger leaves.
    C) growing more slowly.
    D) increasing photosynthesis.

Answer: A
Topic: Section 6.10

33) All the following are plant adaptations to low temperatures, except:
    A) shedding leaves at the onset of cold weather.
    B) production of antifreeze molecules.
    C) a shifting of T$_{opt}$.
    D) increased photosynthetic rate to heat leaves.

Answer: D
Topic: Section 6.11

34) Which of the following elements is considered a plant micronutrient?
    A) iron
    B) nitrogen
    C) phosphorus
    D) oxygen

Answer: A
Topic: Section 6.12

35) Which of the following is considered a plant adaptation to low-nutrient environments?
    A) faster growth rate
    B) decreased root production
    C) increased leaf longevity
    D) None of the above

Answer: C
Topic: Section 6.12

36) Some plant species are able to release _____ from flooded or submerged roots to increase aeration and prevent anaerobic conditions.
    A) methane
    B) ethylene
    C) oxygen
    D) nitrogen

Answer: B
Topic: Section 6.13

37) Pneumatophores are typical of plants (particularly trees)
    A) in arid environments.
    B) exposed to fluctuating water levels.
    C) flooded once each year.
    D) in salt marshes.

Answer: B
Topic: Section 6.13

True/False Questions

1) All life on Earth is carbon based.

Answer: TRUE
Topic: Introduction to Chapter 6

2) Photosynthesis transforms oxygen and carbon dioxide into carbohydrates and water.

Answer: FALSE
Topic: Section 6.1

3) Photosynthesis produces more water than it uses.

Answer: FALSE
Topic: Section 6.1

4) The light and dark reactions of photosynthesis occur in different areas of the chloroplast.

Answer: TRUE
Topic: Section 6.1

5) At light levels below the light compensation point, the rate of carbon loss due to respiration exceeds the rate of uptake in the process of photosynthesis.

Answer: TRUE
Topic: Section 6.2

6) Photoinhibition is the negative effect of high light levels on respiration.

Answer: FALSE
Topic: Section 6.2

7) A plant takes in water and loses carbon dioxide through its open stomata.

Answer: FALSE
Topic: Section 6.3

8) The drier the air outside a leaf, the faster water will be lost from the leaf through the stomata.

Answer: TRUE
Topic: Section 6.3

9) In nature, water potential values (ψ) typically range from zero to increasingly positive values.

Answer: FALSE
Topic: Section 6.4

10) The higher the concentration of solutes in a solution, the lower that solution's osmotic potential.

Answer: TRUE
Topic: Section 6.4

11) Water moves from regions of high water potential to regions of low water potential.

Answer: TRUE
Topic: Section 6.4

12) Submerged aquatic plants typically have stomata.

Answer: FALSE
Topic: Section 6.5

13) Submerged aquatic plants are different from terrestrial plants in that they can use HCO_3^- as a carbon source for photosynthesis.

Answer: TRUE
Topic: Section 6.5

14) Small compound leaves dissipate heat more readily than broad, unlobed leaves.

Answer: TRUE
Topic: Section 6.6

15) Plants lose heat to the environment through direct contact of leaves with the air or water.

Answer: TRUE
Topic: Section 6.6

16) Total carbon loss through respiration is a function of the total mass of living tissue.

Answer: TRUE
Topic: Section 6.7

17) Allocation of carbon to roots directly increases both respiration and photosynthesis rates.

Answer: FALSE
Topic: Section 6.7

18) Features of the physical environment that directly influence plants, such as light and temperature, typically act on plants independently from each other.

Answer: FALSE
Topic: Section 6.8

19) Allocation to increased root production would be expected to increase both mineral nutrient acquisition and the rate of carbon gain through photosynthesis.

Answer: FALSE
Topic: Sections 6.7 and 6.8

20) Plants growing in shade tend to produce less rubisco and more chlorophyll than plants growing in full sun.

Answer: TRUE
Topic: Section 6.9

21) Plants growing in shade tend to allocate more to leaf production than to root production compared with plants growing in full sun.

Answer: TRUE
Topic: Section 6.9

22) Relative growth rate is the change in size of a plant during some period of time.

Answer: FALSE
Topic: Quantifying Ecology 6.1

23) Drought deciduous plants lose leaves just as the dry season begins.

Answer: TRUE
Topic: Section 6.10

24) CAM plants use the enzyme PEP carboxylase to capture CO_2.

Answer: TRUE
Topic: Section 6.10

25) Members of the same plant species always exhibit the same response to changes in temperature.

Answer: FALSE
Topic: Section 6.11

26) Dehydration can be a problem for plants in cold habitats.

Answer: TRUE
Topic: Section 6.11

27) Nitrogen is a plant micronutrient.

Answer: FALSE
Topic: Section 6.12

28) Some plants have adapted to low nutrient environments by having long-lived leaves.

Answer: TRUE
Topic: Section 6.12

29) Plants adapted to low-nutrient environments attain maximum growth rate at much lower nitrogen levels than high-nutrient plants.

Answer: TRUE
Topic: Section 6.12

30) Halophytes accumulate high levels of ions within their cells.

Answer: TRUE
Topic: Section 6.13

31) The growth of adventitious roots is an adaptation to saline environments.

Answer: FALSE
Topic: Section 6.13

Essay Questions

1) Explain why all of life on Earth ultimately depends on photosynthesis.

Topic: Introduction to Chapter 6 and Section 6.1

2) Explain why the opening of stomata has both benefits and costs for plants in dry environments.

Topic: Sections 6.3 and 6.4

3) Describe how water moves from the soil, through plant tissues, into the atmosphere through transpiration. Define and utilize the concept of water potential in your answer.

Topic: Section 6.4

4) Describe the differences in carbon acquisition between terrestrial and aquatic plants.

Topic: Section 6.5

5) Draw a graph to illustrate how gross photosynthesis and respiration respond to temperature change. Label T_{opt} on the graph.

Topic: Section 6.6

6) Explain how the allocation of carbon to plant roots influences net carbon gain by plants.

Topic: Section 6.7

7) Give an example of how different aspects of the physical environment interact to influence plants.

Topic: Section 6.8

8) Describe two plant adaptations to low light and explain why these adaptations are unsuitable for plants in high-light environments.

Topic: Section 6.9

9) Suggest how seed mass might be related to the growth and survival of species in different light environments.

Topic: Field Studies: Kaoru Kitajima

10) Describe the features of the C_4 and CAM photosynthetic strategies. Relate your description to why C_4 and CAM plants are successful in hot and/or arid environments.

Topic: Section 6.10

11) Compare how CO_2 uptake and net photosynthetic rates change with temperature between cold-weather and warm-weather plants. Use one or more graphs in your answer.

Topic: Section 6.11

12) Explain the link between nutrient availability and plant performance. Use the specific example of nitrogen to illustrate the interdependence of plant processes.

Topic: Section 6.12

13) Explain why a plant growing in waterlogged soil suffers similar symptoms as a plant exposed to drought conditions. Describe the responses these plants can make to survive in such extreme environments.

Topic: Section 6.13

Chapter 7 Animal Adaptations to the Environment

Short Answer Questions

1) An organism that obtains its energy and most nutrients from consuming plants or animals is called a(n) _____.

Answer: heterotroph
Topic: Introduction to Chapter 7

2) The predictable change in morphological and physiological features as a function of body size is referred to as _____.

Answer: scaling
Topic: Section 7.1

3) The relationship between surface area and _____ imposes a critical constraint on animal form.

Answer: volume
Topic: Section 7.1

4) Animals that feed exclusively on plant tissue as food are called _____.

Answer: herbivores
Topic: Section 7.2

5) Herbivores are unable to digest _____ and thus rely on the help of specialized bacteria and protozoa living in their digestive tracts.

Answer: cellulose
Topic: Section 7.2

6) Herbivores with compartmentalized digestive systems that house microbes that facilitate the breakdown of cellulose are known as _____.

Answer: ruminants
Topic: Section 7.2

7) _____ amino acids are those that animals are unable to synthesize for themselves and thus, these must be supplied by the diet.

Answer: Essential
Topic: Section 7.3

8) The highest-quality plant food for herbivores is high in _____.

Answer: nitrogen
Topic: Section 7.3

9) As ocean temperatures increase around the Galapagos Islands, the density of _____ algae increases.

Answer: brown
Topic: Field Studies: Martin Wikelski

10) _____ is often the least available nutrient in terrestrial environments.

Answer: Sodium
Topic: Section 7.4

11) Oxygen is required in _____, a cellular process that releases energy through the breakdown of organic compounds.

Answer: respiration
Topic: Section 7.5

12) _____ is the maintenance by an animal of a relatively constant internal environment in a varying external environment.

Answer: Homeostasis
Topic: Section 7.6

13) _____ is the ability to transmit heat.

Answer: Conductivity
Topic: Section 7.7

14) If the value of $H_{conduction}$ of the body core is positive, then the direction of heat flow is _____.

Answer: outward
Topic: Quantifying Ecology 7.1

15) Animals that maintain a fairly constant internal temperature independent of external temperatures are called _____.

Answer: homeotherms
Topic: Section 7.8

16) Environmental sources of heat control the rates of metabolism and activity among most _____.

Answer: poikilotherms
Topic: Sections 7.8 and 7.9

17) Amphibians and reptiles can quickly raise body temperature by _____ in the sun.

Answer: basking
Topic: Section 7.9

18) The _____ zone is a range of environmental temperatures within which homeothermic metabolic rates are minimal.

Answer: thermoneutral
Topic: Section 7.10

19) A process of temporarily dropping body temperature to the temperature of the environment for part of the day is called _____.

Answer: torpor, or daily torpor
Topic: Sections 7.11 and 7.13

20) Large reptiles (e.g., alligators) are all restricted to _____ environments.

Answer: warm tropical
Topic: Section 7.11

21) The smaller a homeotherm, the _____ the loss of heat to the surrounding environment.

Answer: greater
Topic: Section 7.11

22) _____ is a long, seasonal torpor characterized by a cessation of activity.

Answer: Hibernation
Topic: Section 7.13

23) _____ of body fluids takes place when the body temperature falls below the freezing point without actually freezing.

Answer: Supercooling
Topic: Section 7.14

24) Birds and reptiles reabsorb water from the _____ back into the body.

Answer: cloaca
Topic: Section 7.15

25) Many insects undergo _____, a stage of arrested development in their lifecycle from which they emerge when conditions improve.

Answer: diapause
Topic: Section 7.15

26) Aquatic organisms that have a lower salt concentration in their bodies than the surrounding water are considered _____.

Answer: hypoosmotic
Topic: Section 7.16

27) Living tissue is _____ dense than water.

Answer: more
Topic: Section 7.17

28) _____ are less dense than seawater and are present in fish that lack swim bladders.

Answer: Lipids
Topic: Section 7.17

29) In animals, a cycle of physiological activity that occurs within a 24-hour period is called a _____.

Answer: circadian rhythm
Topic: Section 7.18

30) The circadian rhythm of an animal is controlled by _____.

Answer: light
Topic: Section 7.18

31) The reproductive, or seasonal, activity is unaffected by day length in _____ organisms.

Answer: day neutral
Topic: Section 7.19

32) The circadian rhythm of many intertidal species is determined by _____.

Answer: tides, or tidal cycles
Topic: Section 7.20

33) That organisms rely on multiple environmental cues to determine circadian rhythms is known as _____.

Answer: redundancy, or redundancies
Topic: Section 7.20

Multiple-Choice Questions

1) An organism that derives energy and most nutrients through the consumption of plants and animals is a(n)
   A) autotroph.
   B) heterotroph.
   C) organotroph.
   D) detritovore.

Answer: A
Topic: Introduction to Chapter 7

2) The isometric scaling exponent (0.67) represents the interaction of
   A) body weight and length.
   B) body length and volume.
   C) body surface area and weight.
   D) body volume and surface area.

Answer: D
Topic: Section 7.1

3) What factor is known to constrain animal body shape and size?
   A) access to water
   B) atmospheric pressure
   C) oxygen diffusion rate
   D) nitrogen availability

Answer: C
Topic: Section 7.1

4) Which of the following is a feature that allows for long-distance transport of oxygen to animal cells?
   A) brain
   B) heart
   C) stomach
   D) mouth

Answer: B
Topic: Section 7.1

5) Detritivores
   A) feed exclusively on live plant material.
   B) eat other live animals.
   C) drink only water.
   D) feed on dead plant and animal material.

Answer: D
Topic: Section 7.2

6) Which of the following is incorrect?
   A) A grazer has a high cellulose diet.
   B) By itself, a browser is unable to extract all the nutrients from woody material.
   C) An herbivore may also be a frugivore.
   D) A granivore feeds on fruits.

Answer: D
Topic: Section 7.2

7) Which of the following statements is true?
   A) Carnivores usually have longer intestines and more complex stomachs than herbivores.
   B) Some fish access nutrients in algal cells by having a low stomach pH.
   C) Seed-eating birds rely on chewing alone to mechanically process seeds.
   D) Fatty acids produced in the rumen are later absorbed in the omasum.

Answer: B
Topic: Section 7.2

8) Which of the following is an incorrect match of animal nutrient and nutrient role?
   A) fluorine: a basic constituent of proteins
   B) phosphorus: important for bone and tooth formation
   C) calcium: gives rigidity to the skeletons of vertebrates
   D) cobalt: required by ruminants for the synthesis of vitamin B_{12}

Answer: A
Topic: Section 7.3

9) _____ is concentrated in the growing tips, new leaves, and buds of plants.
   A) Carbon
   B) Hydrogen
   C) Nitrogen
   D) Oxygen

Answer: C
Topic: Section 7.3

10) Researcher Martin Wikelski has found that as ocean temperature decreases along the coast of several Galapagos Islands.
   A) the size and productivity of algae pastures decrease.
   B) the size and productivity of algae pastures increase.
   C) the productivity of algae pastures increases but the size decreases.
   D) the size and productivity of algae pastures do not change.

Answer: B
Topic: Field Studies: Martin Wikelski

11) What unusual adaptation is documented in marine iguanas during El Niño events?
   A) improved digestion of brown algae
   B) migration to Chile
   C) a switch to eating bird eggs
   D) body size shrinkage

Answer: D
Topic: Field Studies: Martin Wikelski

12) All the following minerals are provided to animals at a mineral-lick, except:
   A) sulfur.
   B) sodium.
   C) magnesium.
   D) calcium.

Answer: A
Topic: Section 7.4

13) Which of the following animals does not use lungs to acquire oxygen?
    A) whale
    B) frog
    C) bird
    D) butterfly

Answer: D
Topic: Section 7.5

14) Water flows over gills in the opposite direction as blood flow in a process known as
    A) inhalation.
    B) respiration.
    C) diffusion.
    D) countercurrent exchange.

Answer: D
Topic: Section 7.5

15) The maintenance of a relatively constant internal environment in a varying external environment is called
    A) thermoregulation.
    B) diapause.
    C) acclimatization.
    D) homeostasis.

Answer: D
Topic: Section 7.6

16) Which of the following is not expected in response to an increase in human body temperature?
    A) sweating
    B) cooling due to evaporation of water from skin
    C) shivering
    D) increased blood flow to the skin

Answer: C
Topic: Section 7.6

17) Which of the following factors does not influence animal heat exchange?
    A) oxygen diffusion rate
    B) conductivity of fat
    C) movement of blood to the body's surface
    D) fat thickness

Answer: A
Topic: Section 7.7

18) Which of the following will always decrease an organism's thermal conductivity (k)?
    A) fur
    B) density
    C) fat
    D) feathers

Answer: B
Topic: Quantifying Ecology 7.1

19) The transfer of heat energy between a solid and a moving fluid (air or water) is known as
   A) conduction.
   B) evaporation.
   C) convection.
   D) radiation.

   Answer: C
   Topic: Quantifying Ecology 7.1

20) The regulation of body temperature in an animal by internal metabolism is called
   A) endothermy.
   B) ectothermy.
   C) poikilothermy.
   D) homeostasis.

   Answer: A
   Topic: Section 7.8

21) The regulation of body temperature in an animal by the external environment is called
   A) heterothermy.
   B) ectothermy.
   C) endothermy.
   D) homeostasis.

   Answer: C
   Topic: Section 7.8

22) For every _____ rise in temperature, the poikilothermic metabolic rate approximately doubles.
   A) 1^oC
   B) 2^oC
   C) 5^oC
   D) 10^oC

   Answer: D
   Topic: Section 7.9

23) Sharks and tuna are able to maintain a higher internal body temperature than the surrounding water because they possess
   A) lungs.
   B) a rete.
   C) smaller fins.
   D) a swim bladder.

   Answer: B
   Topic: Section 7.9

24) The homeothermic respiration rate is proportional to
   A) surface area to volume ratio (SA/V).
   B) nitrogen availability.
   C) body mass.
   D) air temperature.

   Answer: C
   Topic: Section 7.10

25) Which of the following is unique to some small mammals in order to increase heat production?
    A) fur
    B) brown fat
    C) shivering
    D) evaporative cooling

Answer: B
Topic: Section 7.10

26) The basal metabolic rate per unit of body mass is highest in a
    A) large endotherm.
    B) small endotherm.
    C) large ectotherm.
    D) small ectotherm.

Answer: B
Topic: Section 7.11

27) Which of the following is an advantage of homeothermy?
    A) high caloric intake
    B) maximum allocation of energy to growth
    C) activity regardless of external temperature
    D) wide fluctuations in body temperature

Answer: C
Topic: Section 7.11

28) The dropping of body temperature to approximately ambient temperature for part of a day is called
    A) diapause.
    B) hibernation.
    C) behavioral thermoregulation.
    D) torpor.

Answer: D
Topic: Section 7.11

29) Immediately prior to flight in cool temperatures, some insects
    A) must consume hundreds of calories.
    B) increase heat production by shivering flight muscles of the thorax.
    C) seek shade.
    D) increase anaerobic respiration.

Answer: B
Topic: Section 7.12

30) The seasonal cessation of activities accompanied by a reduction in metabolism in response to cold
    temperatures during winter is called
    A) hibernation.
    B) torpor.
    C) heterothermy.
    D) diapause.

Answer: A
Topic: Section 7.13

31) All of the following characterize a hibernating homeotherm, except:
    A) low blood pH.
    B) high CO_2 level in blood.
    C) increased heart rate.
    D) decrease in body temperature.

Answer: C
Topic: Section 7.13

32) This solute is known to provide protection against freezing damage in some animals.
    A) glucose
    B) glycerol
    C) salt
    D) sucrose

Answer: B
Topic: Section 7.14

33) Which of the following is not a known countercurrent heat exchange mechanism?
    A) porpoise fluke
    B) beaver tail
    C) African desert antelope sinus
    D) primate hands

Answer: D
Topic: Section 7.14

34) _____ can cool nasal membranes enough to cause condensation from inhaled air.
    A) Spadefoot toads
    B) African ungulates
    C) Small desert rodents
    D) Kangaroos

Answer: C
Topic: Section 7.15

35) Which of the following is a major problem for animals that live in hyperosmotic environments?
    A) preventing heat loss
    B) access to mineral nutrients
    C) preventing water loss
    D) obtaining enough oxygen

Answer: C
Topic: Section 7.16

36) A freshwater fish is _____ and _____ water to/from the environment.
    A) hyperosmotic; gains
    B) hyperosmostic; loses
    C) hypoosmotic; gains
    D) hypoosmotic; loses

Answer: A
Topic: Section 7.16

37) Which of the following is not a mechanism used by some animals to stay afloat?
   A) swim bladder
   B) rete
   C) lungs
   D) lipid deposits

Answer: B
Topic: Section 7.17

38) Secretion of _____ from the pineal gland peaks at night and declines during the day.
   A) melatonin
   B) melanin
   C) carbon dioxide
   D) glucose

Answer: A
Topic: Section 7.18

39) Parietel eyes are found in all the following animals, except:
   A) frogs.
   B) lizards.
   C) tuna.
   D) birds.

Answer: D
Topic: Section 7.18

40) An organism's response to seasonal change in spring and fall is determined by both critical day length and
   A) direction of light.
   B) temperature.
   C) rainfall.
   D) food availability.

Answer: A
Topic: Section 7.19

41) In seasonal breeders (e.g., sheep) an increase in melatonin
   A) occurs in the summer.
   B) causes the anterior pituitary to release luteinizing hormone.
   C) increases the sensitivity of the pituitary gland to negative feedback.
   D) corresponds with a reduction in fertility.

Answer: B
Topic: Section 7.19

True/False Questions

1) As the surface area of a body increases, the surface-area to volume ratio (SA/V) also increases.

Answer: FALSE
Topic: Section 7.1

2) An omnivore feeds primarily on dead plant or animal matter.

Answer: FALSE
Topic: Section 7.1

3) Coprophagy is common among detritus-feeding animals.

Answer: TRUE
Topic: Section 7.2

4) Ruminants regurgitate food to further break food down into smaller pieces.

Answer: TRUE
Topic: Section 7.2

5) The primary problem for carnivores is to digest enough cellulose.

Answer: FALSE
Topic: Section 7.2

6) Herbivores can detect the nitrogen content of plants by odor and/or taste.

Answer: TRUE
Topic: Section 7.3

7) Marine iguanas are herbivorous reptiles that feed on submerged algae.

Answer: TRUE
Topic: Field Studies: Martin Wikelski

8) During spring, vegetation is higher in potassium relative to calcium and magnesium.

Answer: TRUE
Topic: Section 7.4

9) All marine animals lack lungs.

Answer: FALSE
Topic: Section 7.5

10) Air flow through bird lungs is a continuous circuit, the air flows in one direction only.

Answer: TRUE
Topic: Section 7.5

11) Homeostasis refers to the maintenance of a fluctuating internal environment, varying in response to changes in the external environment.

Answer: FALSE
Topic: Section 7.6

12) A living organism must maintain each internal condition (e.g., body temperature) to a fixed set point.

Answer: FALSE
Topic: Section 7.6

13) Terrestrial animals are usually subjected to more radical changes in their thermal environment than aquatic animals.

Answer: TRUE
Topic: Section 7.7

14) Convective heat transfer is the movement of heat through solids or between two solids that are in direct contact.

Answer: FALSE
Topic: Quantifying Ecology 7.1

15) The regulation of body temperature by internal metabolism is called ectothermy.

Answer: FALSE
Topic: Section 7.8

16) Poikilotherms exploit microclimates to regulate temperature.

Answer: TRUE
Topic: Section 7.9

17) Some aquatic poikilotherms (e.g., sharks) are able to maintain a higher internal body temperature than the surrounding water.

Answer: TRUE
Topic: Section 7.9

18) Homeotherms can sustain a higher level of physical activity for longer periods of time than poikilotherms.

Answer: TRUE
Topic: Section 7.10

19) Only animals with sweat glands can take advantage of evaporative cooling.

Answer: FALSE
Topic: Section 7.10

20) The smallest animals are endotherms.

Answer: FALSE
Topic: Section 7.11

21) An ectotherm has a lower caloric requirement than an endotherm of similar size.

Answer: TRUE
Topic: Section 7.11

22) Flying insects have a high metabolic rate when flying and can produce as much heat as homeotherms or more.

Answer: TRUE
Topic: Section 7.12

23) Countercurrent heat exchange is an adaptation for both conserving body heat in a cold environment and losing body heat in a hot environment.

Answer: TRUE
Topic: Section 7.14

24) Liquid water is the sole source of water to terrestrial animals.

Answer: FALSE
Topic: Section 7.15

25) Freshwater aquatic organisms are faced with the problem of preventing excessive uptake or retention of water.

Answer: TRUE
Topic: Section 7.16

26) Seabirds cannot drink saltwater but are able to obtain water directly from the food they eat.

Answer: FALSE
Topic: Section 7.16

27) Most fish control their buoyancy by regulating the amount of gas in their gills.

Answer: FALSE
Topic: Section 7.17

28) The 24-hour cycle of activities in animals is called a circannual rhythm.

Answer: FALSE
Topic: Section 7.18

29) Melatonin is secreted by the pineal gland at greater levels during the day.

Answer: FALSE
Topic: Section 7.18

30) Seasonal changes in the behavior of animals is usually stimulated by changing critical daylengths.

Answer: TRUE
Topic: Section 7.19

31) Fiddler crabs are still dependent on tidal cycles for circadian rhythms of body color in a controlled lab setting.

Answer: FALSE
Topic: Section 7.20

Essay Questions

1) Explain the relationship between the surface area and volume of a body as it increases in size. How have some animals adapted to the constraints imposed by cellular respiration and delivery of oxygen?

Topic: Section 7.11

2) Discuss and describe several different strategies that herbivores use to extract nutrients from a cellulose-rich diet.

Topic: Section 7.2

3) Discuss and explain the impact of El Niño events on the success of marine iguanas of the Galapagos Islands.

Topic: Field Studies: Martin Wikelski

4) Describe the physiological consequences suffered by ruminants when the mineral content of vegetation is low (e.g., springtime).

Topic: Section 7.4

5) Compare and contrast the mechanisms used by animals for the uptake of oxygen from the terrestrial and aquatic environments.

Topic: Section 7.5

6) Explain the importance of negative feedback to the maintenance of homeostatic plateaus in animals.

Topic: Section 7.6

7) Discuss the distinctions between ectothermy, endothermy, poikilothermy, and homeothermy.

Topic: Sections 7.8, 7.9, 7.10, and 7.11

8) Use an example to explain how poikilotherms change behavior and exploit microclimates to regulate body temperature.

Topic: Section 7.9

9) Contrast the advantages of a fur coat on a camel and a squirrel.

Topic: Section 7.10

10) Discuss the tradeoffs between ectothermy and endothermy. Under what conditions is each strategy beneficial and why?

Topic: Section 7.11

11) Use an example to explain the strategy used by a temporal heterotherm.

Topic: Section 7.12

12) Compare and contrast the torpor states of a bat, chipmunk, and black bear.

Topic: Section 7.13

13) Explain the countercurrent heat exchange mechanism. How does this mechanism serve opposite purposes for animals in cold and hot environments?

Topic: Section 7.14

14) Describe two animal adaptations for conserving water in arid environments.

Topic: Section 7.15

15) Describe and contrast the osmotic challenges faced by marine and freshwater animals.

Topic: Section 7.16

16) Explain the pathway involved to determine an animal's circadian rhythm. Include the following terms in your explanation: critical day length, light, melatonin, photoperiod, photoreception, pineal gland, and pituitary gland.

Topic: Sections 7.18 and 7.19

Chapter 8 Life History Patterns

Short Answer Questions

1) An organism's _____ is its lifetime pattern of growth, development, and reproduction.

Answer: life history
Topic: Introduction to Chapter 8

2) Reproduction by a single parent, in which the offspring are genetically identical to the parent, is referred to as _____ reproduction.

Answer: asexual
Topic: Section 8.1

3) _____ is a form of asexual reproduction in which the ovum develops without fertilization by a male.

Answer: Parthenogenesis
Topic: Section 8.1

4) _____ plants are those with separate male and female individuals.

Answer: Dioecious
Topic: Section 8.2

5) Individual organisms that possess both male and female organs are considered _____.

Answer: hermaphroditic, or hermaphrodites
Topic: Section 8.2

6) The mating system most prevalent in birds is _____.

Answer: monogamy
Topic: Section 8.3

7) The type of mating system in which an individual female pairs with two or more males is known as

_____.

Answer: polyandry
Topic: Section 8.3

8) _____ selection occurs when members of the same sex compete for access to the opposite sex.

Answer: Intrasexual
Topic: Section 8.4

9) Generally, female peacocks prefer a male peacock with a larger _____.

Answer: tail
Topic: Section 8.4

10) A longer "sword" in male green swordtails increases mating success but negatively affects _____.

Answer: swimming or swimming ability
Topic: Field Studies: Alexandra L. Basolo

11) Communal courtship grounds, or _____, are areas where males congregate to display to females.

Answer: leks
Topic: Section 8.5

12) The amount of time and energy that an organism allocated to reproduction is called _____.

Answer: reproductive effort
Topic: Section 8.6

13) Seed number is negatively correlated with seed _____.

Answer: size
Topic: Quantifying Ecology 8.1

14) _____ is a mode of reproduction in which an organism expends all its energy in growth and reproduction and then dies.

Answer: Semelparity
Topic: Section 8.7

15) The mode of reproduction in which individuals produce fewer young at one time and repeat reproduction multiple times throughout their life is known as _____.

Answer: iteroparity
Topic: Section 8.7

16) _____ young are offspring that are relatively helpless at birth and require considerable parental care.

Answer: Altricial
Topic: Section 8.8

17) Little parental care is required by _____ offspring.

Answer: precocial
Topic: Section 8.8

18) For many species, the number of offspring produced varies with the age and _____ of the parent.

Answer: size
Topic: Section 8.9

19) The production of offspring, or _____, generally increases with size.

Answer: fecundity
Topic: Section 8.9

20) _____ is the killing of one sibling by another.

Answer: Siblicide
Topic: Section 8.10

21) The environment, or place, in which an organism lives is known as its _____.

Answer: habitat
Topic: Section 8.12

22) The process in which organisms actively choose a specific location to inhabit is called _____.

Answer: habitat selection
Topic: Section 8.12

23) Habitats that are variable in time or short-lived will favor _____ strategists.

Answer: r
Topic: Section 8.13

24) _____ are competitive species with stable populations of long-lived individuals.

Answer: K-strategists
Topic: Section 8.13

25) Native Americans cultivate maize from several genera of Central and South American grasses called

_____.

Answer: teosinte, or *Zea*
Topic: Ecological Issues: The Life History of Maize: A Story of Unnatural Selection

Multiple-Choice Questions

1) The true measure of an organism's reproductive success is
    A) its fitness.
    B) its survival.
    C) the total number of offspring produced.
    D) its life span.

Answer: A
Topic: Introduction to Chapter 8

2) Which of the following is not a form of asexual reproduction?
    A) budding
    B) parthenogenesis
    C) growth of a rhizome
    D) sequential hermaphroditism

Answer: D
Topic: Section 8.1

3) The development of an ovum without fertilization by a male is called
    A) budding.
    B) parthenogenesis.
    C) hermaphroditism.
    D) monoecy.

Answer: B
Topic: Section 8.1

4) Plants with male and female flowers on the same plant are
    A) gonochuristic.
    B) dioecious.
    C) monoecious.
    D) dichogamous.

Answer: C
Topic: Section 8.2

5) An individual that experiences a sex reversal during its lifetime is a
    A) simultaneous hermaphrodite.
    B) sequential hermaphrodite.
    C) result of parthenogenesis.
    D) dioecious individual.

Answer: B
Topic: Section 8.2

6) When one male mates and stays with one female, the relationship is called
   A) polygamous.
   B) monogamous.
   C) monoecious.
   D) promiscuous.

Answer: B
Topic: Section 8.3

7) The mating system in which males and females mate with one or many of the opposite sex and form no pair bond is known as
   A) monogamy.
   B) polygyny.
   C) polyandry.
   D) promiscuity.

Answer: D
Topic: Section 8.3

8) Intrasexual selection
   A) is only documented for females.
   B) is associated with elaborate secondary sexual characteristics.
   C) is a passive process.
   D) has no effect on evolution.

Answer: B
Topic: Section 8.4

9) Direct, aggressive competition among individuals for the opportunity to mate with the opposite sex is characteristic of
   A) intrasexual selection.
   B) polygyny.
   C) polyandry.
   D) intersexual selection.

Answer: A
Topic: Section 8.4

10) A male swordtail fish with a tail fin longer than its rivals is
    A) more likely to be selected by a female and consume less oxygen while swimming.
    B) more likely to be selected by a female and consume more oxygen while swimming.
    C) less likely to be selected by a female and consume less oxygen while swimming.
    D) less likely to be selected by a female and consume more oxygen while swimming.

Answer: B
Topic: Field Studies: Alexandra L. Basolo

11) A female exhibits two major approaches in choosing a mate; the phenotypic characteristics of the mate or the
    A) number of other females the males has in his harem.
    B) ability of the male to provide resources.
    C) number of offspring the male has previously produced.
    D) age of the male.

Answer: B
Topic: Section 8.5

12) A lek is characterized by
    A) females displaying in small, clumped territories lacking resources.
    B) males defending resources in small, clumped territories.
    C) females mating with only a small percentage of displaying males.
    D) a group of females defended by a single dominant male.

Answer: C
Topic: Section 8.5

13) As an individual _____ its reproductive effort, it _____ its survivorship.
    A) increases; reduces
    B) increases; increases
    C) increases; does not change
    D) decreases; reduces

Answer: A
Topic: Section 8.6

14) The more seeds that a plant produces in a single reproductive episode, the _____ of each seed.
    A) greater the probability of survival
    B) smaller the size
    C) greater the size
    D) more irregular the shape

Answer: B
Topic: Quantifying Ecology 8.1

15) The reproductive strategy in which relatively few young are produced at repeated intervals during an individual's life is referred to as
    A) semelparity.
    B) iteroparity.
    C) altricial.
    D) precocial.

Answer: B
Topic: Section 8.7

16) Altricial young are relatively
    A) independent at birth and require relatively little time for incubation/gestation.
    B) independent at birth and require a relatively long time for incubation/gestation.
    C) helpless at birth and require relatively little time for incubation/gestation.
    D) helpless at birth and require a relatively long time for incubation/gestation.

Answer: C
Topic: Section 8.8

17) Parental care is documented for all the following animals, except:
    A) bees.
    B) crocodiles.
    C) humans.
    D) cod.

Answer: D
Topic: Section 8.8

18) All of the following are organisms without a particular adult size or that have indeterminate growth, except:
   A) fish.
   B) amphibians.
   C) mammals.
   D) annual plants.

   Answer: C
   Topic: Section 8.9

19) Which of the following statements is not true?
   A) Perennial plants generally delay reproduction until they have attained a certain size.
   B) Fecundity in poikilothermic animals, such as fish, increases with age.
   C) The number of eggs produced by a female loggerhead sea turtle is constrained by her body size.
   D) Fecundity generally declines with body size in endotherms.

   Answer: D
   Topic: Section 8.9

20) Asynchronous hatching
   A) ensures survival of all offspring in times of limited resources.
   B) is practiced by many insect species.
   C) favors the survival of the early hatched young.
   D) is the same as siblicide.

   Answer: C
   Topic: Section 8.10

21) Which of the following is not proposed to explain the change in clutch size of birds with latitude?
   A) Clutch size has evolved to equal the largest number of young the parents can feed.
   B) Clutch size results from different allocations of energy to egg production, avoidance of predators, and competition.
   C) Clutch size is a fixed evolutionary feature within any given taxonomic lineage of bird species.
   D) Clutch size varies in direct proportion to seasonal variation in resources, especially food.

   Answer: C
   Topic: Section 8.11

22) Which of the following statements is incorrect?
   A) Seed dispersal is the primary component of plant habitat selection.
   B) Birds tend to assess the general features of the landscape before any other factor when selecting a habitat.
   C) Even though a habitat may provide all the resources required, it still may not be selected.
   D) The presence of predators may encourage a species to occupy a particular habitat.

   Answer: D
   Topic: Section 8.12

23) An r-strategist is characterized by
   A) slow population growth.
   B) a slow rate of development.
   C) a long life expectancy.
   D) density-independent mortality.

   Answer: D
   Topic: Section 8.13

24) J. Philip Grime developed a life history classification for
   A) plants.
   B) mollusks.
   C) vertebrates.
   D) marine fish.

   Answer: A
   Topic: Section 8.13

25) R-strategists (MacArthur et al.) are most similar to Grime's
   A) C strategy.
   B) S strategy.
   C) R strategy.
   D) CS strategy.

   Answer: C
   Topic: Section 8.13

26) Plant species that exhibit Grime's S strategy
   A) rapidly colonize disturbed sites.
   B) are superior competitors and allocate most energy to growth.
   C) are tolerant of stressful conditions and primarily allocate resources to maintenance.
   D) have a lifespan of many years and produce large seeds.

   Answer: C
   Topic: Section 8.13

27) The development of modern corn from teosinte, a group of large Central and South American grasses, is an example of
   A) sexual selection.
   B) selective breeding.
   C) natural selection.
   D) random genetic drift.

   Answer: B
   Topic: Ecological Issues: The Life History of Maize: A Story of Unnatural Selection

True/False Questions

1) Offspring that are produced via asexual reproduction are genetically identical to the parent.
   Answer: TRUE
   Topic: Section 8.1

2) Organisms reproduce either sexually or asexually, but never both.
   Answer: FALSE
   Topic: Section 8.1

3) Dioecious plants have both male and female parts on the same plant.
   Answer: FALSE
   Topic: Section 8.2

4) Some plant and animal species can naturally change their sex from male to female or vice versa.
   Answer: TRUE
   Topic: Section 8.2

5) Polygamy is the acquisition by an individual of two or more mates.

Answer: TRUE
Topic: Section 8.3

6) Polygyny is much more common than polyandry.

Answer: TRUE
Topic: Section 8.3

7) Polygyny is more likely to occur as differences in territory quality increase between territorial males.

Answer: TRUE
Topic: Section 8.3

8) The dominant phenotypes in a population may be determined by factors other than natural selection.

Answer: TRUE
Topic: Section 8.4

9) The size and color of a potential mate rarely correlates with fitness.

Answer: FALSE
Topic: Section 8.4

10) Female choice is most apparent in situations in which males congregate at a lek.

Answer: TRUE
Topic: Section 8.5

11) The more energy an organism spends on reproduction, the less it has available for growth.

Answer: TRUE
Topic: Section 8.6

12) An individual's fitness is defined by the number of offspring it produces.

Answer: FALSE
Topic: Section 8.6

13) Semelparous organisms initially allocate energy into growth, development, and energy storage and later allocate energy into one massive reproductive effort before dying.

Answer: TRUE
Topic: Section 8.7

14) Most species of vertebrates are iteroparous.

Answer: TRUE
Topic: Section 8.7

15) In general, parental investment has a positive correlation with the number of young produced.

Answer: FALSE
Topic: Section 8.8

16) Humans are precocial because their offspring are born helpless and require intensive parental care.

Answer: FALSE
Topic: Section 8.8

17) Many species of plants and ectothermic animals continue growing throughout their adult lives, a condition known as indeterminate growth.

Answer: TRUE
Topic: Section 8.9

18) Large body size is often positively correlated with fecundity.

Answer: TRUE
Topic: Section 8.9

19) In birds, siblicide is more likely to occur when the hatching of eggs is asynchronous rather than synchronous.

Answer: TRUE
Topic: Section 8.10

20) The number of offspring produced by birds and mammals per reproductive event is fewer in temperate areas than in tropical areas.

Answer: FALSE
Topic: Section 8.11

21) Established plants are unable to select a new habitat.

Answer: TRUE
Topic: Section 8.12

22) Species that are r-strategists usually live longer than those that are K-strategists.

Answer: FALSE
Topic: Section 8.13

23) Species that are K-strategists tend to develop more rapidly than those that are r-strategists.

Answer: FALSE
Topic: Section 8.13

24) According to Grime's model of life history variation in plants, trees and shrubs generally are categorized as CS strategists.

Answer: TRUE
Topic: Section 8.13

25) The major difference between ancestral teosinte and modern corn is the amount of resources allocated to seed production.

Answer: TRUE
Topic: Ecological Issues: The Life History of Maize: A Story of Unnatural Selection

Essay Questions

1) Contrast sexual and asexual reproduction. What conditions would favor the evolution of one reproductive strategy over the other?

Topic: Section 8.1

2) Explain the advantage of the ability for an organism to possess both male and female organs.

Topic: Section 8.2

3) Explain why most bird species are monogamous while most mammal species are polygynous.

Topic: Section 8.3

4) Explain sexual dimorphism from a Darwinian perspective.

   Topic: Section 8.4

5) Contrast semelparous and iteroparous reproductive strategies and explain the trade-offs of each.

   Topic: Section 8.7

6) Contrast altricial and precocial offspring and describe the conditions under which each is considered most advantageous.

   Topic: Section 8.8

7) Explain why siblicide is common among bird species when resources are rare. Why is this an effective strategy under these conditions?

   Topic: Section 8.10

8) Describe the three hypotheses proposed to explain the increase in bird clutch size with an increase in latitude. Discuss which one of these hypotheses seems most probably to you and why.

   Topic: Section 8.11

9) Discuss the differences between r-strategists and K-strategists. Give an example of each.

   Topic: Section 8.13

10) Describe the different strategies (S, C, and R) as presented in Grime's model of life history variation in plants.

   Topic: Section 8.13

Chapter 9 Properties of Populations

Short Answer Questions

1) A group of individuals of the same species inhabiting a given area is called a(n) _____.

   Answer: population
   Topic: Introduction to Chapter 9

2) A module developed asexually from a genet is known as a _____.

   Answer: ramet
   Topic: Section 9.1

3) The _____ of a population describes its spatial location.

   Answer: distribution
   Topic: Section 9.2

4) When referring to a population, it is important to explicitly define its _____.

   Answer: boundaries
   Topic: Section 9.2

5) _____ defines the size of a population.

   Answer: Abundance
   Topic: Section 9.3

6) Population _____ is the number of individuals per unit area, or per unit volume.

   Answer: density
   Topic: Section 9.3

7) In most cases, population density must be estimated by _____.

   Answer: sampling
   Topic: Section 9.4

8) A sampling method that is commonly used to study plants or other sessile animals involves _____.

   Answer: quadrats
   Topic: Section 9.4

9) Populations can be divided into three ecologically important age classes: prereproductive, reproductive, and _____.

   Answer: postreproductive
   Topic: Section 9.5

10) A graph that compares the relative size of different age groups within a population is called a(n) _____.

    Answer: age pyramid
    Topic: Section 9.5

11) In most mammalian populations, the _____ sex ratio at birth is often weighted toward males.

    Answer: secondary
    Topic: Section 9.6

12) When individuals move out of a subpopulation, it is referred to as _____.

Answer: emigration
Topic: Section 9.7

13) A round-trip movement of an individual from one place to another and back again is called _____.

Answer: migration
Topic: Section 9.7

14) The primary factors driving the dynamics of population abundance are the demographic processes of _____ and _____.

Answer: birth, death
Topic: Section 9.8

Multiple-Choice Questions

1) A group of individuals of the same species living in a given area is called a
   A) genet.
   B) population.
   C) community.
   D) ramet.

Answer: B
Topic: Introduction to Chapter 9

2) Which of the following is not a feature of a population?
   A) size
   B) density
   C) number of species
   D) distribution

Answer: C
Topic: Introduction to Chapter 9

3) An individual organism produced by sexual reproduction is called a
   A) genet.
   B) ramet.
   C) clone.
   D) module.

Answer: A
Topic: Section 9.1

4) Which of the following is a modular organism?
   A) frog
   B) coral
   C) cat
   D) butterfly

Answer: B
Topic: Section 9.1

5) A collective of local subpopulations is called a(n)
   A) genet.
   B) ramet.
   C) metapopulation.
   D) ecogroup.

Answer: C
Topic: Section 9.2

6) The area inhabited by all individuals of a particular species is known as this population's
   A) geographic range.
   B) distribution.
   C) ecosystem.
   D) habitat.

Answer: A
Topic: Section 9.2

7) Abundance is a function of
   A) the area over which the population is distributed.
   B) temperature.
   C) population density and temperature.
   D) population density and area of distribution.

Answer: D
Topic: Section 9.3

8) The most common spatial distribution of individuals within a population is
   A) homogenous.
   B) clumped.
   C) random.
   D) uniform.

Answer: B
Topic: Section 9.3

9) The clumping of individuals into scattered groups can result from all the following, except:
   A) resource availability.
   B) social behavior.
   C) electromagnetic force.
   D) geography.

Answer: C
Topic: Section 9.3

10) The most widely used technique to estimate the size of animal populations is
    A) quadrat sampling.
    B) mark-recapture.
    C) counts of animal scat.
    D) direct counts of all individuals.

Answer: B
Topic: Section 9.4

11) The age of a tree is commonly determined by
A) estimating tree height.
B) assessing the rate of CO_2 consumption.
C) measuring the diameter of a trunk at breast height (dbh).
D) counting the number of leaves.

Answer: C
Topic: Section 9.5

12) Which of the following is a graphical depiction of the age structure of a population?
A) phase plane plot
B) life table
C) age pyramid
D) age tower

Answer: C
Topic: Section 9.5

13) Which of the following would not be expected to change with the age of individuals in a population?
A) sex ratio
B) reproductive output
C) probability of survival
D) species identity

Answer: D
Topic: Sections 9.5 and 9.6

14) The movement of individuals in space is called
A) distribution.
B) migration.
C) dispersal.
D) density.

Answer: C
Topic: Section 9.7

15) Which of the following organisms is listed as a Federal Noxious Weed because of its profound negative impacts on ecosystems of the southeastern United States?
A) gypsy moth
B) corn
C) ivy
D) kudzu

Answer: D
Topic: Ecological Issues: Human–Assisted Dispersal

True/False Questions

1) A population will decrease in size when the number of individuals born exceeds the number of individuals that die.

Answer: FALSE
Topic: Introduction to Part 3

2) The population is a genetic unit.

Answer: TRUE
Topic: Introduction to Chapter 9

3) An individual plant is often more difficult to recognize than an individual animal.

Answer: TRUE
Topic: Section 9.1

4) A ramet possesses the exact same genetic makeup as its parent.

Answer: TRUE
Topic: Section 9.1

5) The distribution of species is rarely determined by minimum and maximum temperature tolerances.

Answer: FALSE
Topic: Section 9.2

6) Individuals are usually distributed as one large population across the landscape and not as separate disjunct subpopulations in patches.

Answer: FALSE
Topic: Section 9.2

7) A uniform distribution of individuals within a population occurs if each individual's position is independent of others' positions.

Answer: FALSE
Topic: Section 9.3

8) Ecological density is a measure of the number of individuals per unit of available living space.

Answer: TRUE
Topic: Section 9.3

9) The distribution of a population is influenced by suitable habitat availability, while the abundance of a population is not.

Answer: FALSE
Topic: Sections 9.3 and 9.4

10) The most common approach to sampling animal population size is to count every individual.

Answer: FALSE
Topic: Section 9.4

11) For plants, the distribution of age classes in an age pyramid is often highly skewed.

Answer: TRUE
Topic: Section 9.5

12) The age of a fish can be determined by counting the annual rings of otoliths (ear stones).

Answer: TRUE
Topic: Section 9.5

13) Most properties of a population do not change with the age of individuals.

Answer: FALSE
Topic: Sections 9.5 and 9.6

14) The sex ratio in a population is usually fixed and does not vary among age classes.

Answer: FALSE
Topic: Section 9.6

15) All animals disperse actively, while all plants disperse passively.

Answer: FALSE
Topic: Section 9.7

16) Unlike the one-way movement of an individual in emigration and immigration, migration is a round-trip.

Answer: TRUE
Topic: Section 9.7

Essay Questions

1) Give an example of how environmental variation affects the distribution of a population.

Topic: Section 9.2

2) Discuss the three distribution patterns of individuals within a population and explain the conditions that give rise to each pattern.

Topic: Section 9.3

3) Provide the mark-recapture equation used for estimating population size and define the terms of the equation. Why is mark-recapture such a popular and effective method for determining animal population densities?

Topic: Section 9.4

4) Describe several approaches used by ecologists to establish age structure for plant and animal populations.

Topic: Section 9.5

5) Describe several ways that plants disperse.

Topic: Section 9.7

6) Some animals migrate daily while others migrate seasonally. Give an example of each migration pattern and explain the benefit of this lifestyle to the organisms that you present.

Topic: Section 9.7

7) Using examples, discuss the impact of increased human travel in the 20th century on long-distance dispersal of plants and animals. Describe how and why introduced species typically alter native ecosystems.

Topic: Ecological Issues: Human–Assisted Dispersal

Chapter 10 Population Growth

Short Answer Questions

1) _____ refers to the rate at which the number of individuals in a population increases or decreases with time.

Answer: Growth
Topic: Introduction to Chapter 10

2) Movement in and out of a population does not occur in a(n) _____ population.

Answer: closed
Topic: Introduction to Chapter 10

3) There is no change in population size when the instantaneous per capita rate of growth (r) is equal to

_____ .

Answer: zero
Topic: Section 10.1

4) If population size $N(t)$ is plotted as a linear function of time (t), the _____ of the resulting line will remain constant between any two points.

Answer: slope or rate of population change
Topic: Quantifying Ecology 10.2

5) To obtain a clear and systematic picture of mortality and survival within a population, ecologists construct _____ .

Answer: life tables
Topic: Section 10.2

6) A group of individuals born in the same period of time is called a(n) _____ .

Answer: cohort
Topic: Section 10.2

7) Life _____ refers to the average number of years that an individual is expected to live from the time of his or her birth.

Answer: expectancy
Topic: Quantifying Ecology 10.3

8) Ecologists develop a _____ life table to follow the fate of a group of individuals, who were all born at a given time, from birth to death.

Answer: cohort, or dynamic
Topic: Section 10.3

9) A _____ life table is constructed by sampling the population to obtain a distribution of age classes during a single time period.

Answer: time-specific
Topic: Section 10.3

10) A mortality curve plots mortality rate (q_x) against _____ .

Answer: age
Topic: Section 10.4

11) A type _____ survivorship curve is typical of populations in which the mortality rate of juveniles is very high.

Answer: III
Topic: Section 10.4

12) Adult birds exhibit a type _____ survivorship curve.

Answer: II
Topic: Section 10.4

13) The _____ birthrate is expressed as the births per 1000 individuals per unit of time.

Answer: crude
Topic: Section 10.5

14) _____ is the study of populations.

Answer: Demography
Topic: Section 10.5

15) The net reproductive rate (R_0) is equal to _____ when females, on average, replace themselves in a population.

Answer: one
Topic: Section 10.6

16) An _____ is the proportion of individuals in the various age classes for any one year.

Answer: age distribution
Topic: Section 10.7

17) Demographic _____ is the random variation in birth and death rates that occur in populations from year to year.

Answer: stochasticity
Topic: Section 10.8

18) _____ stochasticity is the random variation in birth and death rates that occur in populations from year to year due to natural disasters and other annual variations in the environment.

Answer: Environmental
Topic: Section 10.8

19) A population eventually goes _____ when its population growth (r) remains negative without reversing.

Answer: extinct
Topic: Section 10.9

20) The _____ effect is the decline in either reproduction or survival under conditions of low population density.

Answer: Allee
Topic: Section 10.10

21) _____ populations are more susceptible to both demographic and environmental stochasticity than _____ populations.

Answer: Small; large
Topic: Section 10.10

Multiple-Choice Questions

1) A population that is decreasing in size has an intrinsic rate of population growth (r) that is
   A) < 0.
   B) = 0.
   C) > 0.
   D) > 1.

   Answer: A
   Topic: Section 10.1

2) Colonizing populations generally exhibit _____ population growth while they establish in a new environment.
   A) exponential
   B) logistic
   C) tangential
   D) dynamic

   Answer: A
   Topic: Section 10.1

3) An equation in which the derivative appears on the left-hand side is referred to as a(n)
   A) calculation.
   B) tangential equation.
   C) differential equation.
   D) derivative equation.

   Answer: C
   Topic: Quantifying Ecology 10.1

4) Which of the following equations reflects the exponential model of population growth?
   A) $N(t) = b - d$
   B) $s = \triangle N/\triangle t$
   C) $N(t) = N(0)e^{rt}$
   D) $dN/dt = rN$

   Answer: C
   Topic: Section 10.2 and Quantifying Ecology 10.2

5) A systematic compilation of mortality and survival data for a population is called a(n)
   A) age pyramid.
   B) cohort group.
   C) life table.
   D) probability summary.

   Answer: C
   Topic: Section 10.2

6) In a life table, the value l_x represents the
   A) age-specific mortality rate.
   B) age-specific life expectancy.
   C) age-specific mortality.
   D) the probability at birth of surviving to any given age.

   Answer: D
   Topic: Section 10.2

7) Most life tables have been constructed for
   A) short-lived plants.
   B) insects.
   C) long-lived vertebrates.
   D) short-lived mammals.

Answer: C
Topic: Section 10.3

8) The life table is most useful in studying the following areas of plant demography except:
   A) life cycles of perennial plants.
   B) life cycles of annual plants.
   C) seedling mortality and survival.
   D) population dynamics of perennial plants marked as seedlings.

Answer: A
Topic: Section 10.3

9) A _____ survivorship curve is typical of humans and other mammals, in which survival rate is high throughout the life span followed by heavy mortality at the end.
   A) type I
   B) type II
   C) type III
   D) type IV

Answer: A
Topic: Section 10.4

10) Survivorship curves plot _____ against x.
   A) d_x
   B) l_x
   C) $\log l_x$
   D) q_x

Answer: C
Topic: Section 10.4

11) The _____ equals the number of births per female of age x.
   A) crude birth rate
   B) age-specific birth rate
   C) gross reproductive rate
   D) net reproductive rate

Answer: B
Topic: Section 10.5

12) The average number of female offspring born to a female over her lifetime is the
   A) crude birth rate.
   B) age-specific birth rate.
   C) gross reproductive rate.
   D) net reproductive rate.

Answer: C
Topic: Section 10.5

13) A fecundity table includes all the following information, except:
    A) age-specific birthrates.
    B) survivorship.
    C) net reproductive rate.
    D) age.

Answer: C
Topic: Section 10.6

14) A population reaches a stable-age distribution when
    A) the population stops growing.
    B) the birthrate is less than the deathrate.
    C) the net reproductive rate (R_0) is zero.
    D) the proportion of individuals in each age group remains the same.

Answer: D
Topic: Section 10.7

15) Which of the following is incorrect?
    A) s_x is the average survival rate of the population.
    B) l is the rate of population growth.
    C) $N(t)$ is the total population size for a given year.
    D) b_x is the age-specific birthrate.

Answer: A
Topic: Section 10.7

16) If N(0) = 30 and λ = 1.20, what is the population size for year one?
    A) 25
    B) 28.8
    C) 30
    D) 36

Answer: D
Topic: Section 10.7

17) A leading cause of current population extinctions is
    A) global warming.
    B) habitat destruction.
    C) hunting.
    D) diseases.

Answer: B
Topic: Section 10.9

18) A small population is at a greater risk of extinction because
    A) there is less competition within the population.
    B) of an increase in the genetic diversity within the population.
    C) most of the individuals would likely die in a stochastic event (e.g., wildfire).
    D) females can no longer reproduce.

Answer: C
Topic: Section 10.10

True/False Questions

1) Immigration and emigration occurs within an open population.

Answer: TRUE

Topic: Introduction to Chapter 10

2) Exponential growth is characteristic of populations that inhabit favorable environments at high densities.

Answer: FALSE

Topic: Section 10.1

3) The instantaneous per capita rate of growth (r) of a stable population is equal to zero.

Answer: TRUE

Topic: Section 10.1

4) Exponential population growth does not occur in natural populations.

Answer: FALSE

Topic: Section 10.1 and Quantifying Ecology 10.2

5) A cohort refers to a group of individuals born in the same period of time.

Answer: TRUE

Topic: Section 10.2

6) In a given life table, x represents the age classes of that population.

Answer: TRUE

Topic: Section 10.2

7) Life expectancy (e) is the same for an individual regardless of age.

Answer: FALSE

Topic: Quantifying Ecology 10.3

8) A time-specific life table is easier to create and more accurate than a dynamic life table.

Answer: FALSE

Topic: Section 10.3

9) There are two general types of survivorship curves.

Answer: FALSE

Topic: Section 10.4

10) The probability of survival and death usually varies with age.

Answer: TRUE

Topic: Section 10.4

11) The net reproductive rate represents the number of births per 1000 population per unit of time.

Answer: FALSE

Topic: Section 10.5

12) When a population is stable, the net reproductive rate (R_0) is equal to zero.

Answer: FALSE

Topic: Section 10.6

13) A population in which λ equals one has reached a stable-age distribution.

Answer: TRUE
Topic: Section 10.7

14) Because birth and death rates are not constant, tables and models developed by a demographer may have limited relevance to real populations.

Answer: TRUE
Topic: Section 10.8

15) The introduction of a novel organism into an ecosystem can lead to extinction/s of the natural population/s.

Answer: TRUE
Topic: Section 10.9

16) Genetic drift occurs at a faster rate in a large population than in a small population.

Answer: FALSE
Topic: Section 10.10

Essay Questions

1) What is the significance of constructing a life table to an ecologist? What information is required to develop a life table and what is this information used for?

Topic: Section 10.2

2) Compare and contrast the two basic types of life tables. Discuss the advantages and disadvantages of each.

Topic: Section 10.3

3) Illustrate three types of survivorship curves and give examples of each. What factors cause the three different types to appear in nature?

Topic: Section 10.4

4) Explain how λ is used by demographers to predict the future size of a population.

Topic: Section 10.7

5) Discuss two stochastic processes and describe how each influences population dynamics.

Topic: Section 10.8

6) Discuss five factors known to cause extinction. Which of these factors is considered the leading cause of current extinctions and why?

Topic: Section 10.9

7) What is the Allee effect? Give several examples that illustrate the potential catastrophic impact of small size on population persistence.

Topic: Section 10.10

Chapter 11 Intraspecific Population Regulation

Short Answer Questions

1) The per capita death rate (d) _____ with population size.

   Answer: increases
   Topic: Section 11.1

2) The maximum sustainable population size for the prevailing environment is called the _____.

   Answer: carrying capacity
   Topic: Section 11.1

3) The factors that influence a population in proportion to its size are called _____ factors.

   Answer: density-dependent
   Topic: Section 11.2

4) _____ occurs when individuals use a common resource that is in short supply relative to the number seeking it.

   Answer: Competition
   Topic: Section 11.3

5) Competition among individuals of the same species is referred to as _____ competition.

   Answer: intraspecific
   Topic: Section 11.3

6) When competing individuals deplete a shared resource without direct interaction, it is called _____ competition.

   Answer: exploitation
   Topic: Section 11.3

7) _____ growth is the inverse relationship between population density and individual growth.

   Answer: Density-dependent
   Topic: Section 11.4

8) The progressive decline in density and increase in biomass of remaining individuals in a population is known as _____.

   Answer: self-thinning
   Topic: Section 11.5

9) A plant grown at high density will produce _____ seeds than the same plant grown at low density.

   Answer: more
   Topic: Section 11.6

10) One hypothesis of population regulation in animals is that increased crowding and _____ cause stress.

    Answer: social contact
    Topic: Section 11.7

11) Researcher T. Scott Sillett studied the response of warbler survival and fecundity to _____.

    Answer: El Niño-Southern Oscillation (ENSO), or effects of climate
    Topic: Field Studies: T. Scott Sillett

12) The _____ individual is dominant over all other members of the social group.

Answer: alpha
Topic: Section 11.9

13) The area that an animal normally uses during a year is its _____.

Answer: home range
Topic: Section 11.10

14) The part of an animal's home range that is defended against intruders is its _____.

Answer: territory
Topic: Section 11.10

15) Individual organisms spaced out more than is expected from a random occupancy of suitable habitat is an alternate (and appropriate) definition of _____.

Answer: territoriality
Topic: Section 11.11

16) Factors that influence population growth that do not change systematically with the density of the population are called _____ factors.

Answer: density-independent
Topic: Section 11.12

Multiple-Choice Questions

1) The exponential model of population growth assumes
   A) that essential resources are unlimited.
   B) a changeable environment.
   C) that all individuals in the population are the same age.
   D) a constant mortality rate throughout the population.

Answer: A
Topic: Section 11.1

2) As population size (N) increases, the
   A) birth rate increases.
   B) birth rate decreases.
   C) death rate decreases.
   D) carrying capacity increases.

Answer: B
Topic: Section 11.1

3) In logistic growth, the level at which population growth ceases is referred to as the
   A) threshold of security.
   B) Malthusian parameter.
   C) saturation point.
   D) carrying capacity.

Answer: D
Topic: Section 11.1

4) Which of the following is considered to be a density-dependent factor that regulates population growth?
    A) hurricane
    B) disease
    C) earthquake
    D) forest fire

Answer: B
Topic: Section 11.2

5) Density-independent population regulation
    A) is usually catastrophic.
    B) primarily affects large populations.
    C) may involve disease transmission among individuals of the population.
    D) is the result of the competition for available resources.

Answer: A
Topic: Section 11.2

6) The form of competition in which some competing individuals claim enough resources while denying others a share is called
    A) scramble competition.
    B) contest competition.
    C) exploitation competition.
    D) interference competition.

Answer: B
Topic: Section 11.3

7) _____ competition occurs when an organism actively defends a site and/or resource and denies access to other individuals.
    A) Scramble
    B) Contest
    C) Exploitation
    D) Interference

Answer: C
Topic: Section 11.3

8) As the density of a population increases, the
    A) survival rate increases.
    B) reproductive rate increases.
    C) intensity of intraspecific competition decreases.
    D) individual growth rate increases.

Answer: D
Topic: Sections 11.4 and 11.5

9) When experimental plants (*Atriplex prostrata*) were grown at high densities
    A) individual growth rates increased.
    B) the proportion of resources allocated to leaf production increased.
    C) individual plant weight increased.
    D) net photosynthetic rate increased.

Answer: B
Topic: Section 11.4

10) Self-thinning
    A) is found only in populations of sessile organisms.
    B) occurs at high population densities.
    C) functions to increase the survival rate of all individuals in the population.
    D) is a type of scramble competition.

Answer: B
Topic: Section 11.5

11) Fecundity
    A) is unrelated to population density.
    B) decreases as population density increases.
    C) increases as population density increases.
    D) decreases for females only as population density increases.

Answer: A
Topic: Section 11.6

12) Which statement about stress is incorrect?
    A) Stress increases as population density increases.
    B) Stress may trigger the release of specific chemical signals or pheromones.
    C) Stress can stimulate growth and increase the rate of reproduction.
    D) Stress may result in increased vulnerability to disease.

Answer: C
Topic: Section 11.6

13) The individuals that disperse as a response to high population density
    A) are the oldest members of the population.
    B) rarely survive.
    C) include mostly females.
    D) are usually superior competitors.

Answer: B
Topic: Section 11.8

14) Which statement is correct?
    A) When a resource shortage brings about dispersal, it is usually the reproductive adults that are forced out.
    B) Dispersal rarely leads to the expansion of a population's range.
    C) Dispersal functions as an important mechanism regulating the growth of populations.
    D) Dispersal is one way to reduce the chance of inbreeding.

Answer: D
Topic: Section 11.8

15) Social organization
    A) is restricted to invertebrates and rarely appears in vertebrate populations.
    B) becomes disruptive to normal social interaction.
    C) stabilizes relationships and minimizes fighting.
    D) is not believed to play a role in population regulation.

Answer: C
Topic: Section 11.9

16) In a wolf pack, the beta male
     A) mates with all the females of the pack.
     B) is subordinate to the alpha female.
     C) is dominant over all members of the pack.
     D) is usually very closely related to the alpha male.

Answer: D
Topic: Section 11.9

17) In general, the size of an animal's territory
     A) is smaller when food is abundant and concentrated.
     B) is larger when food is abundant and concentrated.
     C) is unrelated to animal body size.
     D) is unrelated to food availability.

Answer: A
Topic: Section 11.10

18) The home range of an animal is usually larger for
     A) a carnivorous species than for a herbivorous species of the same body size.
     B) females than males of the same species.
     C) an immature male than for an adult male of the same species.
     D) a smaller species than for a larger species.

Answer: A
Topic: Section 11.10

19) Which of the following factors is most likely to be a density-independent regulator of population growth?
     A) drought
     B) disease
     C) starvation
     D) parasites

Answer: A
Topic: Section 11.12

True/False Questions

1) Most natural populations grow in size indefinitely.

Answer: FALSE
Topic: Introduction to Chapter 11

2) The carrying capacity (K) of a population can vary depending on the supply of resources.

Answer: TRUE
Topic: Section 11.1

3) Resource availability is the only density-dependent factor affecting a population.

Answer: FALSE
Topic: Section 11.2

4) Competition for resources is a density-dependent factor affecting a population.

Answer: TRUE
Topic: Section 11.2

5) The influence of density-independent factors on populations is generally less predictable than the influence of density-dependent factors.

Answer: TRUE
Topic: Section 11.2

6) Contest competition results in some individuals in the population getting more resources than others.

Answer: TRUE
Topic: Section 11.3

7) As intraspecific competition increases, the growth of individuals decreases.

Answer: TRUE
Topic: Section 11.4

8) High-density conditions caused no noticeable shift in the behavior of experimental tadpoles (*Rana sylvatica*).

Answer: FALSE
Topic: Section 11.4

9) As the density of a population increases, the rate of reproduction increases.

Answer: FALSE
Topic: Section 11.5

10) Fecundity is unrelated to body size.

Answer: FALSE
Topic: Section 11.6

11) The rate of aggressive interactions among individuals increases as population density increases.

Answer: TRUE
Topic: Section 11.6

12) As the density of a population increases, dispersal usually decreases.

Answer: FALSE
Topic: Section 11.8

13) Dispersal plays an active part in regulating population size.

Answer: FALSE
Topic: Section 11.8

14) Within a social group of animals, resources are usually divided up evenly and peaceably, thus strengthening group cohesion.

Answer: FALSE
Topic: Section 11.9

15) Among mammal species, the home range size is negatively correlated with body size.

Answer: FALSE
Topic: Section 11.10

16) When a given area is saturated with territories, excluded individuals who lack a territory soon die of starvation.

Answer: FALSE
Topic: Section 11.10

17) Territorial behavior includes some form of advertisement, threat, and combat.

Answer: TRUE
Topic: Section 11.10

18) Plants can capture and defend space.

Answer: TRUE
Topic: Section 11.11

19) Fire is an example of a density-independent factor that affects a population.

Answer: TRUE
Topic: Section 11.12

Essay Questions

1) What is the difference between exponential growth and logistic growth? Under what ecological conditions does each occur?

Topic: Section 11.1

2) Discuss some of the important issues involved when trying to determine Earth's carrying capacity (K) for humans. Why is it difficult to calculate K for the human population?

Topic: Ecological Issues: The Human Carrying Capacity

3) Contrast the density-dependent and density-independent mechanisms of population regulation.

Topic: Sections 11.2–11.12

4) What is competition? Compare and contrast scramble and contest competition.

Topic: Section 11.3

5) Discuss the impact of high-density conditions on wood frog tadpoles (*Rana sylvatica*). How did these experimental tadpoles respond to increased intraspecific competition?

Topic: Section 11.4

6) Explain why high population density might stress an organism. Provide several examples of some of the negative impacts of stress on an organism.

Topic: Section 11.7

7) Explain why El Niño or La Niña conditions might affect survival and reproductive rates of a migratory bird species (e.g., black-throated blue warbler).

Topic: Field Studies: T. Scott Sillett

8) Explain why the timing of dispersal during low- or high-population density states can have very different impacts on the population.

Topic: Section 11.8

9) Why are social organization and territoriality adaptive? How do human populations exhibit these two behaviors?

Topic: Sections 11.9 and 11.10

10) Why do some species have a larger home range than others? Explain why a carnivorous mammal requires a larger home range than an herbivorous mammal of similar body size.

Topic: Section 11.10

11) Give a specific example of how a density-independent factor affects a population. Explain why density-independent factors are less predictable in their effects than density-dependent factors.

Topic: Section 11.12

Chapter 12 Metapopulations

Short Answer Questions

1) A _____ consists of a group of local, interacting subpopulations that are linked by dispersal.

Answer: metapopulation
Topic: Introduction to Chapter 12

2) At the _____, or within-patch scale, individuals move and interact with each other in the course of their routine feeding and breeding activities.

Answer: local
Topic: Section 12.1

3) At the metapopulation, or _____ scale, population dynamics are governed by the interaction of local populations.

Answer: regional
Topic: Section 12.1

4) Metapopulation persistence is a dynamic balance between the _____ and (re)colonization of empty habitat patches.

Answer: extinction
Topic: Section 12.2

5) The extinction rate (E) of a metapopulation _____ as the proportion of patches occupied (P) increases.

Answer: increases
Topic: Section 12.2

6) With habitat _____, formerly continuous populations are separated into a network of local populations with varying degrees of isolation and risk.

Answer: fragmentation
Topic: Ecological Issues: The Metapopulation Concept in Conservation Ecology

7) _____ size and _____ influence the dynamics of patch occupancy.

Answer: Patch; isolation
Topic: Section 12.3

8) Increasing patch size has the potential to increase environmental _____.

Answer: heterogeneity
Topic: Section 12.4

9) The _____ effect refers to the increasing population size and decreasing risk of extinction, which occurs with an increasing rate of immigration.

Answer: rescue
Topic: Section 12.5

10) A _____ population maintains a positive growth rate, producing a surplus of individuals who immigrate elsewhere.

Answer: source
Topic: Section 12.5

11) A _____ population cannot support a positive population growth and is only able to persist when individuals immigrate from elsewhere.

Answer: sink
Topic: Section 12.5

12) _____ rate is affected by fecundity and mode of reproduction.

Answer: Dispersal
Topic: Section 12.7

13) Population densities are usually _____ in smaller species than in large species.

Answer: higher, or greater
Topic: Section 12.7

14) A _____ is a collection of metapopulations in a geographic region.

Answer: subspecies
Topic: Section 12.8

Multiple-Choice Questions

1) In a typical metapopulation,
   A) suitable habitat is relatively uniform rather than patchy.
   B) even the largest subpopulations are at risk of extinction.
   C) the isolation of habitat patches prevent recolonization after local extinction.
   D) the dynamics of local populations are synchronized.

Answer: B
Topic: Section 12.1

2) In a metapopulation, within-patch population dynamics are governed primarily by
   A) birth and death rates.
   B) dispersal and colonization.
   C) predation and parasitism.
   D) stochastic processes.

Answer: A
Topic: Section 12.1

3) Which of the following is not an assumption of the model of population dynamics developed by Levins?
   A) Each patch contributes equally to the pool of emigrants.
   B) Patches are of equal size.
   C) The probability of local population extinction is independent of all other populations.
   D) Some patches supply more resources than others.

Answer: D
Topic: Section 12.2

4) In the equation, $P = 1 - e/m$, e represents
   A) the probability of extinction.
   B) the probability of colonization.
   C) the rate of local population extinction.
   D) the rate of colonization.

Answer: A
Topic: Quantifying Ecology 12.1

5) In a metapopulation, the probability of local extinction increases with
     A) increasing patch size and increasing isolation.
     B) increasing patch size and decreasing isolation.
     C) decreasing patch size and increasing isolation.
     D) decreasing patch size and decreasing isolation.

Answer: C
Topic: Section 12.3

6) In a metapopulation, the probability of (re)colonization increases with
     A) increasing patch size and increasing isolation.
     B) increasing patch size and decreasing isolation.
     C) decreasing patch size and increasing isolation.
     D) decreasing patch size and decreasing isolation.

Answer: B
Topic: Section 12.3

7) As the habitat heterogeneity of a patch increases,
     A) environmental stochasticity has a greater impact.
     B) the probability of extinction decreases.
     C) the probability of colonization decreases.
     D) birth rates decrease.

Answer: B
Topic: Section 12.4

8) The rescue effect is a function of
     A) birthrate.
     B) death rate.
     C) immigration.
     D) fecundity.

Answer: C
Topic: Section 12.5

9) A source population
     A) must be maintained by immigrants from a sink population.
     B) has a high rate of extinction.
     C) is usually located in small, isolated patches.
     D) maintains a positive growth rate.

Answer: D
Topic: Section 12.5

10) The persistence of metapopulations increases when
     A) heterogeneity of habitat decreases.
     B) isolation of local populations increase.
     C) environmental stochasticity decreases.
     D) the size of local populations decreases.

Answer: C
Topic: Sections 12.3–12.6

11) Which of the following factors can synchronize metapopulation dynamics?
   A) environmental stochasticity
   B) prevention of dispersal
   C) death of immigrants
   D) heterogeneous patch quality

Answer: A
Topic: Section 12.6

12) The rate of dispersal is highest in species that
   A) occupy stable habitats.
   B) occupy isolated habitats.
   C) reproduce asexually.
   D) have high fecundity.

Answer: D
Topic: Section 12.7

13) Which of the following is the correct hierarchy of the population concept?
   A) local population < metapopulation < subspecies < species
   B) metapopulation < local population < subspecies < species
   C) local population < metapopulation < species < subspecies
   D) metapopulation < local population < species < subspecies

Answer: A
Topic: Section 12.8

True/False Questions

1) The dynamics of local populations are synchronized in most metapopulations.

Answer: FALSE
Topic: Section 12.1

2) The probability of core population extinction is less than that of satellite populations in a metapopulation.

Answer: TRUE
Topic: Section 12.1

3) The model of metapopulation growth is similar to the logistic model of population growth in that both are regulated by density-dependent factors.

Answer: TRUE
Topic: Section 12.2

4) The probability of local extinction decreases with decreasing patch size.

Answer: FALSE
Topic: Section 12.3

5) The probability of colonization increases with increasing patch size.

Answer: TRUE
Topic: Section 12.3

6) A large patch of habitat tends to be more spatially heterogeneous than a small patch of habitat.

Answer: TRUE
Topic: Section 12.4

7) As heterogeneity of habitat in a local population increases, the population density fluctuates more.

Answer: FALSE
Topic: Section 12.4

8) A sink population maintains a positive growth rate and produces a surplus of individuals who immigrate elsewhere.

Answer: FALSE
Topic: Section 12.5

9) Local extinctions will tend to strike the smallest populations.

Answer: TRUE
Topic: Section 12.5

10) The conversion of natural ecosystems to agricultural production tends to synchronize metapopulation dynamics.

Answer: TRUE
Topic: Section 12.6

11) The rate of dispersal is greater in species occupying temporary habitats than in stable habitats.

Answer: TRUE
Topic: Section 12.7

12) Sexually reproducing plants tend to have lower rates of local extinction than asexually reproducing plants.

Answer: FALSE
Topic: Section 12.7

13) A subspecies encompasses the largest geographic range in the population concept hierarchy.

Answer: FALSE
Topic: Section 12.8

Essay Questions

1) Describe the four conditions necessary for the term metapopulation to apply to a system of local populations.

Topic: Section 12.1

2) Describe the assumptions made to mathematically model metapopulation dynamics. Are these assumptions appropriate? Why or why not?

Topic: Section 12.2

3) In the context of a metapopulation, explain how patch size and its degree of isolation affect the equilibrium value of P (proportion of patches occupied).

Topic: Section 12.3

4) Explain the relationship between patch size and habitat heterogeneity. Why is habitat heterogeneity a benefit to a population?

Topic: Section 12.4

5) Contrast sink and source populations. Discuss the importance of source-sink dynamics to species conservation.

Topic: Section 12.5

6) Discuss three characteristics of species that affect their potential rates of colonization and extinction.

Topic: Section 12.7

7) Critique the classic definition of a population as "a group of organisms of the same species occupying a particular area at a particular time." Describe the alternative hierarchical approach for describing the concept of a population.

Topic: Section 12.8

Chapter 13 Interspecific Competition

Short Answer Questions

1) _____ is a relationship that affects the populations of two or more species adversely.

Answer: Competition
Topic: Section 13.1

2) _____ competition occurs when the occupation by one sessile individual precludes the establishment by others.

Answer: Preemptive, or Preemption
Topic: Section 13.1

3) Chemical interaction competition in plants is called _____.

Answer: allelopathy
Topic: Section 13.1

4) _____ competition results from the behavioral exclusion of some individuals by others from a specific space that is defended.

Answer: Territorial
Topic: Section 13.1

5) _____ competition results when non-territorial behavioral interactions between two species result in negative effects on both species.

Answer: Encounter
Topic: Section 13.1

6) The _____ equations predict the outcomes of interspecific competition under different conditions.

Answer: Lotka-Volterra
Topic: Section 13.2

7) In a competitive interaction in which species 1 has a higher carrying capacity (K_1) than species 2 (K_2), it is expected that species _____ will go extinct.

Answer: 2
Topic: Section 13.2

8) In the Lotka-Volterra equations, the zero _____ represent the combined values of species 1 and species 2 under which population growth is zero ($dN/dt = 0$).

Answer: isoclines
Topic: Quantifying Ecology 13.1

9) The Russian biologist G. Gause was one of the first to support the Lotka-Volterra equations by studying the competitive interactions of _____.

Answer: *Paramecium* species
Topic: Section 13.3

10) The _____ principle states that two "complete competitors" cannot coexist.

Answer: competitive exclusion
Topic: Section 13.4

11) Periods of drought or extreme environmental conditions may depress _____ below carrying capacity (*K*).

Answer: population size, or *N*
Topic: Section 13.6

12) Interspecific _____ is where the competition for space influences access to food and nesting sites.

Answer: territoriality
Topic: Section 13.7

13) Ecologist K. Suding applied two soil treatments, three neighborhood treatments, and planted three grass species in each plot, giving a total of _____ treatments.

Answer: 18
Topic: Field Studies: Katherine N. Suding

14) The _____ coefficients represent the per capita effect of an individual of one species on the other.

Answer: competition
Topic: Quantifying Ecology 13.2

15) The full range of conditions and resources under which an organism can survive and reproduce is that organism's _____ niche.

Answer: fundamental
Topic: Section 13.9

16) The portion of the fundamental niche that an organism actually exploits in the presence of competitors is called its _____ niche.

Answer: realized
Topic: Section 13.9

17) When two organisms use a portion of the same resource simultaneously, it is referred to as _____ overlap.

Answer: niche
Topic: Section 13.9

18) When a species expands its niche in response to the removal of a competitor, the species has experienced competitive _____.

Answer: release
Topic: Section 13.9

19) The coexistence of competitors due to differences in the range of resources used or environmental tolerances is referred to as niche _____.

Answer: differentiation, or partitioning
Topic: Section 13.10

20) The limnologist G. E. Hutchinson proposed the idea of the niche as a multidimensional response called a(n) _____.

Answer: hypervolume
Topic: Section 13.10

21) A shift in a species' morphology, behavior, or physiology in response to resource competition is referred to as _____.

Answer: character displacement
Topic: Section 13.11

Multiple-Choice Questions

1) Interspecific competition through the exploitation of a shared resource is sometimes referred to as _____ competition.
   A) preemption
   B) consumption
   C) overgrowth
   D) encounter

   Answer: B
   Topic: Section 13.1

2) Competition in which the occupation of space by one individual prevents establishment in that space by another individual is referred to as _____ competition.
   A) preemption
   B) consumption
   C) overgrowth
   D) territorial

   Answer: A
   Topic: Section 13.1

3) _____ competition results when nonterritorial behavioral interactions between species result in negative effects on one or both species.
   A) Consumption
   B) Preemption
   C) Encounter
   D) Overgrowth

   Answer: C
   Topic: Section 13.1

4) According to the Lotka-Volterra equations, which of the following is not an expected outcome of competitive interactions between two species?
   A) Species 1 drives species 2 to extinction.
   B) Species 2 drives species 1 to extinction.
   C) Both species coexist.
   D) The population sizes of both species increase to infinity.

   Answer: D
   Topic: Section 13.2

5) The diagonal line that represents $dN/dt = 0$ in the graphical depiction of the Lotka-Volterra competitions equations is called
   A) a competition coefficient.
   B) the carrying capacity.
   C) a zero-growth isocline.
   D) a competitive exclusion parameter.

   Answer: C
   Topic: Section 13.2

6) _____ studied the competitive interactions of several *Paramecium* species and supported the Lotka-Volterra competition models.
   A) Charles Darwin
   B) Gregor Mendel
   C) Thomas Schoener
   D) G. F. Gause

Answer: D
Topic: Section 13.3

7) The biologist Thomas Park used _____ to study competition between species.
   A) diatoms
   B) prairie plants
   C) *Paramecium*
   D) flour beetles

Answer: D
Topic: Section 13.3

8) In theory, when two species compete for the same resources, _____ will result.
   A) competitive exclusion
   B) coexistence
   C) initial competition followed by mutualism
   D) parasitism

Answer: A
Topic: Section 13.4

9) Which of the following is an assumption of the competitive exclusion principle?
   A) The competitors have different resource requirements.
   B) The competitors have the same carrying capacity (K).
   C) The environmental conditions remain constant.
   D) The superior competitor will have a lower population growth rate than the inferior competitor.

Answer: C
Topic: Section 13.4

10) Which of the following statements is incorrect?
   A) Competition between species can occur for multiple resources.
   B) Competition can be influenced by non-resource factors such as relative humidity.
   C) The competitive relationship between two species may change over time as the environment changes.
   D) The conditions assumed by the competitive exclusion principle are often observed in nature.

Answer: D
Topic: Sections 13.4–13.7

11) Which of the following is a nonresource (or nonconsumable resource) that can influence the outcome of competition among plant species?
   A) temperature
   B) light
   C) water
   D) nitrogen

Answer: A
Topic: Section 13.5

12) Which of the following is incorrect?
    A) The relative competitive ability of annual plants shift along moisture gradients.
    B) The ability of several thistle species to access nutrients is similar in both monoculture and mixed population experiments.
    C) The distribution of chipmunk species on the eastern slope of the Sierra Nevada is a function of the tolerance of heat stress.
    D) Salt marsh plant zones of the New England coast are influenced by a species' ability to tolerate the physical stress of increasing water depth.

Answer: B
Topic: Section 13.8

13) In the grassland study conducted by ecologist K. Suding, what natural disturbance was simulated to test the effects on competitive interactions among three plant species?
    A) hurricane
    B) grazing by cattle
    C) fire
    D) small mammal burrows

Answer: D
Topic: Field Studies: Katherine N. Suding

14) Two bird species compete in the forest for the same seeds. If $\alpha = 0.75$ and $\beta = 0.25$, then
    A) the rate of seed consumption is the same for both species.
    B) the environment can supply both species since the sum of competition coefficients equals 1.
    C) species 1 "wins" and will outcompete species 2.
    D) species 2 "wins" and will outcompete species 1.

Answer: C
Topic: Quantifying Ecology 13.2

15) When two organisms use a portion of the same resource simultaneously, it is referred to as
    A) niche overlap.
    B) competitive release.
    C) intraspecific competition.
    D) territoriality.

Answer: A
Topic: Section 13.9

16) The portion of potential resources and conditions that an organism actually exploits as a result of interactions with other species is its
    A) home range.
    B) territory.
    C) realized niche.
    D) fundamental niche.

Answer: C
Topic: Section 13.9

17) When two or more organisms use a portion of the same resource simultaneously, it is referred to as
    A) niche overlap.
    B) competitive release.
    C) commensalisms.
    D) amensalism.

Answer: A
Topic: Section 13.9

18) Which of the following is not expected following competition?
    A) evolution of character displacement
    B) evolution of increased niche overlap
    C) competitive exclusion
    D) increase in resources

Answer: B
Topic: Sections 13.9–13.11

19) In general, demonstrating the occurrence of competition under natural field conditions is problematic for all of the following reasons, except:
    A) It is difficult to know whether a population is at carrying capacity.
    B) Competition is impossible to measure in a natural setting.
    C) Scientists cannot control the environment.
    D) Scientists lack full knowledge of the life history requirements of natural populations.

Answer: B
Topic: Section 13.12

True/False Questions

1) Interactions among species are always negative.

Answer: FALSE
Topic: Introduction to Part 4

2) Competition has been regarded as a major force behind species divergence and specialization.

Answer: TRUE
Topic: Introduction to Chapter 13

3) Encounter competition results from the behavioral exclusion of some individuals by others from a specific space that is defended.

Answer: FALSE
Topic: Section 13.1

4) Preemptive competition occurs primarily among mobile organisms, such as small mammals.

Answer: FALSE
Topic: Section 13.1

5) According to the Lotka-Volterra equations, there are two possible outcomes of interspecific competition.

Answer: FALSE
Topic: Section 13.2

6) The Lotka-Volterra competition models do not take into account variation between different environments.

Answer: FALSE
Topic: Section 13.2 and Quantifying Ecology 13.2

7) The biologist G. F. Gause conducted experiments with *Paramecium* that supported the predictions of the Lotka-Volterra competition models.

Answer: TRUE
Topic: Section 13.3

8) In the experiments carried out by biologist David Tilman, two diatom species were able to coexist as long as silica was continually added to the water.

Answer: TRUE
Topic: Section 13.3

9) The competitive exclusion principle assumes that environmental conditions remain constant.

Answer: TRUE
Topic: Section 13.4

10) The outcome of competitive interactions is determined solely by resource availability.

Answer: FALSE
Topic: Section 13.5

11) The competitive ability of a species remains constant even when environmental conditions change.

Answer: FALSE
Topic: Section 13.6

12) Climatic variation can have both density-dependent and density-independent effects on populations.

Answer: TRUE
Topic: Section 13.6

13) Competition for one resource often influences the ability of an organism to access other resources.

Answer: TRUE
Topic: Section 13.7

14) The outcome of interspecific competition varies with environmental changes over time but does not vary over space.

Answer: FALSE
Topic: Section 13.8

15) Changes in the outcome of competition over an environmental gradient are mediated by multiple environmental variables.

Answer: TRUE
Topic: Section 13.8

16) Because of competition, a species rarely is allowed to utilize all of its fundamental niche.

Answer: TRUE
Topic: Section 13.9

17) When two or more organisms use a portion of the same resource simultaneously, it is referred to as resource partitioning.

Answer: FALSE
Topic: Section 13.9

18) The expansion of a species' niche in response to the removal of a competition is referred to as competitive release.

Answer: TRUE
Topic: Section 13.9

19) Because all plants require the same few resources (light, water, essential nutrients), resource partitioning is rarely observed for plants.

Answer: FALSE
Topic: Section 13.10

20) Competition rarely influences the evolution of species' niches.

Answer: FALSE
Topic: Section 13.11

21) Competition can be difficult to demonstrate in the field because it is difficult to know whether populations are at or below their carrying capacity.

Answer: TRUE
Topic: Section 13.12

22) The findings of a laboratory study are more useful and applicable than the results of a field study.

Answer: FALSE
Topic: Section 13.12

Essay Questions

1) According to T. Schoener, there are six types of competitive interactions among species. Use examples to describe four types of these competitive interactions.

Topic: Section 13.1

2) Use a graph of the Lotka-Volterra equations to show how the outcome of competition between two species depends on the population carrying capacity.

Topic: Section 13.2 and Quantifying Ecology 13.1

3) Describe the competitive exclusion principle and outline its major assumptions. Provide an example of a scientific study that supports the competitive exclusion principle.

Topic: Sections 13.3 and 13.4

4) Give an example to show how nonresource factors influence the outcome of competition

Topic: Section 13.5

5) Give several examples to illustrate how temporal and spatial variation in the environment can influence the outcome of competition.

Topic: Sections 13.6 and 13.8

6) Give an example of how a disturbance can affect competition between different plant species.

Topic: Field Studies: Katherine N. Suding

7) Explain how the outcome of competition between two species is a function of both species and environmental characteristics.

Topic: Quantifying Ecology 13.2

8) Explain the difference between a fundamental niche and a realized niche. Use an example to illustrate the role of competition in the establishment of each niche type.

Topic: Section 13.9

9) Explain how is it possible for a diversity of potential competitors to coexist in the same community, despite the competitive exclusion principle.

Topic: Section 13.10

10) Explain the idea of "ghosts of competition past" coined by ecologist J. Connell. What does this concept refer to and why is it important to our understanding of evolution and diversity?

Topic: Section 13.11

11) Why is it difficult for ecologists to demonstrate the importance of competition in natural field conditions? Discuss the different problems inherent to controlled versus natural settings.

Topic: Section 13.12

Chapter 14 Predation

Short Answer Questions

1) _____ is the consumption of one living organism by another.

Answer: Predation
Topic: Introduction to Chapter 14

2) A predator that consumes animal tissue is called a _____.

Answer: carnivore
Topic: Section 14.1

3) The form of predation in which an animal predator consumes all or part of a plant is called _____.

Answer: herbivory
Topic: Section 14.1

4) A(n) _____ is an organism that lives on or within another without killing the host.

Answer: parasite
Topic: Section 14.1

5) The per capita rate at which predators consume prey is assumed to increase _____ with the number of prey.

Answer: linearly
Topic: Section 14.2

6) The cycle of change in the size of predator and prey populations in response to the other is known as

_____.

Answer: oscillations
Topic: Section 14.2

7) The relationship between the per capita rate of consumption and the number of prey is known as the predator's _____.

Answer: functional response
Topic: Section 14.3

8) A predator's _____ is the increase in predator reproduction in response to an increase in the consumption of prey.

Answer: numerical response
Topic: Section 14.3

9) The functional response is the relationship between the per capita rate of predation and _____.

Answer: prey population size
Topic: Section 14.4

10) A type _____ functional response describes the per capita rate of predation, which increases linearly with prey density.

Answer: I
Topic: Section 14.4

11) A type _____ functional response occurs when the number of prey taken per predator increases quickly at first with prey density and then increases at a much slower rate as prey density continues to increase.

Answer: II
Topic: Section 14.4

12) The recognition of a particular species by a predator is called the _____ image.

Answer: search
Topic: Section 14.4

13) A numerical response of predators through movement of predators into areas of high prey density is referred to as a _____ response.

Answer: aggregative
Topic: Section 14.5

14) The trade-off between conflicting demands faced by a predator is described by the _____ theory.

Answer: optimal foraging
Topic: Section 14.6

15) Costs can be measured in terms of the _____ and energy expended in the act of foraging, and benefits should be measured in terms of _____.

Answer: time; fitness
Topic: Section 14.6

16) The _____ theorem predicts the length of time an individual should stay in a resource patch before leaving and seeking another.

Answer: marginal value
Topic: Section 14.7

17) Most predators are also _____.

Answer: prey
Topic: Section 14.8

18) The concept of _____ energy is the basis for models of optimal foraging.

Answer: maximizing
Topic: Quantifying Ecology 14.1

19) _____ involves the development of novel adaptations in predator and prey populations in response to advances that make each more successful, either at obtaining prey or evading a predator.

Answer: Coevolution
Topic: Section 14.9

20) _____ coloration allows prey to blend into the background and avoid predation.

Answer: Cryptic
Topic: Section 14.10

21) _____ mimicry involves a non-toxic species that resembles a toxic species while _____ mimicry is the shared color pattern of unpalatable or toxic species.

Answer: Batesian; Mullerian
Topic: Section 14.10

22) _____ defenses are fixed features of an organism.

Answer: Constitutive
Topic: Section 14.10

23) _____ defenses are not permanently present but, rather, are brought about by the presence or action of predators.

Answer: Induced
Topic: Section 14.10

24) Predators have three general methods of hunting: ambush, _____, and _____.

Answer: stalking; pursuit
Topic: Section 14.11

25) Typically, _____ do not kill the individuals they feed on.

Answer: herbivores
Topic: Section 14.12

26) _____, or the amount of biomass eaten, is not necessarily the best measure of the importance of herbivory within a community.

Answer: Consumption
Topic: Section 14.12

27) In the presence of dragonfly predators (*Anax*), grey tree frog tadpoles (*Hyla*) _____ foraging activity.

Answer: reduced
Topic: Field Studies: Rick A. Relyea

28) Many plants use _____ defenses, such as hairy leaves, thorns, or spines to deter herbivory.

Answer: structural
Topic: Section 14.13

29) Plants contain a wide variety of chemicals, called _____, that are not involved in the basic metabolism of their cells but may be used to prevent or deter herbivory.

Answer: secondary compounds
Topic: Section 14.13

30) As lynx populations increase, snowshoe hare populations _____ and browse vegetation populations _____.

Answer: decrease; increase
Topic: Section 14.14

Multiple-Choice Questions

1) Which of the following is considered a predator?
   A) autotroph
   B) scavenger
   C) omnivore
   D) decomposer

Answer: C
Topic: Section 14.1

2) Which of the following is functionally a true predator?
   A) parasite
   B) planktivore
   C) grazer
   D) parasitoid

Answer: B
Topic: Section 14.1

3) A _____ wholly consumes animal tissue.
   A) carnivore
   B) parasitem
   C) herbivore
   D) decomposer

Answer: A
Topic: Section 14.1

4) A parasitoid
   A) is a true predator.
   B) actively pursues its prey.
   C) attacks the host indirectly by laying its eggs in or on the prey's body.
   D) only preys on animals.

Answer: C
Topic: Section 14.1

5) What does the slope represent in a graph that plots prey population (N_{prey}) against the per capita consumption rate of predation?
   A) efficiency of predation (c)
   B) efficiency with which food is converted into predator reproduction (b)
   C) predator population growth rate (r)
   D) the rate of increase in prey availability

Answer: A
Topic: Section 14.2

6) In the basic Lotka-Volterra equations that describe predator-prey interactions, the growth rate of the prey population (dN_{prey}/dt) is zero when the density of predators (N_{prey}) is equal to
   A) r/N.
   B) N/r.
   C) r/c.
   D) c/r.

Answer: C
Topic: Section 14.2

7) The net outcome of predator-prey interactions in the basic Lotka-Volterra models is that
   A) the predator drives its prey to extinction and then goes extinct itself.
   B) the prey population declines and this causes the predator population to also decline.
   C) predator and prey populations eventually converge on equilibrium population sizes that are maintained into infinity.
   D) predator and prey populations oscillate, with each predictably increasing and decreasing in response to the other.

Answer: D
Topic: Section 14.2

8) The change in prey consumed per predator as prey numbers increase is called the predator's
    A) numerical response.
    B) functional response.
    C) foraging optimum.
    D) oscillation.

Answer: B
Topic: Section 14.3

9) The _____ functional response depicts a sigmoidal rate of predation.
    A) type I
    B) type II
    C) type III
    D) type IV

Answer: C
Topic: Section 14.4

10) The sigmoidal relationship between prey density and per capita predation rate in a type III functional response can be explained by all of the following factors, except:
    A) prey access to refuge.
    B) predator preference.
    C) recognition of prey by predator.
    D) predator density.

Answer: D
Topic: Section 14.4

11) Which of the following is a positive numerical response made by a predator in response to an increase in prey density?
    A) decrease in predator mortality rate
    B) increase in predator survival rate
    C) immigration of predators to an area of high prey density
    D) decrease in predator reproduction rate

Answer: C
Topic: Section 14.5

12) According to the optimal foraging theory, a predator will select prey 1 (P_1) over prey 2 (P_2) when
    A) $E_1 < E_2$.
    B) $T_{h1} < T_{h2}$.
    C) $E_1/T_{h1} < E_2/T_{h2}$.
    D) $N_{prey1} > N_{prey2}$.

Answer: B
Topic: Section 14.6 and Quantifying Ecology 14.1

13) Under the marginal value theorem, when patch quality is equal, what other factor is expected to influence the time a predator spends foraging in a patch?
    A) handling time of prey
    B) time spent traveling to the patch
    C) patch size
    D) prey density

Answer: B
Topic: Section 14.7

14) According to the optimal foraging theory, a predator should abandon a patch
    A) when the rate of energy gain is at a maximum.
    B) at low values of G.
    C) when the preferred prey species is unavailable.
    D) any time a higher-quality patch is available.

Answer: A
Topic: Section 14.7

15) The profitability of a prey item
    A) increases as its handling time (T_h) increases.
    B) decreases as its search time (T_s) decreases.
    C) increases as its energy content (E) decreases.
    D) increases as its E/T_h increases.

Answer: D
Topic: Quantifying Ecology 14.1 and Section 14.6

16) The Red Queen hypothesis refers to
    A) Hardy-Weinberg evolution.
    B) coevolution.
    C) directional selection.
    D) predator-prey oscillation.

Answer: B
Topic: Section 14.9

17) Which of the following is not considered to be an evolved defense of prey against predators?
    A) cryptic coloration
    B) Batesian mimicry
    C) flashing coloration
    D) character displacement

Answer: D
Topic: Section 14.10

18) Which of the following is an example of apoematism?
    A) the flashing of the tail of a white-tailed deer
    B) an insect that resembles its habitat
    C) an edible species that mimics a toxic species
    D) a poisonous snake with bold color patterns

Answer: D
Topic: Section 14.10

19) _____ occurs when prey produce so many offspring in a short period of time that predators can only attack a fraction of them.
    A) Numerical response
    B) Functional defense
    C) Predator satiation
    D) Cryptic reproduction

Answer: C
Topic: Section 14.10

20) These are stimulated by the presence of predators.
   A) constitutive defenses
   B) induced defenses
   C) Batesian mimicries
   D) aposematic responses

Answer: B
Topic: Section 14.10

21) Which animal does not employ protective armor for predator defense?
   A) armadillo
   B) beetle
   C) scorpion
   D) porcupine

Answer: C
Topic: Section 14.10

22) Which of the following is not a hunting method used by predators?
   A) satiation
   B) ambush
   C) stalking
   D) pursuit

Answer: A
Topic: Section 14.11

23) Which of the following is considered a nonlethal effect of predation?
   A) reduced activity of prey
   B) prey consumption
   C) reduced competition
   D) increased predator mortality

Answer: A
Topic: Field Studies: Rick A. Relyea and Section 14.15

24) Which of the following gray tree frog (*Hyla*) tadpole body forms is most common in populations raised in the presence of predators (aquatic dragonfly larvae, *Anax*)?
   A) a long body and great tail depth
   B) a long body and minimal tail depth
   C) a great tail depth and short overall body length
   D) a minimal tail depth and short overall body length

Answer: C
Topic: Field Studies: Rick A. Relyea

25) Which of the following is not a class of plant secondary compounds?
   A) terpenoids
   B) phenolics
   C) nitrogen-based compounds
   D) alkanes

Answer: D
Topic: Section 14.13

26) Qualitative inhibitors
   A) are produced in large quantities by a plant.
   B) are toxic to herbivores.
   C) reduce digestibility of plant material.
   D) include resins and tannins.

Answer: B
Topic: Section 14.13

27) In response to the nonlethal presence of predatory damsel bugs (*Nabis*), pea aphids (*Acyrrhosiphon*) did all of the following, except:
   A) increased reproductive rates.
   B) stopped feeding.
   C) walked away from the predator.
   D) dropped off the plant.

Answer: A
Topic: Section 14.15

True/False Questions

1) Unlike a scavenger, a predator is a heterotroph.

Answer: FALSE
Topic: Introduction to Chapter 14

2) A parasitoid usually kills its host.

Answer: TRUE
Topic: Section 14.1

3) In the Lotka-Volterra models of predator-prey interactions, prey density does not influence predator mortality.

Answer: TRUE
Topic: Section 14.2

4) In the Lotka-Volterra equations that represent predator-prey interactions, predators are a source of density-independent mortality for prey.

Answer: FALSE
Topic: Section 14.2

5) The basic Lotka-Volterra equations that describe predator-prey interactions assume both a functional response and a numerical response of the predators to the prey.

Answer: TRUE
Topic: Section 14.3

6) The central importance of predator-prey interactions to the population regulation of each is widely accepted by ecologists.

Answer: FALSE
Topic: Section 14.3

7) The response of a predator's consumption rate to prey density is a key factor as to whether a predator can regulate a prey population.

Answer: TRUE
Topic: Section 14.4

8) A type I functional response leads to regulation of the prey population by the predator.

Answer: FALSE
Topic: Section 14.4

9) A type II functional response is the most commonly reported for predators.

Answer: TRUE
Topic: Section 14.4

10) One explanation for the shape of the type III functional response is that predators develop a search image for prey after they have encountered them.

Answer: TRUE
Topic: Section 14.4

11) The type of functional response has a strong influence on the ability of a predator to regulate a prey population, while the degree of numerical response has little effect.

Answer: FALSE
Topic: Section 14.5

12) If a predator encounters a different prey species than it was searching for, the predator will usually switch and pursue the new prey species.

Answer: FALSE
Topic: Section 14.6

13) Optimal foraging theory suggests that foraging for food should be much more important to an animal than other time constraints such as defense, avoiding predators, searching for mates, or caring for young.

Answer: FALSE
Topic: Section 14.6

14) According to the marginal value theorem, the amount of time a predator spends foraging in a patch will vary with resource quality and the time required to extract the resource.

Answer: FALSE
Topic: Section 14.7

15) The risk of predation can sometimes have a significant impact on the foraging choices made by animals.

Answer: TRUE
Topic: Section 14.8

16) The Red Queen Hypothesis describes the response that predators make to increasing prey density.

Answer: FALSE
Topic: Section 14.9

17) Object resemblance is an effective but very uncommon predator avoidance strategy among insects.

Answer: FALSE
Topic: Section 14.10

18) In Mullerian mimicry, one poisonous prey species has evolved the same warning coloration as another poisonous prey species.

Answer: FALSE
Topic: Section 14.10

19) Cryptic coloration is a strategy employed by both predators and prey.

Answer: TRUE
Topic: Section 14.11

20) Pursuit hunting is typical of reptile and amphibian species.

Answer: FALSE
Topic: Section 14.11

21) Defoliation kills deciduous plant species.

Answer: FALSE
Topic: Section 14.12

22) Some plants may be able to compensate for the loss of leaves to herbivores by increasing the rate of photosynthesis in remaining leaves.

Answer: TRUE
Topic: Section 14.12

23) Most grasses tolerate grazing and actually benefit from it.

Answer: TRUE
Topic: Section 14.12

24) Quantitative inhibitors may constitute up to 60% of the dry weight of a leaf.

Answer: TRUE
Topic: Section 14.13

25) Some plants are able to attract beneficial insects that act as predators on the herbivores of that plant.

Answer: TRUE
Topic: Section 14.13

26) Carnivores can have an indirect, positive effect on plants by reducing populations of herbivores.

Answer: TRUE
Topic: Section 14.14

27) Predators can influence prey only through lethal, rather than nonlethal, effects.

Answer: FALSE
Topic: Section 14.15

Essay Questions

1) Compare and contrast the three types of predation.

Topic: Section 14.1

2) What is the primary prediction of the basic Lotka-Volterra equations of predator-prey interactions? Is this prediction realistic? Does it fit with our observations of predators and prey in nature?

Topic: Sections 14.2 and 14.3

3) Use a graph to illustrate the differences among the three types of functional responses. Explain the importance of the time a predator spends searching and handling prey to the different functional response types. In which functional responses can predators regulate prey populations and how?

Topic: Section 14.4

4) Explain why there was no lag seen between the irruption of rodents in response to high resources and weasel reproduction. Why is a lag usually observed in a predator-prey relationship?

Topic: Section 14.5

5) Give two examples of considerations besides food acquisition that might influence an animal's decision of whether and for how long to forage in a given resource patch. What rules might an animal use to make a decision?

Topic: Section 14.6–14.8

6) When glaucous-winged gulls forage for prey (e.g., mussels and urchins), what factors are expected to influence prey selection?

Topic: Quantifying Ecology 14.1

7) Use a real or hypothetical example to describe coevolution. What happens when a predator and/or its prey is unable to respond appropriately?

Topic: Section 14.9

8) Describe several different types of prey defenses against predators and give an example of each.

Topic: Section 14.10

9) Discuss the costs and benefits of each of the three hunting methods employed by predators.

Topic: Section 14.11

10) Describe several different strategies that a plant can employ to counteract herbivory before, during, and after it occurs. What are some of the costs associated with these defense mechanisms?

Topic: Sections 14.12 and 14.13

11) Use the tadpole-dragonfly case study presented in the text to explain the direct and indirect impacts that a predator (dragonfly larvae) can have on individuals of prey populations (tadpoles).

Topic: Field Studies: Rick A. Relyea and Section 14.15

12) Graphically illustrate an example of the three-way interaction between a carnivore, an herbivore, and a plant. Explain how the plant is affected by both direct and indirect interactions.

Topic: Section 14.14

13) Explain how nonlethal effects of predators on prey can have important impacts on prey population dynamics.

Topic: Section 14.15

Chapter 15 Parasitism and Mutualism

Short Answer Questions

1) _____ is the intimate and protracted association between two or more organisms of different species.

Answer: Symbiosis
Topic: Introduction to Chapter 15

2) A _____ lives on or within the host organism for some period of its life.

Answer: parasite
Topic: Introduction to Chapter 15

3) A heavy load of parasites is termed a(n) _____.

Answer: infection
Topic: Section 15.1

4) The outcome of an infection is called a(n) _____.

Answer: disease
Topic: Section 15.1

5) Relatively small parasites, such as viruses, bacteria, and protozoans, are referred to as _____-parasites.

Answer: micro
Topic: Section 15.1

6) Parasites that live on the skin of their host are called _____-parasites.

Answer: ecto
Topic: Section 15.2

7) Parasites that live within their host rather than on the skin are referred to as _____-parasites.

Answer: endo
Topic: Section 15.2

8) _____ transmission is the transfer of a parasite from one host to another without the involvement of an intermediate organism.

Answer: Direct
Topic: Section 15.3

9) A(n) _____ is an intermediate organism that aids the spread of a parasite from one host to another.

Answer: vector
Topic: Section 15.4

10) The _____ host is the host species in which a parasite becomes an adult and reaches maturity.

Answer: definitive
Topic: Section 15.5

11) The _____ host is a host species that harbors a developmental stage of a parasite, but in which the parasite does not reach maturity.

Answer: intermediate
Topic: Section 15.5

12) After infection occurs, the first line of defense for a host against a parasite is the _____ response.

Answer: inflammatory
Topic: Section 15.6

13) Plants often react to attacks on the leaf, stem, fruit, or seed by forming abnormal structures called

_____.

Answer: galls
Topic: Section 15.6

14) When a foreign object, such as a virus or bacterium, enters the bloodstream, it elicits a(n) _____ response.

Answer: immune
Topic: Section 15.6

15) A relationship between two species in which one species benefits and the other is not significantly affected is called _____.

Answer: commensalism
Topic: Section 15.9

16) A relationship between two species in which both species benefit is called _____.

Answer: mutualism
Topic: Section 15.9

17) The mutualistic fungi that can live within the roots of certain plants are called _____.

Answer: mycorrhizae
Topic: Section 15.10

18) In a _____ mutualism, an animal transfers pollen from one plant to another in exchange for some reward such as nectar.

Answer: pollination
Topic: Section 15.13

19) A species that interacts with many other species rather than only a few, such as a nectivore that gathers nectar from many plant species, is called a _____.

Answer: generalist
Topic: Section 15.13

20) Plants that rely on ants to disperse their seeds are called _____.

Answer: myrmecochores
Topic: Section 15.14

Multiple-Choice Questions

1) The intimate and protracted association between two or more organisms of different species is referred to as a(n)
   A) mutualism.
   B) parasitism.
   C) commensalism.
   D) symbiosis.

Answer: D
Topic: Introduction to Chapter 15

2) A heavy load of parasites is called a(n)
- A) infection.
- B) disease.
- C) macroparasitism.
- D) parasitoidism.

Answer: A
Topic: Section 15.1

3) Which of the following is a microparasite?
- A) virus
- B) flea
- C) fluke
- D) mistletoe

Answer: A
Topic: Section 15.1

4) Which of the following is an ectoparasite?
- A) virus that inhabits the lymphatic system
- B) bacterium that attacks the brain
- C) tick that attaches to the skin
- D) fluke that inhabits the bloodstream

Answer: C
Topic: Section 15.2

5) The most debilitating external parasites of birds and mammals are spread by
- A) a vector.
- B) an intermediate host.
- C) a definitive host.
- D) direct contact.

Answer: D
Topic: Section 15.3

6) Plant parasites that are photosynthetic but draw water and nutrients from their host plant are referred to as:
- A) mycorrhizae.
- B) vectors.
- C) parasitoids.
- D) hemiparasites.

Answer: D
Topic: Section 15.4

7) A host species that harbors only a developmental phase of a parasite is called a(n)
- A) intermediate host.
- B) direct host.
- C) definitive host.
- D) macrohost.

Answer: A
Topic: Section 15.5

8) Which of the following is a potential response by a plant host to a parasite?
   A) formation of a gall
   B) allelopathy
   C) production of lymphocytes
   D) growing more rapidly

Answer: A
Topic: Section 15.6

9) Which of the following is likely to be the first response of an animal host to a new parasite?
   A) formation of a cyst
   B) allelopathy
   C) inflammatory response
   D) immune response

Answer: C
Topic: Section 15.6

10) When infected by a parasite, an animal typically
    A) grows more rapidly than a healthy individual.
    B) produces fewer offspring than a healthy individual.
    C) behaves less conspicuously than a healthy individual.
    D) is less likely to be preyed on than a healthy individual.

Answer: D
Topic: Section 15.7

11) Which of the following symbiotic mutualisms involves a fungus?
    A) lichens
    B) legume-*Rhizobium* interactions
    C) corals and zooxanthellae
    D) gut microbe-ruminant interactions

Answer: A
Topic: Sections 15.9 and 15.10

12) Which of the following types of mutualisms is a defensive mutualism?
    A) corals and zooxanthellae
    B) bees and flowers
    C) ants and acacias
    D) birds and fruits

Answer: C
Topic: Sections 15.10–15.14

13) A mutualism in which two species must live together and cannot survive when apart is referred to as a(n)
    A) obligatory mutualism.
    B) trophic mutualism.
    C) dispersive mutualism.
    D) facultative mutualism.

Answer: A
Topic: Section 15.15

True/False Questions

1) Symbiosis is an interaction between two species that is beneficial to both species.

Answer: FALSE
Topic: Introduction to Chapter 15

2) Microparasites are relatively small, including organisms such as flatworms, flukes, lice, fleas, and ticks.

Answer: FALSE
Topic: Section 15.1

3) A major problem for parasites is gaining access to the host.

Answer: TRUE
Topic: Section 15.2

4) Animal parasites can be either ecto- or endoparasites, whereas all plant parasites live inside the plant tissue as endoparasites.

Answer: FALSE
Topic: Section 15.2

5) Parasites are always transmitted between hosts via an intermediate vector organism.

Answer: FALSE
Topic: Section 15.3

6) Direct transmission of a parasite involves an intermediate organism known as a vector.

Answer: FALSE
Topic: Section 15.3

7) Hemiparasites are plants that do not conduct photosynthesis because they obtain water and nutrients from another host plant.

Answer: FALSE
Topic: Section 15.4

8) Parasites always complete their life cycle in a single host species.

Answer: FALSE
Topic: Section 15.5

9) After infection occurs, the first line of defense by a host against invasion of a parasite is an inflammatory response.

Answer: TRUE
Topic: Section 15.6

10) An immune response is triggered when a foreign object, such as a virus or bacteria, enters the bloodstream.

Answer: TRUE
Topic: Section 15.6

11) Parasites typically impact host survival but not reproduction.

Answer: FALSE
Topic: Section 15.7

12) Parasites may regulate host populations.

Answer: TRUE
Topic: Section 15.8

13) The number of parasites per individual is relatively high in most individuals and low in a few individuals.

Answer: FALSE
Topic: Section 15.8

14) In a commensalistic relationship between two species, both species benefit.

Answer: FALSE
Topic: Section 15.9

15) In a mutualistic relationship between two species, both species benefit.

Answer: TRUE
Topic: Section 15.9

16) In a mutualism, the interaction between two species is often more a reciprocal exploitation than a cooperative effort between individuals.

Answer: TRUE
Topic: Section 15.9

17) Zooxanthellae are algae living within the tissues of reef-forming corals.

Answer: TRUE
Topic: Section 15.9

18) A lichen is a symbiotic mutualism between a fungus and an alga.

Answer: TRUE
Topic: Section 15.10

19) Symbiotic mutualisms usually involve the exchange of services such as pollination or seed dispersal.

Answer: FALSE
Topic: Section 15.10

20) Nitrogen is important in the mutualism between legume plants and *Rhizobium* bacteria.

Answer: TRUE
Topic: Section 15.11

21) Mycorrhizae are nitrogen-fixing bacteria living within the roots of certain tropical trees.

Answer: FALSE
Topic: Section 15.11

22) Some symbiotic mutualisms involve defense against herbivores.

Answer: TRUE
Topic: Section 15.11

23) The relationship between ants and acacias represents a pollination mutualism.

Answer: FALSE
Topic: Section 15.12

24) Plants do not benefit from insects that prey on their nectar.

Answer: FALSE
Topic: Section 15.13

25) Nectar is often produced by plants as an enticement or reward for pollinating animals.

Answer: TRUE
Topic: Section 15.13

26) Myrmechochores are plants that attract ants to their seeds.

Answer: TRUE
Topic: Section 15.14

27) Plants benefit from frugivores, which aid in the dispersal of their seeds.

Answer: TRUE
Topic: Section 15.14

28) The simple Lotka-Volterra models for mutualism describe the dynamics of an obligate interaction in which neither species can survive and reproduce in the absence of the other.

Answer: FALSE
Topic: Quantifying Ecology 15.1

Essay Questions

1) What is the difference between parasitism and mutualism?

Topic: Introduction to Chapter 15

2) Discuss the differences between direct and indirect transmission of a parasite.

Topic: Sections 15.3 and 15.4

3) Describe one pre-infection and two post-infection responses that animal hosts might have to parasites.

Topic: Section 15.6

4) How might a plant respond to invasion by a fungal or bacterial parasite?

Topic: Section 15.6

5) Use an example to illustrate the fact that parasites can impact both the survival and reproduction of their hosts.

Topic: Section 15.7

6) Discuss the difference between mutualism and commensalism.

Topic: Section 15.9

7) Give two examples of mutualisms involving the transfer of nutrients.

Topic: Sections 15.10 and 15.11

8) Explain the potential benefit to a plant of having either ants or fungi living in its tissues.

Topic: Sections 15.11 and 15.12

9) Discuss the potential benefits of pollination between a plant and a pollinator.

Topic: Section 15.13

10) Discuss how the production and dispersal of seeds by plants may represent a mutualism between two species.

Topic: Section 15.14

11) Explain how the consumption of seeds or fruit by an animal could result in either parasitism or mutualism.

Topic: Sections 15.14

12) Give two reasons that it can be difficult to detect the effects of mutualism on the population dynamics of species.

Topic: Section 15.15

13) Describe the relationship between coralline algae (*Neogoniolithon strictum*) and herbivorous crabs (*Mithrax sculptus*) elucidated by the research of ecologist John J. Stachowicz.

Topic: Field Studies: John J. Stachowicz

14) Draw a graph that illustrates the impact of one species on the carrying capacity of another according to the Lotka-Volterra models of mutualism.

Topic: Quantifying Ecology 15.1

Chapter 16 Community and Structure

Short Answer Questions

1) The group of species that occupies a given area is called a(n) _____.

   Answer: community
   Topic: Introduction to Chapter 16

2) The simplest measure of community structure is a count of the number of species present, and is referred to as species _____.

   Answer: richness
   Topic: Section 16.1

3) The percentage of individuals in a community that belong to one species is called the relative _____ of that species.

   Answer: abundance
   Topic: Section 16.1

4) If one community has a more equitable distribution of individuals among species than another community, it is said to have a high level of species _____.

   Answer: evenness
   Topic: Section 16.1

5) _____ index (D) represents the probability that two individuals randomly selected from a sample will belong to the same species.

   Answer: Simpson's
   Topic: Section 16.1

6) When a single or few species are most prevalent in a community, the species are called _____.

   Answer: dominants
   Topic: Section 16.2

7) A species that has a disproportionate impact on a community, relative to its abundance, is called a(n) _____ species.

   Answer: keystone
   Topic: Section 16.3

8) A set of interconnected food chains with linkages representing a wide variety of species interactions is referred to as a food _____.

   Answer: web
   Topic: Section 16.4

9) In a food web diagram, top _____ are species that prey on intermediate and basal species but are not fed upon themselves.

   Answer: predators
   Topic: Section 16.4

10) In a food web diagram, groups of species that derive food energy from a similar source are called _____ levels.

   Answer: trophic
   Topic: Section 16.4

11) Within a community, a group of species that carry out similar functions or exploit the same resource is called a(n) _____.

Answer: guild
Topic: Section 16.5

12) In a forest community, the upper layer is called the _____.

Answer: canopy
Topic: Section 16.6

13) In a forest community, the layer containing tall shrubs, small trees, and young trees is called the

_____.

Answer: understory
Topic: Section 16.6

14) In a forest community, the site where decomposition occurs and decaying organic matter releases nutrients for reuse by plants is called the forest _____ .

Answer: floor
Topic: Section 16.6

15) In a well-stratified lake during summer, the upper layer of freely circulating water is called the

_____.

Answer: epilimnion
Topic: Section 16.6

16) In aquatic habitats, the upper zone of water where the availability of light supports photosynthesis by phytoplankton is called the _____ zone.

Answer: photic
Topic: Section 16.6

17) In aquatic habitats, the bottom zone where decomposition is most active is referred to as the _____ zone.

Answer: benthic
Topic: Section 16.6

18) Changes in the physical and biological structure of communities as you move across the landscape are referred to as _____.

Answer: zonation
Topic: Section 16.7

19) The view developed by Frederick Clements that sees communities as unified entities, is referred to as the _____ concept of communities.

Answer: organismic
Topic: Section 16.9

20) The view developed by H. A. Gleason that communities result from similarities in species' requirements and tolerances for environmental factors is referred to as the _____ concept of communities.

Answer: individualistic, or continuum
Topic: Section 16.9

Multiple-Choice Questions

1) The group of species that occupy a given area, interacting either directly or indirectly, is called a(n)
   A) ecosystem.
   B) community.
   C) population.
   D) population.

Answer: B
Topic: Introduction to Chapter 16

2) The total number of species present within a community is called
   A) species evenness.
   B) species diversity.
   C) species richness.
   D) relative abundance.

Answer: C
Topic: Section 16.1

3) Ecologists usually define the species diversity of a community as
   A) the number of species in a community.
   B) the evenness of relative abundances of the species in a community.
   C) a combination of A and B
   D) none of the above

Answer: C
Topic: Section 16.1

4) Which description is true for most communities?
   A) All species have approximately equal abundances.
   B) All species are rare.
   C) All species are common.
   D) A few species are common and the remainder are rare.

Answer: D
Topic: Section 16.2

5) Which statement best describes a keystone species?
   A) a species that takes up a great deal of space in a community
   B) an abundant species that may or may not affect other species
   C) a rare species that has a strong effect on its community
   D) a common species that has a strong effect on its community

Answer: C
Topic: Section 16.3

6) A diagram that illustrates the flow of energy, linking several species as prey and predators, is referred to
as a
   A) food web.
   B) food chain.
   C) trophic level.
   D) gene pool.

Answer: B
Topic: Section 16.4

7) A diagram that describes the interactions between species within a community, focusing on which species eat which other species, is called a
   A) food web.
   B) food chain.
   C) trophic level.
   D) guild.

Answer: A
Topic: Section 16.4

8) To which category or trophic level does a typical plant belong?
   A) basal species
   B) intermediate species
   C) decomposer
   D) top predator

Answer: A
Topic: Section 16.4

9) A group of species in a community that all exploit the same common resource is called a
   A) niche.
   B) guild.
   C) trophic level.
   D) food chain.

Answer: B
Topic: Section 16.5

10) In a forest community, the layer in which most photosynthesis occurs is the
   A) canopy.
   B) midstory.
   C) understory.
   D) forest floor.

Answer: A
Topic: Section 16.6

11) The layer of a forest that contains tall shrubs, small trees, and young trees is called the
   A) canopy.
   B) understory.
   C) herb layer.
   D) forest floor.

Answer: B
Topic: Section 16.6

12) In a well-stratified lake in summer, the second layer of water, which is characterized by a steep and rapid decline in temperature with depth, is called the
   A) epilimnion.
   B) metalimnion.
   C) hypolimnion.
   D) benthic zone.

Answer: B
Topic: Section 16.6

13) In a well-stratified lake in summer, the bottom zone, in which decomposition is most active, is called the
_____ zone.
   A) photic
   B) benthic
   C) aphotic
   D) hypolimnion

Answer: B
Topic: Section 16.6

14) Changes in the physical and biological structure of a community across the landscape are called
   A) succession.
   B) stratification.
   C) zonation.
   D) ecotones.

Answer: C
Topic: Section 16.7

15) Defining boundaries between communities is generally
   A) not attempted by ecologists.
   B) difficult.
   C) not difficult due to the variety of methods that have been developed.
   D) attempted only as a last resort.

Answer: B
Topic: Section 16.8

16) The view of communities as a cluster of species associating together as an interacting, integrated
component, is referred to as the _____ concept of communities.
   A) unified
   B) organismic
   C) individualistic, or continuum
   D) successional

Answer: B
Topic: Section 16.15

True/False Questions

1) A community refers to the group of species that occupy a given area, interacting either directly or
indirectly.

Answer: TRUE
Topic: Introduction to Chapter 16

2) The species diversity of a community is defined by both the number of species and the evenness of the
species' relative abundances.

Answer: TRUE
Topic: Section 16.1

3) Most communities have a few common species and many rare species.

Answer: TRUE
Topic: Section 16.2

4) Dominance is the converse or opposite of diversity.

Answer: TRUE
Topic: Section 16.2

5) A species that has a disproportionate effect on other species in its community relative to its abundance is referred to as a keystone species.

Answer: TRUE
Topic: Section 16.3

6) Basal species in a food web do not feed on other species.

Answer: TRUE
Topic: Section 16.4

7) All the hummingbirds and other nectar-feeding birds in a community could be considered a guild.

Answer: TRUE
Topic: Section 16.5

8) The physical structure of terrestrial communities is usually defined more by the plants than the animals present.

Answer: TRUE
Topic: Section 16.6

9) In a forest, the primary site of photosynthesis is in the midstory.

Answer: FALSE
Topic: Section 16.6

10) The vertical structure of the plant community provides the physical framework in which many forms of animal life are adapted to live.

Answer: TRUE
Topic: Section 16.6

11) The herb layer of a forest is where most of the decomposition takes place.

Answer: FALSE
Topic: Section 16.6

12) The benthic zone of a lake is where most of the decomposition takes place.

Answer: TRUE
Topic: Section 16.6

13) In aquatic ecosystems, the thermocline occurs in the epilimion.

Answer: FALSE
Topic: Section 16.6

14) Species composition does not usually differ much within a local area, such as between a hilltop and a stream bottomland.

Answer: FALSE
Topic: Section 16.7

15) The boundaries between communities are usually sharply defined and easily discerned.

Answer: FALSE
Topic: Section 16.8

16) Ecologists have a variety of useful sampling and statistical techniques for delineating and classifying communities.

Answer: TRUE
Topic: Section 16.8

17) The characteristics of a community are generally not dependent on the spatial scale at which the community is examined because communities are tightly integrated groups of species.

Answer: FALSE
Topic: Section 16.8

18) The organismic concept of communities views communities as clusters of species associating together as an interacting, integrated component.

Answer: TRUE
Topic: Section 16.9

19) It is usually straightforward to determine the species richness of any given community since species richness is simply the number of species in a community.

Answer: FALSE
Topic: Ecological Issues

Essay Questions

1) Explain how ecologists define species diversity. What data must be collected to determine the diversity of a community?

Topic: Section 16.1 and Ecological Issues, Chapter 16

2) Use examples to illustrate the difference between a dominant species and a keystone species.

Topic: Sections 16.2 and 16.3

3) Draw a diagram of a simple food web with three trophic levels, and describe the difference between a food chain and a food web

Topic: Section 16.4

4) Explain the difference between a guild and a functional type, and discuss why it may be useful for ecologists to classify species in these ways.

Topic: Section 16.5

5) Discuss the physical structure of either a forest or a lake, and explain how the physical structure affects the biological structure.

Topic: Section 16.6

6) Explain why defining the boundaries of a community can sometimes be very difficult. Do you think this detracts from the usefulness of the concept of community?

Topic: Sections 16.7–16.9

7) Explain the difference between the organismal concept of communities and the individualistic continuum concept. Which of these concepts best describes the majority of communities? Explain your answer.

Topic: Section 16.9

8) Give two reasons why it is difficult to accurately determine the species diversity of any given community, and suggest how you might go about trying to do so.

Topic: Ecological Issues

9) Choose either of the two most common indices of community similarity (Sorenson's coefficient of similarity and percent similarity), and explain how it is calculated. For what purpose might such an index be used?

Topic: Quantifying Ecology 16.1

Chapter 17 Factors Influencing the Structure of Communities

Short Answer Questions

1) The _____ is a group of plant and animal species that inhabit a given area.

Answer: community
Topic: Introduction to Chapter 17

2) A(n) _____ model of community structure assumes that interactions among species have no impact on community structure.

Answer: null
Topic: Section 17.1

3) When interspecific interactions involve more than just two species, they are said to be _____.

Answer: diffuse
Topic: Section 17.2

4) Food _____ are diagrams of communities that depict the trophic relationships among species.

Answer: webs
Topic: Section 17.3

5) Food webs are useful for depicting _____ interactions among species in which the interaction between two species is mediated by an intermediate species.

Answer: indirect
Topic: Section 17.3

6) A type of indirect interaction in which a predator enhances the success of one or more inferior competitors by reducing the abundance of a superior competitor is called _____ predation.

Answer: keystone
Topic: Section 17.3

7) When an indirect interaction is beneficial to two interacting species, the indirect interaction is termed indirect _____.

Answer: mutualism
Topic: Section 17.3

8) _____ or functional groups are groups of species in a community that are thought to have similar roles in the community.

Answer: Guilds
Topic: Section 17.4

9) When prey populations are controlled by predators in a trophic level above them they are said to be under _____ control.

Answer: top-down
Topic: Section 17.4

10) The structure of plant communities along environmental gradients can sometimes be explained by a tradeoff between stress tolerance and _____ ability among the plant species.

Answer: competitive
Topic: Section 17.5

11) Variation in environmental conditions within a community, or environmental _____, can have a strong influence on the diversity of a community.

Answer: heterogeneity
Topic: Section 17.6

12) In all experimental studies to date, the effect of increasing nutrient availability to plants has been to _____ plant diversity.

Answer: decrease
Topic: Section 17.7

13) _____ describes the number of trophic links in a food web.

Answer: Connectance
Topic: Quantifying Ecology 17.1

14) The _____ model, proposed by Paul and Anne Ehrlich, suggests that each loss of a species results in a slight weakening of the ecosystem, and if species losses continue, the ecosystem will abruptly lose function.

Answer: rivet
Topic: Ecological Issues

Multiple-Choice Questions

1) A null model of community structure assumes that the presence and abundance of species within a community is
   A) determined mostly by direct species interactions.
   B) determined mostly by indirect species interactions.
   C) not affected by species interactions.
   D) both A and B

Answer: C
Topic: Section 17.1

2) Interspecific interactions often
   A) involve multiple species.
   B) involve only two species.
   C) have no effect on either species.
   D) have no effect on the rest of the community.

Answer: A
Topic: Section 17.2

3) Indirect interactions occur when
   A) one species is influenced by interactions with many species.
   B) one species does not interact with a second species but influences a third species, which interacts directly with the second.
   C) a prey species is controlled by a predator species.
   D) a predator species is controlled by a prey species.

Answer: B
Topic: Section 17.3

4) Food webs can be arranged into _____ levels based on whether organisms obtain their nutrition from photosynthesis, from eating plants, or from eating animals.
   A) niche
   B) guild
   C) trophic
   D) predation

Answer: C
Topic: Section 17.4

5) When populations at a given trophic level are controlled by populations in the trophic level above them, they are said to be under
   A) top-down control.
   B) indirect control.
   C) bottom-up control.
   D) functional control.

Answer: A
Topic: Section 17.4

6) Plant community structure along an environmental gradient can often be explained by
   A) differences among species in their competitive abilities.
   B) differences among species in their abilities to tolerate stress.
   C) differences among species in their resistance to herbivores.
   D) a tradeoff among species with respect to competitive ability and stress tolerance.

Answer: D
Topic: Section 17.5

7) The two major determinants of regional and global patterns of vegetation distribution include
   A) soil and temperature.
   B) soil and moisture.
   C) temperature and moisture.
   D) temperature and animal communities.

Answer: C
Topic: Section 17.5

8) In general, the degree of environmental heterogeneity of a community has a _____ effect on the species diversity of that community.
   A) positive
   B) negative
   C) neutral
   D) complicated

Answer: A
Topic: Section 17.6

9) Increasing nutrient availability tends to _____ plant diversity in a community.
   A) not affect
   B) decrease
   C) increase
   D) increase the first year but thereafter decrease

Answer: B
Topic: Section 17.7

10) In a food web, the average number of feeding links per species, or linkage _____, provides one measure of community complexity.
    A) richness
    B) diversity
    C) density
    D) number

Answer: C
Topic: Quantifying Ecology 17.1

11) Brian Walker's _____ model asserts that most species are superfluous, and functional groups of species are more important than individual species for ecosystems to continue functioning.
    A) redundancy
    B) rivet
    C) food web
    D) interactive

Answer: A
Topic: Ecological Issues

True/False Questions

1) There is considerable evidence that community structure is influenced by species interactions.

Answer: TRUE
Topic: Section 17.1

2) Environmental conditions often vary spatially but do not tend to change over time in a given place.

Answer: FALSE
Topic: Section 17.1

3) A null model for the impact of species interactions on communities assumes that species interactions have strong influences on community structure.

Answer: FALSE
Topic: Section 17.1

4) Species interactions within a community rarely involve only two species.

Answer: TRUE
Topic: Section 17.2

5) Competitive interactions are often diffuse while mutualisms are not.

Answer: FALSE
Topic: Section 17.2

6) Keystone predators have strong indirect effects on inferior competitors.

Answer: TRUE
Topic: Section 17.3

7) In its simplest form, apparent competition involves two predators and one prey species.

Answer: FALSE
Topic: Section 17.3

8) The removal of a single species from a community can have unpredictable consequences.

Answer: TRUE
Topic: Section 17.3

9) The control of an herbivore population by a parasitoid is an example of top-down control.

Answer: TRUE
Topic: Section 17.4

10) The "world is green" hypothesis of Hairston et al. suggests that predators keep herbivore populations in check.

Answer: TRUE
Topic: Section 17.4

11) Within a community, most species have a similar range of environmental tolerances.

Answer: FALSE
Topic: Section 17.5

12) Competition among plant species rarely involves only a single resource.

Answer: TRUE
Topic: Section 17.5

13) Environmental heterogeneity is often negatively correlated with species diversity across habitats.

Answer: FALSE
Topic: Section 17.6

14) The diversity of an animal community is unrelated to the physical structure of a plant community.

Answer: FALSE
Topic: Section 17.6

15) When nutrient availability increases within a plant community, diversity usually increases.

Answer: FALSE
Topic: Section 17.7

16) Competition for belowground resources is considered to be asymmetric because larger plants have a disproportionate advantage in competition for those resources.

Answer: FALSE
Topic: Section 17.7

17) Recent studies suggest that as species richness in a food web increases, the number of trophic links increases but the connectance decreases.

Answer: TRUE
Topic: Quantifying Ecology 17.1

18) The research of Sally Hacker has demonstrated that *Juncus* plants are strong antagonists, causing increases in conditions such as salinity that hinder the growth of other plants such as *Iva*.

Answer: FALSE
Topic: Researcher Profile: Sally D. Hacker

Essay Questions

1) Explain the differing roles of fundamental niches and species interactions in controlling community structure.

Topic: Section 17.1

2) Explain what an indirect interaction is, and give an example of an indirect interaction that has a strong effect on a specific species in a community.

Topic: Section 17.3

3) Explain the difference between bottom-up and top-down control of community structure. Do you think one or the other is most important, or some combination of both? Why?

Topic: Section 17.4

4) Summarize the "world is green" hypothesis of Hairston, Smith, and Slobodkin. Is this an example of bottom-up or top-down control?

Topic: Section 17.4

5) Identify at last three resources involved in competition among plants and explain how these resources may lead to zonation along a gradient.

Topic: Section 17.5

6) Explain the potential relationship between the physical structure of a plant community and the diversity of an animal community in the same habitat. Give a real or hypothetical example to support your answer.

Topic: Section 17.6

7) Describe the response that plant communities typically exhibit when nutrients are added, and summarize the prevailing hypothesis to explain this response.

Topic: Section 17.7

8) What are the possible explanations for the paradox that diversity in plant communities decreases when nutrient availability increases?

Topic: Section 17.7

9) Explain the differences between the rivet model and the redundancy model of ecosystems. Which do you think more accurately described ecosystems?

Topic: Ecological Issues

Chapter 18 Community Dynamics

Short Answer Questions

1) _____ is a temporal change in community composition and structure.

   Answer: Succession
   Topic: Section 18.1

2) The sequence of communities from the pioneer community to the climax community is called a
   _____.

   Answer: sere
   Topic: Section 18.1

3) High growth rates, smaller size, high degree of dispersal, and high rates of population growth are typical
   of _____ successional species.

   Answer: early
   Topic: Section 18.1

4) Succession that occurs on a site that was previously occupied by another community is called _____
   succession.

   Answer: secondary
   Topic: Section 18.1

5) _____ environmental change is change that is a direct result of the organisms within the community.

   Answer: Autogenic
   Topic: Section 18.5

6) _____ environmental change is due to a change in the physical environment that is independent of
   the species in the community.

   Answer: Allogenic
   Topic: Section 18.5

7) Within an area, a group of sites that are at different stages of succession is known as a _____.

   Answer: chronosequence, or chronosere
   Topic: Section 18.6

8) The hypothesis that moderate frequencies of disturbance result in the highest species diversity is called
   the _____ hypothesis.

   Answer: intermediate disturbance
   Topic: Section 18.6

9) The study of the distribution and abundance of ancient organisms and their relationship to the
   environment is _____.

   Answer: paleoecology
   Topic: Section 18.9

Multiple-Choice Questions

1) Changes in community composition and structure over time are called
   A) succession.
   B) stratification.
   C) zonation.
   D) characterization.

   Answer: A
   Topic: Section 18.1

2) Succession that occurs on a site not previously occupied by a community is called _____ succession.
   A) primary
   B) secondary
   C) initial
   D) basic

   Answer: A
   Topic: Sections 18.1–18.3

3) An example of secondary succession is
   A) grasses colonizing sand dunes.
   B) lichens colonizing a rock.
   C) weeds colonizing a volcanic lava flow.
   D) crabgrass colonizing an abandoned wheat field.

   Answer: A
   Topic: Sections 18.1–18.3

4) The _____ model proposes that later successional species are neither inhibited nor aided by species of earlier stages, and they establish themselves independently of species that precede or follow them.
   A) facilitation
   B) inhibition
   C) tolerance
   D) seral

   Answer: C
   Topic: Section 18.4

5) In succession, _____ environmental changes occur when the physical environment changes, such as an increase in temperature or salinity.
   A) allopatric
   B) allogenic
   C) autozygous
   D) autogenic

   Answer: B
   Topic: Section 18.5

6) Groups of sites within an area that are at different stages of succession are known as
   A) autosequences.
   B) ecotypes.
   C) clines.
   D) chronosequences.

   Answer: D
   Topic: Section 18.6

7) During the early stages of succession, diversity typically
   A) increases.
   B) decreases.
   C) stays the same.
   D) varies frequently.

Answer: A
Topic: Section 18.6

8) Succession involves
   A) only autotrophic species.
   B) only heterotrophic species.
   C) both autotrophic and heterotrophic species.
   D) only plants.

Answer: C
Topic: Section 18.7

9) Which of the following is an example of an allogenic change that drives succession?
   A) seasonal changes in temperature, photoperiod, and light intensity
   B) increased shading of seedlings by adult trees in a forest
   C) increased nitrogen availability in soil due to the presence of leguminous plants
   D) reduced salinity due to surface shading by grasses in a salt marsh

Answer: A
Topic: Section 18.8

10) The view of communities as species responding independently to the underlying features of the environment rather than being interdependent is referred to as the _____ concept of communities.
   A) autogenic
   B) organismal
   C) individualistic, or continuum
   D) allogenic

Answer: C
Topic: Section 18.10

True/False Questions

1) Communities vary in composition over space but usually not in composition over time.

Answer: FALSE
Topic: Introduction to Chapter 18

2) Early successional species are usually long-lived and slow-growing.

Answer: FALSE
Topic: Section 18.1

3) Primary succession occurs when the community at a site is disturbed and then replaced by a different community.

Answer: FALSE
Topic: Sections 18.1–18.3

4) The colonization of sand dunes by grasses is an example of secondary succession.

Answer: FALSE
Topic: Sections 18.1–18.3

5) Egler's initial floristic composition hypothesis posits that the process of succession at any site is dependent on which species get there first.

Answer: TRUE
Topic: Section 18.4

6) The inhibition model of succession involves strong competitive interactions with the first species to arrive maintaining its position until it is weakened or dies, after which it yields space to another species.

Answer: TRUE
Topic: Section 18.4

7) The tolerance model of succession posits that later successional species are neither inhibited nor aided by species of earlier stages.

Answer: TRUE
Topic: Section 18.4

8) Autogenic environmental change is a direct result of the organisms within a community.

Answer: TRUE
Topic: Section 18.5

9) In the early stages of plant succession, shade-intolerant species are often common.

Answer: TRUE
Topic: Section 18.5

10) Although community composition changes during succession, diversity rarely changes.

Answer: FALSE
Topic: Section 18.6

11) Disturbances, such as fire, can sometimes increase coexistence between species and can increase diversity.

Answer: TRUE
Topic: Section 18.6

12) Diversity often decreases during the later stages of succession.

Answer: TRUE
Topic: Section 18.6

13) Succession usually involves only autotrophic species such as plants.

Answer: FALSE
Topic: Section 18.7

14) A good example of succession involving heterotrophic species occurs when dead organic matter is decomposed over long periods of time.

Answer: TRUE
Topic: Section 18.7

15) Community structure changes over relatively short time scales through succession, but generally is stable over longer geological time scales.

Answer: FALSE
Topic: Section 18.9

16) Pollen preserved within lake sediments can be used to reconstruct historical changes in the geographic ranges of plant species.

Answer: TRUE
Topic: Section 18.9

17) The organismal concept of communities argues that species distributions along environmental gradients form clusters because they are interdependent.

Answer: TRUE
Topic: Section 18.10

18) Most forests in the eastern United States are greater than 100 years old.

Answer: FALSE
Topic: Ecological Issues: American Forests

19) Rates of species turnover during succession are defined by rates of immigration and local extinction.

Answer: TRUE
Topic: Quantifying Ecology 18.1

Essay Questions

1) Using a specific example, discuss the ecological differences between early successional species and late successional species within a sere.

Topic: Section 18.1

2) Using specific examples for each, explain the differences between primary and secondary succession.

Topic: Sections 18.1–18.3

3) Explain how a chronosequence can be used to understand succession.

Topic: Section 18.6

4) Describe the process of succession of heterotrophic organisms associated with decomposition of a fallen tree.

Topic: Section 18.7

5) Using specific examples for each, describe the differences between autogenic and allogenic environmental changes that drive succession.

Topic: Section 18.8

6) Explain the difference between the organismal concept of communities and the individualistic continuum concept. Which do you think most accurately describes real communities and why?

Topic: Section 18.10

7) Explain the link between the rise of large-scale, commercial agriculture in the American west and increases in forest habitat in the east, as well as the role of succession in this link.

Topic: Ecological Issues: American Forests

Chapter 19 Landscape Ecology

Short Answer Questions

1) The patchwork of different types of land cover is called a _____.

Answer: mosaic
Topic: Introduction to Chapter 19

2) The study of the causes and ecological consequences of spatial patterns on the landscape is called

_____.

Answer: landscape ecology
Topic: Introduction to Chapter 19

3) Stable, permanent edges along landscape patches are called _____ edges.

Answer: inherent
Topic: Section 19.2

4) Edges along landscape patches that are caused by disturbances and are subject to successional changes over time are called _____ edges.

Answer: induced
Topic: Section 19.2

5) The place where the edge of one landscape patch meets the edge of another is called a(n) _____.

Answer: border
Topic: Section 19.2

6) A wide transition zone between one patch and another, in which the characteristics of one patch blend gradually with the characteristics of the other, is called a(n) _____.

Answer: ecotone
Topic: Section 19.2

7) Species that are adapted to living at the borders of patches of habitat are called _____ species.

Answer: edge
Topic: Section 19.2

8) The _____ effect refers to the rich diversity of life that occurs along the border between adjacent habitat patches, represented by species from both adjacent patches and species adapted to edge habitats.

Answer: edge
Topic: Section 19.2

9) A(n) _____ species lives within the borders of a habitat patch, avoiding edges where habitat change is abrupt.

Answer: interior
Topic: Section 19.3

10) MacArthur and Wilson's theory of _____ was developed to explain the number of species on islands, but it has been applied to patches of habitat as well.

Answer: island biogeography
Topic: Section 19.4

Copyright © 2009 Pearson Education, Inc.

11) In the theory of island biogeography, species diversity on an island is determined by the _____ of an island, as well as its distance from the mainland.

Answer: size, or area
Topic: Section 19.4

12) Strips of habitat that connect habitat patches are referred to as _____.

Answer: corridors
Topic: Section 19.5

13) The phenomenon in which different-sized gaps in corridors allow certain organisms to cross and restrict others is referred to as the _____ effect.

Answer: filter
Topic: Section 19.5

14) A set of spatially separated subpopulations connected by the movement of individuals, is referred to as a(n) _____.

Answer: metapopulation
Topic: Section 19.6

15) A(n) _____ is any relatively discrete event, such as fire, that disrupts community structure and function.

Answer: disturbance
Topic: Section 19.7

16) The _____ of a disturbance is measured by the spatial extent of the impact of a disturbance relative to the size of the affected landscape.

Answer: scale
Topic: Section 19.7

17) The _____ of a disturbance is the mean number of disturbances that occur within a particular time interval.

Answer: frequency
Topic: Section 19.7

18) An opening in a community, created by a disturbance, that becomes a site of regeneration and growth is referred to as a(n) _____.

Answer: gap
Topic: Section 19.7

19) The _____ mosaic view of the landscape considers landscapes as composed of multiple patches or communities, each in a different phase of successional development due to disturbances.

Answer: shifting
Topic: Section 19.10

20) Computer-based systems for handling spatially referenced or geographical data are collectively referred to as _____.

Answer: GIS or geographical information systems
Topic: Quantifying Ecology 19.1

Multiple–Choice Questions

1) The relatively homogeneous areas that make up the landscape mosaic are called
   A) subpopulations.
   B) patches.
   C) pods.
   D) sinks.

   Answer: B
   Topic: Introduction to Chapter 19

2) A relatively stable and permanent habitat edge is called a(n)
   A) inherent edge.
   B) induced edge.
   C) ecotone.
   D) border.

   Answer: A
   Topic: Section 19.2

3) A relatively wide area that forms a gradual zone of transition between two adjoining patches is called a(n)
   A) border.
   B) edge.
   C) ecotone.
   D) matrix.

   Answer: C
   Topic: Section 19.2

4) Plants adapted to edge environments tend to be
   A) tolerant of shade and prefer moisture.
   B) tolerant of shade and dry conditions.
   C) intolerant of shade and prefer moisture.
   D) intolerant of shade and tolerant of dry conditions.

   Answer: D
   Topic: Section 19.2

5) Which of the following statements is true?
   A) Large patches of habitat usually contain fewer species than small patches.
   B) Large animals usually have larger home ranges and smaller animals.
   C) Carnivore home ranges are usually smaller than herbivore home ranges.
   D) Small species are usually limited to small habitat patches.

   Answer: B
   Topic: Section 19.3

6) According to the theory of island biogeography, the islands with the most species will be
   A) small and close to the mainland.
   B) small and far from the mainland.
   C) large and close to the mainland.
   D) large and far from the mainland.

   Answer: C
   Topic: Section 19.4

7) Which of the following does NOT function as a habitat corridor?
    A) a large lake
    B) a hedgerow
    C) the vegetation along a river
    D) a drainage ditch

Answer: A
Topic: Section 19.5

8) A set of partially isolated populations that is interconnected by the movement of individuals is called a(n)
    A) ecotone.
    B) archipelago.
    C) corridor.
    D) metapopulation.

Answer: D
Topic: Section 19.6

9) The impact of a disturbance is determined by its
    A) frequency, period, and scale.
    B) period, scale, and type.
    C) frequency, intensity, and strength.
    D) frequency, intensity, and scale.

Answer: D
Topic: Section 19.7

10) Which of the following is least considered to be a major agent of disturbance?
    A) fire
    B) flooding
    C) a beaver constructing a dam
    D) a rainstorm

Answer: D
Topic: Section 19.8

True/False Questions

1) The size and shape of habitat patches are determined more by the activities of animals than by the interaction of geology, topography, and climate.

Answer: FALSE
Topic: Section 19.1

2) Borders between patches that result from natural disturbances usually do not change over time.

Answer: FALSE
Topic: Section 19.2

3) Habitat fragmentation is harmful because there are no species that are adapted to living along habitat edges.

Answer: FALSE
Topic: Section 19.2

4) Plants adapted to living at the edges of forests are usually tolerant of shade.

Answer: FALSE
Topic: Section 19.2

5) The variety and density of life is usually greatest in and around habitat edges.

Answer: TRUE
Topic: Section 19.2

6) The greater the contrast between two adjoining habitat patches, the greater the diversity of species living along the border between the two patches.

Answer: TRUE
Topic: Section 19.2

7) Large habitat patches typically contain more species than smaller habitat patches.

Answer: TRUE
Topic: Section 19.3

8) As a patch increases in size, the ratio of interior to edge increases.

Answer: TRUE
Topic: Section 19.3

9) Patch size is generally more important for plant populations than for animal populations.

Answer: FALSE
Topic: Section 19.3

10) The theory of island biogeography was developed for islands and cannot be applied to habitat patches within a larger landscape.

Answer: FALSE
Topic: Section 19.4

11) The theory of island biogeography predicts that large islands have more species than smaller islands.

Answer: TRUE
Topic: Section 19.4

12) The theory of island biogeography predicts that the extinction rate is greater on large islands than on small islands.

Answer: FALSE
Topic: Section 19.4

13) Habitat corridors are usually of human origin.

Answer: TRUE
Topic: Section 19.5

14) Habitat corridors have two roles: providing a unique habitat for some plant and animal species and providing a means of dispersal between larger patches of habitat.

Answer: TRUE
Topic: Section 19.5

15) Subpopulations within a metapopulation are isolated from each other with no movement of individuals between subpopulations.

Answer: FALSE
Topic: Section 19.6

16) The intensity of a disturbance is measured by the proportion of total biomass or the population of a species, that is killed or eliminated by a disturbance.

Answer: TRUE
Topic: Section 19.7

17) The scale of a disturbance is measured by the mean number of disturbances that occur within a specific time interval.

Answer: FALSE
Topic: Section 19.8

18) Fire is a human-caused disturbance that is not a natural part of ecosystems.

Answer: FALSE
Topic: Section 19.8

19) Wind can function as an agent of disturbance.

Answer: TRUE
Topic: Section 19.8

20) Animals can function as agents of disturbance.

Answer: TRUE
Topic: Section 19.8

21) Selection cutting is a more severe disturbance to a forest ecosystem than clear cutting.

Answer: FALSE
Topic: Section 19.9

22) The landscape can be thought of as a shifting mosaic of habitat patches, each in a phase of successional development.

Answer: TRUE
Topic: Section 19.10

23) A limitation of geographical information systems (GIS) is that the data cannot be used in hypothesis testing.

Answer: FALSE
Topic: Quantifying Ecology 19.1

24) Butterflies move more frequently between habitats connected by corridors than between unconnected habitats.

Answer: TRUE
Topic: Field Studies: Nick M. Haddad

25) The huge fires in 1988 in Yellowstone National Park ultimately caused land managers to view fire primarily as a destructive force to be suppressed.

Answer: FALSE
Topic: Ecological Issues: The Yellowstone Fires of 1988

Essay Questions

1) Using an example, explain how human and natural forces can combine to create habitat patches.

Topic: Section 19.1

2) Discuss the major ecological differences between edge species and interior species.

Topic: Sections 19.2 and 19.3

3) Discuss the differences in diversity between large and small habitat patches. What are the reasons for these differences?

Topic: Section 19.3

4) Using a graph, illustrate how the number of species on an island can be affected by its size and distance from a mainland. What are the two important demographic variables that vary with the size of an island and its distance from a mainland?

Topic: Section 19.4

5) Explain the potential value of corridors to large-bodied species such as carnivores.

Topic: Section 19.5

6) Give two examples of disturbance, and explain how disturbance can alter a community.

Topic: Sections 19.7 and 19.8

7) Explain the role of disturbances in the shifting-mosaic view of the landscape.

Topic: Section 19.10

8) Using the example of the Yellowstone fires of 1988, explain how disturbances can be beneficial to some species and detrimental to others.

Topic: Ecological Issues: The Yellowstone Fires of 1988

Chapter 20 Ecosystem Energetic

Short Answer Questions

1) A(n) _____ chemical reaction must absorb energy in order to proceed.

Answer: endothermic
Topic: Section 20.1

2) The _____ law of thermodynamics states that energy is neither created nor destroyed.

Answer: first
Topic: Section 20.1

3) The _____ law of thermodynamics states that when energy is transferred or transformed, part of the energy assumes a form that cannot pass on any further.

Answer: second
Topic: Section 20.1

4) _____ primary production is the total rate of photosynthesis, or energy assimilated by plants.

Answer: Gross
Topic: Section 20.2

5) The rate of energy storage as organic matter after respiration is called _____ primary productivity.

Answer: net
Topic: Section 20.2

6) The amount of accumulated organic matter found in an area at a given time is the _____ crop biomass.

Answer: standing
Topic: Section 20.2

7) For photosynthesis and productivity to occur, a plant must open its _____ to take in carbon dioxide.

Answer: stomata
Topic: Section 20.3

8) _____ is the primary factor that limits productivity in aquatic ecosystems.

Answer: Light
Topic: Section 20.4

9) In a body of water, the depth at which the availability of light is such that the rate of photosynthesis equals the rate of respiration is called the _____ depth.

Answer: compensation
Topic: Section 20.4

10) _____ net primary productivity is the ratio of net primary productivity to standing biomass.

Answer: Relative
Topic: Section 20.5

11) The net energy going into growth of new tissues and production of young in heterotrophs is called _____ production.

Answer: secondary
Topic: Section 20.7

12) _____ efficiency is the ratio of assimilation to ingestion and is a measure of the efficiency with which a consumer extracts energy from food.

Answer: Assimilation
Topic: Section 20.8

13) Within any ecosystem there are two major food chains: the _____ food chain and the grazing food chain.

Answer: detrital
Topic: Section 20.9

14) _____ efficiency is the ratio of productivity in a given trophic level to the productivity of the trophic level on which it feeds.

Answer: Trophic
Topic: Section 20.12

Multiple-Choice Questions

1) According to the first law of thermodynamics,
    A) chemical reactions are exothermic.
    B) entropy tends to increase.
    C) potential energy tends to degrade into an unavailable form.
    D) energy is neither created nor destroyed.

Answer: D
Topic: Section 20.1

2) Energy is assimilated by plants through the process of _____.
    A) decomposition
    B) respiration
    C) photosynthesis
    D) regeneration

Answer: C
Topic: Section 20.2

3) Net primary productivity refers to
    A) the total rate of photosynthesis, or energy assimilated, by autotrophs.
    B) the rate of energy storage as organic matter by autotrophs after respiration is deducted.
    C) the amount of accumulated organic matter found in an area at a given time.
    D) the production of new tissues and offspring by heterotrophs.

Answer: B
Topic: Section 20.2

4) The amount of accumulated organic matter found in an area at a given time is referred to as
    A) gross primary productivity.
    B) net primary productivity.
    C) secondary productivity.
    D) standing crop biomass.

Answer: D
Topic: Section 20.2

5) Primary productivity is greatest under
   A) low temperatures and moist conditions.
   B) low temperatures and dry conditions.
   C) high temperatures and moist conditions.
   D) high temperatures and dry conditions.

Answer: C
Topic: Section 20.3

6) In the surface waters of oceans, the major limitation on primary productivity is low
   A) light.
   B) nutrient content.
   C) salinity.
   D) temperature.

Answer: B
Topic: Section 20.4

7) Low moisture conditions favor allocation by a plant to
   A) leaves.
   B) stems.
   C) roots.
   D) flowers.

Answer: C
Topic: Section 20.5

8) Secondary production is limited primarily by
   A) primary production.
   B) nutrient availability.
   C) water availability.
   D) light availability.

Answer: A
Topic: Section 20.7

9) Which organism is most likely to have the highest assimilation efficiency?
   A) an endothermic carnivore, such as a lion
   B) an ectothermic carnivore, such as a snake
   C) an endothermic herbivore, such as a deer
   D) an ectothermic herbivore, such as a grasshopper

Answer: A
Topic: Section 20.8

10) Ecosystems have two major food chains:
   A) producers and consumers.
   B) autotrophs and heterotrophs.
   C) primary and secondary.
   D) grazing and detrital.

Answer: D
Topic: Section 20.9

11) Assimilation efficiency is
  A) the proportion of energy ingested that is not lost to respiration.
  B) the proportion of energy ingested that is assimilated.
  C) the proportion of assimilated energy that is not lost as waste material.
  D) the proportion of assimilated energy that goes to production.

Answer: B
Topic: Section 20.11

12) In most terrestrial and many aquatic ecosystems, the _____ food chain is the dominant pathway of energy flow.
  A) detrital
  B) grazing
  C) consumer
  D) heterotroph

Answer: A
Topic: Section 20.11

13) Aquatic ecosystems dominated by phytoplankton have _____ rates of herbivory than those in which vascular plants dominate.
  A) lower
  B) higher
  C) equal
  D) more variable

Answer: B
Topic: Section 20.11

14) The amount of energy within a food chain is greatest at the trophic level of
  A) producers.
  B) herbivores.
  C) primary carnivores.
  D) secondary carnivores.

Answer: A
Topic: Section 20.12

True/False Questions

1) The first law of thermodynamics states that when energy is transformed or transferred, part of it assumes a form that cannot be passed on any further so that entropy increases.

Answer: FALSE
Topic: Section 20.1

2) When a chemical reaction results in the loss of energy from the system, the reaction is exothermic.

Answer: TRUE
Topic: Section 20.1

3) Energy from primary production that remains after respiration is called net primary production.

Answer: TRUE
Topic: Section 20.2

4) When stomata are open, a plant is gaining CO_2 but losing water.

Answer: TRUE
Topic: Section 20.3

5) Net primary productivity is greater in moist climates than in dry climates.

Answer: TRUE
Topic: Section 20.3

6) Net primary productivity is greater in warm climates than in cold climates.

Answer: TRUE
Topic: Section 20.3

7) Net primary productivity is greater in the open ocean than along the coast.

Answer: FALSE
Topic: Section 20.4

8) In plants, low water availability favors the allocation of energy to the roots.

Answer: TRUE
Topic: Section 20.5

9) In a temperate rain forest, primary productivity remains relatively constant.

Answer: FALSE
Topic: Section 20.6

10) Primary productivity in forests often increases during the early stages of stand development, and then decreases again as the forest ages and standing biomass increases.

Answer: TRUE
Topic: Section 20.6

11) Secondary production in an ecosystem is always less than primary production.

Answer: TRUE
Topic: Section 20.7

12) Production efficiency is the proportion of the energy ingested that is assimilated.

Answer: FALSE
Topic: Section 20.8

13) Endotherms typically have a higher assimilation efficiency than ectotherms.

Answer: TRUE
Topic: Section 20.8

14) Ecosystems have three major food chains: the autotrophs, the heterotrophs, and the decomposers.

Answer: FALSE
Topic: Section 20.9

15) In terrestrial ecosystems, most of the primary production goes into the grazing food chain.

Answer: FALSE
Topic: Section 20.9

16) In a grazing food chain, energy flow is unidirectional, whereas in a detrital food chain, energy is recycled.

Answer: TRUE
Topic: Section 20.9

17) Consumption efficiency is the ratio of ingestion to production.

Answer: TRUE
Topic: Section 20.10

18) In terrestrial and shallow-water ecosystems, the grazing food chain is dominant over the detrital food chain.

Answer: FALSE
Topic: Section 20.11

19) In stream and river ecosystems, the grazing food chain is of minor importance compared with the detrital food chain.

Answer: TRUE
Topic: Section 20.11

20) In most ecosystems, the biomass of carnivores is greater than the biomass of producers.

Answer: FALSE
Topic: Section 20.12

21) Spectral reflectance measurements can be used by scientists to help estimate net primary productivity over large areas.

Answer: TRUE
Topic: Quantifying Ecology 20.1

22) Brian Silliman's research demonstrated that productivity in highly productive coastal salt marshes is controlled by bottom-up forces, such as physical conditions and nutrient availability.

Answer: FALSE
Topic: Field Studies: Brian Silliman

23) Wealthy nations typically have lower rates of human appropriation of net primary productivity (HANPP) than developing nations.

Answer: FALSE
Topic: Ecological Issues: Human Appropriation of Net Primary Productivity

Essay Questions

1) Describe the effects of temperature, moisture, length of photosynthetic period, and nutrient availability on net primary productivity in terrestrial ecosystems.

Topic: Section 20.3

2) Explain why primary productivity is typically higher in coastal areas of the ocean than far from shore in the open ocean.

Topic: Section 20.4

3) Explain the difference between primary production and secondary production. How is secondary production affected by primary production?

Topic: Section 20.7

4) What are the two main food chains of ecosystems? Which is more dominant in terrestrial ecosystems and why?

Topic: Sections 20.9 and 20.11

5) Explain why energy is lost as it is transferred from one trophic level to another. What are the effects of energy loss on the biomass of different trophic levels?

Topic: Sections 20.1 and 20.12

6) How do humans affect net primary productivity? Does the affluence of a society affect how humans appropriate net primary productivity?

Topic: Ecological Issues: Human Appropriation of Net Primary Productivity

Chapter 21   Decomposition and Nutrient Cycling

Short Answer Questions

1) _____ is the process by which plants absorb a portion of their nutrients from senescing tissues to be stored and used for the production of new tissues.

   Answer: Retranslocation, or reabsorption
   Topic: Quantifying Ecology 22.1

2) The breakdown of chemical bonds that were formed during the construction of plant and animal tissues is called _____.

   Answer: decomposition
   Topic: Section 21.2

3) The dominant decomposers of dead animals are _____.

   Answer: bacteria
   Topic: Section 21.2

4) Animals that feed on bacteria and fungi are called _____.

   Answer: microbivores
   Topic: Section 21.2

5) The release of organically bound nutrients into an inorganic form is called _____.

   Answer: mineralization
   Topic: Section 21.5

6) The incorporation of mineral nutrients into an organic form is called _____.

   Answer: immobilization
   Topic: Section 21.5

7) In open water, the undissolved remains of dead organisms and other organic material that drifts toward the bottom is called _____ organic matter.

   Answer: particulate
   Topic: Section 21.6

8) The rate of nutrient cycling in an ecosystem depends on the rates of two key processes: primary productivity and _____.

   Answer: decomposition
   Topic: Section 21.7

9) In streams and rivers, nutrients are continually transported downstream, a process better described as nutrient _____ than nutrient cycling.

   Answer: spiraling
   Topic: Section 21.9

10) In an estuary, the zone of maximum vertical difference in density is called a(n) _____.

   Answer: pycnocline
   Topic: Section 21.10

11) In a process known as the _____ , the rise and fall of water depth with tidal cycles brings nutrients into coastal marshes from coastal ocean waters.

Answer: tidal subsidy
Topic: Section 21.10

Multiple-Choice Questions

1) In plants, the absorption of a portion of nutrients from senescing tissues in order to use the nutrients for production of new tissues is called
   A) leaching.
   B) reabsorption.
   C) recycling.
   D) transpiration.

Answer: B
Topic: Quantifying Ecology 22.1

2) Which of the following is not an important process involved in decomposition?
   A) leaching
   B) fragmentation
   C) mineralization
   D) transpiration

Answer: D
Topic: Section 21.2

3) Which of the following organisms are not important agents of decomposition?
   A) plants
   B) bacteria
   C) fungi
   D) soil invertebrate animals

Answer: A
Topic: Section 21.2

4) The major decomposers of dead plant tissues are
   A) amoeba.
   B) bacteria.
   C) fungi.
   D) insects.

Answer: C
Topic: Section 21.2

5) Which of the following is not a component of plant tissue?
   A) simple sugars
   B) cellulose
   C) chitin
   D) lignin

Answer: C
Topic: Sections 21.3 and 21.4

6) Which of the following breaks down the slowest during decomposition?
   A) simple sugars
   B) cellulose
   C) chitin
   D) lignin

Answer: D
Topic: Sections 21.3 and 21.4

7) The rate of decomposition is greatest in
   A) cold and moist environments.
   B) cold and dry environments.
   C) warm and moist environments.
   D) warm and dry environments.

Answer: C
Topic: Section 21.4

8) The process of conversion of nutrients from an organic form into an inorganic form that plants can use is called
   A) immobilization.
   B) respiration.
   C) transpiration.
   D) mineralization.

Answer: D
Topic: Section 21.5

9) Aquatic arthropods that fragment organic particles and also eat bacteria and fungi on the surface of the litter are called
   A) shredders.
   B) filtering collectors.
   C) gathering collectors.
   D) grazers.

Answer: A
Topic: Section 21.6

10) Which of the following statements is true?
   A) The rate of nutrient cycling in an ecosystem depends only on the rate of photosynthesis.
   B) The rate of nutrient cycling in an ecosystem depends only on the rate of decomposition.
   C) The rate of nutrient cycling in an ecosystem does not depend on the rate of photosynthesis or the rate of decomposition.
   D) The rate of nutrient cycling in an ecosystem depends on both the rate of photosynthesis and the rate of decomposition.

Answer: D
Topic: Section 21.7

11) In open water ecosystems, decomposition occurs primarily in the
   A) thermocline.
   B) hypolimnion.
   C) epilimnion.
   D) benthic zone.

Answer: D
Topic: Section 21.8

12) In _____, the process of nutrient cycling is sometimes described as nutrient spiraling.
   A) streams and rivers
   B) oceans
   C) lakes
   D) forests

Answer: C
Topic: Section 21.9

13) Coastal zones of contact between freshwater from streams and rivers and salt water from the ocean are called
   A) estuaries.
   B) headwaters.
   C) deltas.
   D) coastal upwelling zones.

Answer: A
Topic: Section 21.10

14) In an estuary, the zone of maximum vertical difference in density of water layers is called the
   A) thermocline.
   B) pycnocline.
   C) mixing zone.
   D) hypolimnion.

Answer: B
Topic: Section 21.10

True/False Questions

1) Most of the nutrients in the leaves of a deciduous plant are lost when the leaves senesce and drop to the ground.

Answer: FALSE
Topic: Quantifying Ecology 22.1

2) Aerobic bacteria are decomposers but anaerobic bacteria are not.

Answer: FALSE
Topic: Section 21.2

3) All heterotrophs to some degree function as decomposers.

Answer: TRUE
Topic: Section 21.2

4) Bacteria, fungi, and animals are all important in decomposition.

Answer: TRUE
Topic: Section 21.2

5) The physical fragmentation of organic matter into smaller pieces is achieved primarily by invertebrate detritivores.

Answer: TRUE
Topic: Section 21.2

6) Fungi are the dominant decomposers of dead animal matter, whereas bacteria are the dominant decomposers of dead plant matter.

Answer: FALSE

Topic: Section 21.2

7) Decomposers obtain their energy by photosynthesis.

Answer: FALSE

Topic: Section 21.3

8) Litterbags can be used to estimate the rate of decomposition.

Answer: TRUE

Topic: Section 21.3 and Quantifying Ecology 21.1

9) The rate of decomposition is faster for proteins, simple sugars, cellulose, and hemicellulose than it is for lignin.

Answer: TRUE

Topic: Section 21.4

10) Decomposition proceeds faster in moist environments than in dry environments.

Answer: TRUE

Topic: Section 21.4

11) The release of organically bound nutrients into an inorganic form is called immobilization.

Answer: FALSE

Topic: Section 21.5

12) During the process of decomposition, carbon quality typically declines.

Answer: TRUE

Topic: Section 21.5

13) Aerobic decomposition occurs at a faster rate than anaerobic decomposition.

Answer: TRUE

Topic: Section 21.6

14) The rate of nutrient cycling in an ecosystem is a function of physical characteristics of the ecosystem, not biological processes such as photosynthesis and decomposition.

Answer: FALSE

Topic: Section 21.7

15) In open-water systems such as lakes and oceans, decomposition occurs mostly in the surface layer.

Answer: FALSE

Topic: Section 21.8

16) In open-water ecosystems, turnover prevents the movement of nutrients between the bottom and surface layers.

Answer: FALSE

Topic: Section 21.8

17) Nutrient "spiraling" occurs in streams and rivers.

Answer: TRUE

Topic: Section 21.9

18) Coastal ecosystems are not very productive because they are usually cool.

   Answer: FALSE
   Topic: Section 21.10

19) In salt marshes, only a small portion of primary production is consumed by herbivores.

   Answer: TRUE
   Topic: Section 21.10

20) Estuaries receive nutrients both from tides and from streams and rivers.

   Answer: TRUE
   Topic: Section 21.10

21) The region of the open ocean where the north and south equatorial currents meet is deficient in nutrients and supports little life.

   Answer: FALSE
   Topic: Section 21.11

22) The work of Edward Schuur has found that in some ecosystems, rates of decomposition decline with increased precipitation.

   Answer: TRUE
   Topic: Field Studies: Edward A. G. (Ted) Schuur

23) Nitrogen fertilizers used for crops represent the main source of pollution in the ocean.

   Answer: TRUE
   Topic: Ecological Issues: Nitrogen Fertilizers

Essay Questions

1) Describe the movement of an atom of nitrogen from the leaf of a plant, through the process of decomposition, and back into the root of another plant.
   Topic: Sections 21.1 and 21.2

2) Describe three different processes that are important for decomposition. Explain which organisms are important for each of the processes.
   Topic: Sections 21.1 and 21.2

3) Discuss the effects of temperature, humidity, and oxygen availability on the rate of decomposition.
   Topic: Sections 21.4, 21.6

4) Explain how the "quality" of plant-derived organic matter changes during the course of decomposition.
   Topic: Sections 21.4 and 21.5

5) Define mineralization and immobilization, and discuss the differences between them.
   Topic: Section 21.5

6) Describe two major differences between decomposition in terrestrial environments and decomposition in aquatic environments.
   Topic: Sections 21.6, 21.8

7) Describe one major difference between nutrient cycling in a river and nutrient cycling in a lake.
   Topic: Section 21.9

8) Describe the process of upwelling in the ocean and how it relates to fisheries.

Topic: Section 21.11

9) Describe how you might go about measuring the rate of decomposition of leaf litter in the upper layer of a forest soil.

Topic: Section 21.3 and Quantifying Ecology 21.1

Chapter 22 Biogeochemical Cycles

Short Answer Questions

1) All nutrients flow from the nonliving, to the living, and back to the non-living components of the ecosystem in a path known as a(n) _____ cycle.

Answer: biogeochemical
Topic: Introduction to Chapter 22

2) There are two basic types of biogeochemical cycles: gaseous and _____.

Answer: sedimentary
Topic: Section 22.1

3) In gaseous biogeochemical cycles, the main pools of nutrients are the atmosphere and the _____.

Answer: oceans
Topic: Section 22.1

4) Precipitation brings appreciable quantities of nutrients into ecosystems that are collectively called

_____.

Answer: wetfall
Topic: Section 22.2

5) The element _____ is a basic constituent of all organic compounds and is involved in the fixation of energy by photosynthesis.

Answer: carbon
Topic: Section 22.5

6) The source of all carbon in both living organisms and fossil deposits is carbon _____ in the atmosphere and in all the waters of the Earth.

Answer: dioxide
Topic: Section 22.5

7) The difference between the rate of carbon uptake in photosynthesis and the rate of carbon loss due to autotrophic and heterotrophic respiration is the net _____ productivity.

Answer: ecosystem
Topic: Section 22.5

8) All but a small fraction of the Earth's _____ is buried in sedimentary rocks and is not actively involved in a global cycle.

Answer: carbon
Topic: Section 22.7

9) The ability of the surface waters of the ocean to take up carbon dioxide is governed by the reaction of carbon dioxide with the _____ ion to form bicarbonates.

Answer: carbonate
Topic: Section 22.7

10) Nitrogen is available to plants in two forms: ammonium and _____.

Answer: nitrate
Topic: Section 22.8

11) Biological nitrogen fixation is accomplished by symbiotic _____ living in mutualistic association with plants.

Answer: bacteria
Topic: Section 22.8

12) Nitrogen can be returned to the atmosphere when certain bacteria convert it from nitrate into nitrogen gas, which is a process called _____.

Answer: denitrification
Topic: Section 22.8

13) _____ is the most common form of nitrogen exported from terrestrial ecosystems in stream water.

Answer: Nitrate
Topic: Section 22.8

14) The _____ is the largest pool of nitrogen.

Answer: atmosphere
Topic: Section 22.8

15) The nutrient _____ does not have a gaseous cycle because it occurs in only very minute amounts in the atmosphere.

Answer: phosphorus
Topic: Section 22.9

16) In aquatic ecosystems, the phosphorous cycle moves through three states: particulate organic phosphorous, dissolved organic phosphates, and _____ phosphates.

Answer: inorganic
Topic: Section 22.9

17) The major source of free oxygen that supports life on Earth is the _____.

Answer: atmosphere
Topic: Section 22.12

18) The main reservoirs of oxygen are water and _____.

Answer: carbon dioxide
Topic: Section 22.12

19) The branch of chemistry dealing with the quantitative relationships of elements in combination is called _____.

Answer: stoichiometry
Topic: Section 22.13

Multiple-Choice Questions

1) The flow of nutrients from the non-living to the living and back to the non-living components of an ecosystem is referred to as a(n) _____ cycle.
   A) trophic
   B) biogeochemical
   C) energy
   D) life

Answer: B
Topic: Introduction to Chapter 22

2) In _____ biogeochemical cycles, the main reservoirs of nutrients are the atmosphere and the oceans.
   A) sedimentary
   B) gaseous
   C) aquatic
   D) terrestrial

Answer: B
Topic: Section 22.1

3) In _____ biogeochemical cycles, the main reservoirs of nutrients are the soil, rocks, and minerals.
   A) sedimentary
   B) gaseous
   C) terrestrial
   D) aquatic

Answer: A
Topic: Section 22.1

4) Which of the following does not cause a loss of nutrients from an ecosystem?
   A) the production of carbon dioxide during respiration
   B) the addition of fertilizer to a crop field
   C) the transport of organic matter by a river from one ecosystem to another
   D) the harvesting of a crop by humans

Answer: B
Topic: Section 22.3

5) Which of the following nutrients is most closely linked to the energy cycle in ecosystems?
   A) carbon
   B) nitrogen
   C) lead
   D) sulfur

Answer: A
Topic: Section 22.5

6) The source of all carbon in living organisms is
   A) simple sugars.
   B) carbon dioxide in the atmosphere and in water.
   C) carbon-fixing bacteria.
   D) sedimentary rocks.

Answer: B
Topic: Section 22.5

7) Carbon is released into the atmosphere as carbon dioxide as the result of the process of
   A) photosynthesis.
   B) primary production.
   C) respiration.
   D) fixation.

Answer: C
Topic: Section 22.5

8) The largest active carbon pool is
    A) the atmosphere.
    B) the oceans.
    C) living organisms.
    D) dead organisms.

Answer: B
Topic: Section 22.7

9) Biological nitrogen fixation is accomplished by
    A) protozoans.
    B) bacteria.
    C) fungi.
    D) plants.

Answer: B
Topic: Section 22.8

10) Which of the following does not provide an input of nitrogen into ecosystems?
    A) atmospheric deposition
    B) lightning
    C) biological fixation by cyanobacteria
    D) denitrification by soil bacteria

Answer: D
Topic: Section 22.8

11) The largest pool of nitrogen is
    A) the atmosphere.
    B) the oceans.
    C) living organisms.
    D) dead organisms.

Answer: A
Topic: Section 22.8

12) Which of the following nutrients has a cycle that does not contain an atmospheric phase?
    A) carbon
    B) nitrogen
    C) phosphorus
    D) sulfur

Answer: C
Topic: Section 22.9

13) Which of the following is not a major reservoir for phosphorus?
    A) the atmosphere
    B) rocks
    C) natural phosphate deposits
    D) minerals

Answer: A
Topic: Section 22.9

14) Hydrogen sulfide is transformed into sulfate or elemental sulfur by
    A) protozoans.
    B) bacteria.
    C) fungi.
    D) algae.

Answer: B
Topic: Section 22.10

15) Which of the following represents the largest natural source of sulfur gases released to the atmosphere?
    A) volcanoes
    B) terrestrial organisms
    C) freshwater organisms
    D) oceans

Answer: D
Topic: Section 22.11

16) Which of the following cycles is thought to be most under biological control?
    A) oxygen
    B) phosphorus
    C) sulfur
    D) lead

Answer: A
Topic: Section 22.12

17) Which of the following nutrients is produced by photosynthesis?
    A) nitrogen
    B) phosphorous
    C) oxygen
    D) sulfur

Answer: C
Topic: Section 22.12

True/False Questions

1) There are two basic types of biogeochemical cycles: gaseous and sedimentary.

Answer: TRUE
Topic: Section 22.1

2) In sedimentary biogeochemical cycles, the main reservoirs of nutrients are the atmosphere and the oceans.

Answer: FALSE
Topic: Section 22.1

3) Without the cycling of water, biogeochemical cycles would cease.

Answer: TRUE
Topic: Section 22.1

4) Nutrients with a sedimentary cycle enter the ecosystem via the atmosphere.

Answer: FALSE
Topic: Section 22.2

5) Precipitation can be a significant input of nutrients in ecosystems.
   Answer: TRUE
   Topic: Section 22.2

6) Carbon is exported to the atmosphere via the process of photosynthesis.
   Answer: FALSE
   Topic: Section 22.3

7) The biogeochemical cycles of one ecosystem are typically independent from those of other ecosystems.
   Answer: FALSE
   Topic: Section 22.4

8) Carbon dioxide occurs in both the atmosphere and in oceans.
   Answer: TRUE
   Topic: Section 22.5

9) Carbon cycles more quickly through cold and dry ecosystems than it does through warm and wet ecosystems.
   Answer: FALSE
   Topic: Section 22.5

10) Atmospheric carbon dioxide concentrations in a forest are greater during the day than during the night.
    Answer: FALSE
    Topic: Section 22.6

11) Atmospheric carbon dioxide concentrations are higher during summer than during winter.
    Answer: FALSE
    Topic: Section 22.6

12) Seasonal fluctuations in atmospheric carbon dioxide concentrations are greater in the Northern Hemisphere than in the Southern Hemisphere.
    Answer: TRUE
    Topic: Section 22.6

13) Most carbon is buried in sedimentary rocks.
    Answer: TRUE
    Topic: Section 22.7

14) Of the carbon actively involved in the global cycle, most is in the oceans.
    Answer: TRUE
    Topic: Section 22.7

15) There is more carbon per unit of soil in cold polar regions than in the warm tropics.
    Answer: TRUE
    Topic: Section 22.7

16) Ammonium and nitrate are forms of nitrogen that can be directly used by plants.
    Answer: TRUE
    Topic: Section 22.8

17) Most plants obtain nitrogen directly from gaseous nitrogen in the atmosphere during respiration.

Answer: FALSE
Topic: Section 22.8

18) Certain anaerobic bacteria are capable of converting nitrogen compounds into gaseous nitrogen.

Answer: TRUE
Topic: Section 22.8

19) The atmosphere is the largest pool of nitrogen.

Answer: TRUE
Topic: Section 22.8

20) The phosphorus cycle is a sedimentary cycle with essentially no gaseous cycle.

Answer: TRUE
Topic: Section 22.9

21) The main reservoir for phosphorus is organic matter in the soil.

Answer: FALSE
Topic: Section 22.9

22) Phosphorus is typically in short supply in aquatic and terrestrial ecosystems.

Answer: TRUE
Topic: Section 22.9

23) The sulfur biogeochemical cycle is a sedimentary cycle with essentially no gaseous cycle.

Answer: FALSE
Topic: Section 22.10

24) One way that sulfur enters the atmosphere is through volcanic activity.

Answer: TRUE
Topic: Section 22.10

25) Atmospheric sulfur dioxide returns to Earth in rain as weak sulfuric acid.

Answer: TRUE
Topic: Section 22.10

26) Oceans represent the largest natural source of sulfur gases released to the atmosphere.

Answer: TRUE
Topic: Section 22.11

27) Oxygen is taken up by plants during photosynthesis.

Answer: FALSE
Topic: Section 22.12

28) Oxygen is produced during respiration.

Answer: FALSE
Topic: Section 22.12

29) Stratospheric ozone shields the planet from biologically harmful ultraviolet radiation.

Answer: TRUE
Topic: Section 22.12

30) The various biogeochemical cycles are largely independent of one another.

Answer: FALSE
Topic: Section 22.13

31) The average length of time a molecule resides in any given compartment of an ecosystem is called its turnover time or residence time.

Answer: TRUE
Topic: Quantifying Ecology 22.1

32) Natural levels of atmospheric nitrogen deposition are high, but in recent decades, human activity has disrupted this part of the nitrogen cycle in many parts of the world.

Answer: FALSE
Topic: Ecological Issues: Nitrogen Saturation

33) In the later stages of nitrogen saturation, soils tend to become more acidic, which increases the concentration of aluminum ions in the soil solution.

Answer: TRUE
Topic: Ecological Issues: Nitrogen Saturation

Essay Questions

1) Explain the difference between the two basic types of biogeochemical cycles, using specific examples of each.

Topic: Section 22.1

2) Describe three ways that nutrients can be lost from an ecosystem.

Topic: Section 22.3

3) Describe how atmospheric carbon dioxide levels fluctuate daily, seasonally, and geographically. Explain why such fluctuation occurs.

Topic: Sections 22.5–22.7

4) Describe a pathway of nitrogen from the atmosphere into the body tissue of an herbivore.

Topic: Section 22.8

5) Describe how an atom of phosphorus might move from the crystal lattice of a mineral in a rock, through a plant, and into the ocean.

Topic: Section 22.9

6) List and describe three different inputs of sulfur into the atmosphere.

Topic: Sections 22.10 and 22.11

7) Describe how ozone is formed at different levels of the atmosphere and how biological organisms are affected by ozone.

Topic: Sections 22.12 and 22.13

Chapter 23 Terrestrial Ecosystems

Short Answer Questions

1) _____ is the study of the spatial or geographical distribution of organisms, both past and present.

   Answer: Biogeography
   Topic: Introduction to Part 7

2) A(n) _____ is a classification of plant formations and associated animal life into biotic units based on the predominant plant types, with at least eight major terrestrial types.

   Answer: biome
   Topic: Introduction to Chapter 23

3) Leaves that live for only a single year or growing season are classified as _____.

   Answer: deciduous
   Topic: Section 23.1

4) Leaves that live for more than a year are classified as _____.

   Answer: evergreen
   Topic: Section 23.1

5) More than one-half of all known plant and animal species occur in tropical _____ forests.

   Answer: rain
   Topic: Section 23.2

6) Tropical _____ refers to vegetation in the drier tropics and subtropics that is dominated by a ground cover of grasses with scattered shrubs or trees.

   Answer: savanna
   Topic: Section 23.3

7) Arid environments that occur in the rainshadow of mountain barriers or are located far inland where moist maritime air rarely penetrates are referred to as _____.

   Answer: deserts
   Topic: Section 23.5

8) A _____ climate is characterized by hot, dry summers and cool, moist winters.

   Answer: mediterranean
   Topic: Section 23.6

9) A belt of coniferous forest, known as taiga, or _____ forest, occurs in the high latitudes of the Northern Hemisphere.

   Answer: boreal
   Topic: Section 23.8

10) Frozen, treeless plains dominated by sedges, heaths, and willows at high latitudes and elevations are referred to as _____.

    Answer: tundra
    Topic: Section 23.9

Multiple-Choice Questions

1) The independent evolution of a similar characteristic in two different species, not derived from a recent, common ancestor is referred to as
   A) microevolution.
   B) divergent evolution.
   C) convergent evolution.
   D) macroevolution.

Answer: C
Topic: Introduction to Part 7

2) The study of the distributions of organisms, past and present, is referred to as
   A) biogeography.
   B) community ecology.
   C) ecosystem ecology.
   D) population ecology.

Answer: A
Topic: Introduction to Part 7

3) A classification of plant formations and associated animal life into biotic units based on the predominant plant types, with at least eight major terrestrial types, is referred to as a(n)
   A) community.
   B) biome.
   C) ecosystem.
   D) biosphere.

Answer: B
Topic: Introduction to Chapter 23

4) Which of the following allocates the greatest amount of biomass to photosynthetic tissue and the least amount to supportive tissue?
   A) trees
   B) shrubs
   C) lianas
   D) grasses

Answer: D
Topic: Section 23.1

5) Which of the following is the predominant leaf form of environments where the growing season is very short or where nutrient availability severely constrains photosynthesis and plant growth?
   A) winter-deciduous leaves
   B) drought-deciduous leaves
   C) broad-leaf evergreen leaves
   D) needle-leaf evergreen leaves

Answer: D
Topic: Section 23.1

6) The highest diversity of plant and animal life occurs in
   A) tropical savannas.
   B) tropical rain forests.
   C) temperate deciduous forests.
   D) boreal forests.

Answer: B
Topic: Section 23.2

7) Plants that root and grow on other plants in the tropical rain forest are called
    A) phreatophytes.
    B) succulents.
    C) epiphytes.
    D) halophytes.

Answer: C
Topic: Section 23.2

8) Buttresses, which are broad outgrowths at the base of trees, are best developed in
    A) temperate deciduous forest.
    B) coniferous forest.
    C) tropical rain forest.
    D) temperate shrubland.

Answer: C
Topic: Section 23.2

9) Savannas typically occur in
    A) cold areas with little rainfall in polar regions.
    B) cold areas with little rainfall at high altitudes in the tropics.
    C) very dry areas in the rain shadow of mountains of both temperate and tropical latitudes.
    D) warm areas with seasonal rainfall in the tropics.

Answer: D
Topic: Section 23.3

10) Large grazing ungulates and burrowing animals are most abundant in
    A) deserts.
    B) tropical rain forest.
    C) temperate shrubland.
    D) temperate grassland.

Answer: D
Topic: Section 23.4

11) Most deserts are located
    A) near the equator.
    B) in the southern hemisphere.
    C) in the rainshadow of mountain ranges.
    D) near coastal areas with warm oceanic currents.

Answer: C
Topic: Section 23.5

12) The dominant biome in mediterranean climates with hot, dry summers and cool, moist winters is
    A) temperate shrubland.
    B) temperate deciduous forest.
    C) desert.
    D) tropical savanna.

Answer: A
Topic: Section 23.6

13) In a temperate deciduous forest, the concentration and diversity of animal life is greatest in the
  A) ground layer.
  B) herb layer.
  C) lower canopy.
  D) upper canopy.

Answer: A
Topic: Section 23.7

14) The vegetation formation dominated by needle-leaf evergreen trees and occurring at high latitudes or high elevations where growth is restricted to a few months of the year due to low temperatures is referred to as
  A) temperate deciduous forest.
  B) tundra.
  C) boreal forest.
  D) temperate shrubland.

Answer: C
Topic: Section 23.8

15) Frozen, treeless plains dominated by sedges, heaths, and willows at high latitudes and elevations is referred to as
  A) prairie.
  B) steppe.
  C) tundra.
  D) pampas.

Answer: C
Topic: Section 23.9

16) The vegetation of tundra is dominated by
  A) broadleaf deciduous trees.
  B) short plants such as sedges, heaths, and willow.
  C) needle-leaf evergreen trees.
  D) sclerophyllous broadleaf evergreen shrubs.

Answer: B
Topic: Section 23.9

True/False Questions

1) The independent evolution of a similar characteristic in two different species not derived from a recent, common ancestor is referred to as convergent evolution.

Answer: TRUE
Topic: Introduction to Part 7

2) Biogeography is the study of the distribution and abundance of organisms.

Answer: FALSE
Topic: Introduction to Part 7

3) Classification of the world's major terrestrial biomes is based on the dominant forms of plant life.

Answer: TRUE
Topic: Introduction to Chapter 23

4) Trees, shrubs, and grasses are the dominant plant forms used to classify ecosystems.

Answer: TRUE
Topic: Introduction to Chapter 23

5) Shrubs and grasses allocate more carbon to the production of supportive tissues than do trees.

Answer: FALSE
Topic: Section 23.1

6) Similar climates produce similar vegetation structure around the world.

Answer: TRUE
Topic: Section 23.1

7) Deciduous leaves usually live for more than a single year or growing season.

Answer: FALSE
Topic: Section 23.1

8) The largest and most continuous region of tropical rain forest in the world is in South America.

Answer: TRUE
Topic: Section 23.2

9) More than half of all known plant and animal species occur in tropical rain forests.

Answer: TRUE
Topic: Section 23.2

10) Tropical rain forests typically have a thick layer of litter on the forest floor.

Answer: FALSE
Topic: Section 23.2

11) Deciduous trees and shrubs occur in some areas of the tropics.

Answer: TRUE
Topic: Section 23.2

12) In the tropical latitudes, the length of the dry season increases with distance from the equator.

Answer: TRUE
Topic: Section 23.2

13) The diversity of plant and animal life is higher in tropical savannas than in any other terrestrial biome.

Answer: FALSE
Topic: Section 23.3

14) The dry forests of tropical regions are referred to as tropical savannas.

Answer: FALSE
Topic: Section 23.3

15) Grazing ungulates are relatively common and burrowing rodents are relatively rare in temperate grasslands.

Answer: FALSE
Topic: Section 23.4

16) Deserts are typically hot throughout the year because most are located near the equator.

Answer: FALSE
Topic: Section 23.5

17) Deserts often occur in the rain shadow of mountain ranges.

   Answer: TRUE
   Topic: Section 23.5

18) Mediterranean climates are characterized by relatively dry summers and wet winters.

   Answer: TRUE
   Topic: Section 23.6

19) Temperate shrublands are the dominant biomes in regions with a mediterranean climate.

   Answer: TRUE
   Topic: Section 23.6

20) Rainfall is greater in temperate deciduous forests than in temperate shrublands and grasslands.

   Answer: TRUE
   Topic: Section 23.7

21) In temperate deciduous forests the greatest concentration and diversity of life occurs in the canopy.

   Answer: FALSE
   Topic: Section 23.7

22) Conifer forests are dominated by needle-leaf evergreen trees.

   Answer: TRUE
   Topic: Section 23.8

23) Net primary productivity of boreal forest is generally lower than in temperate deciduous forest.

   Answer: TRUE
   Topic: Section 23.8

24) Tundra occurs only at high latitudes in polar regions.

   Answer: FALSE
   Topic: Section 23.9

25) Tundra occurs at high elevations on mountains.

   Answer: TRUE
   Topic: Section 23.9

26) Topographic features, such as mountains and valleys, influence the climate of a region.

   Answer: TRUE
   Topic: Quantifying Ecology 23.1: Climatic Diagrams

Essay Questions

1) Describe four types of leaf forms and the characteristics of the environment in which each leaf type typically occurs.

   Topic: Section 23.1

2) Discuss the differences in structure and climate between tropical rain forest and dry tropical forest.

   Topic: Section 23.2

3) Explain why the soils of rain forests are poor for agriculture.

   Topic: Section 23.2

4) Discuss the factors that limit the growth of trees in savannas and grasslands.

Topic: Sections 23.3 and 23.4

5) Discuss the differences in structure and climate between tropical savannas and deserts.

Topic: Sections 23.3, 23.5

6) Describe the climatic and topographic factors that favor the formation of deserts.

Topic: Section 23.5

7) Describe the soil conditions in boreal forest and how vegetation affects and is affected by the soil conditions.

Topic: Section 23.8

Chapter 24   Aquatic Ecosystems

Short Answer Questions

1) Nonflowing water ecosystems, such as ponds and lakes, are also called _____ ecosystems.

Answer: lentic
Topic: Introduction to Chapter 24

2) In lakes and ponds, the open water zone extending to the depth of light penetration is referred to as the _____ zone.

Answer: limnetic
Topic: Section 24.2

3) In lakes and ponds, the _____ zone is a shallow water zone along the perimeter in which light reaches the bottom.

Answer: littoral
Topic: Section 24.2

4) In lakes and ponds, the depth at which respiration balances photosynthesis is referred to as the _____ depth of light.

Answer: compensation
Topic: Section 24.2

5) In lakes and ponds, the primary place of decomposition occurs in the _____ zone.

Answer: benthic
Topic: Section 24.2

6) The tiny, photosynthetic, primary producers of open water such as desmids, diatoms, and filamentous algae, are referred to as _____.

Answer: phytoplankton
Topic: Section 24.3

7) In the benthic zone of lakes and ponds, organisms that are attached to or move on a submerged substrate, but do not penetrate it are referred to as _____, or aufwuchs.

Answer: periphyton
Topic: Section 24.3

8) _____ refers to the nutrient enrichment of aquatic ecosystems.

Answer: Eutrophication
Topic: Section 24.4

9) A relatively _____ lake is characterized by an abundance of nutrients, abundant algal growth, and shallow light penetration.

Answer: eutrophic
Topic: Section 24.4

10) Lakes that received large amounts of organic matter from surrounding land, particularly in the form of humic materials that stain the water brown, are called _____ lakes.

Answer: dystrophic
Topic: Section 24.4

11) Flowing-water ecosystems often alternate two different but related habitats: the turbulent _____ and the quiet pool.

Answer: riffle
Topic: Section 24.5

12) In streams and rivers, the group of invertebrates that feeds on coarse particulate organic matter (mostly leaves that fall into the stream) is referred to as the _____.

Answer: shredders
Topic: Section 24.6

13) Streams generally have a(n) _____ temperature at their headwaters than toward their outlet.

Answer: lower
Topic: Section 24.7

14) When rivers flow into the ocean, they create a zone of mixing of freshwater with saltwater referred to as a(n) _____.

Answer: estuary
Topic: Section 24.8

15) The water above the continental shelf belongs to the _____ province of the pelagic zone.

Answer: neritic
Topic: Section 24.9

16) The zone in the ocean from the surface to approximately 200 meters deep is called the _____, or photic, zone.

Answer: epipelagic
Topic: Section 24.9

17) Smaller than diatoms, the _____, which include tiny cyanobaceteria, haptophtyes, and coccolithophores, make up the largest biomass in temperate and tropical water.

Answer: nanoplankton
Topic: Section 24.10

18) _____ refers to the plants and animals living on the bottom of the ocean.

Answer: Benthos
Topic: Section 24.11

19) Reef-building corals have a symbiotic relationship with algal cells called _____ that live within the cells of corals.

Answer: zooxanthella
Topic: Section 24.12

20) A(n) _____ is a ring of coral reefs and islands surrounding a lagoon and are formed when a volcanic mountain subsides beneath the surface.

Answer: atoll
Topic: Section 24.12

Multiple-Choice Questions

1) The general term for flowing bodies of water is
   A) lentic.
   B) lotic.
   C) limnetic.
   D) turbulent.

   Answer: B
   Topic: Introduction to Chapter 24

2) Which of the following bodies of water best represents a lotic ecosystem?
   A) salt pond
   B) marsh
   C) oxbow lake
   D) spring

   Answer: D
   Topic: Introduction to Chapter 24

3) In lakes and ponds, photosynthesis occurs primarily in the
   A) benthic zone.
   B) profundal zone.
   C) limnetic zone.
   D) lotic zone.

   Answer: C
   Topic: Section 24.2

4) In ponds and lakes, the zone beneath the depth of effective light penetration but above the bottom is referred to as the
   A) littoral zone.
   B) limnetic zone.
   C) profundal zone.
   D) benthic zone.

   Answer: C
   Topic: Section 24.2

5) In lakes and ponds, decomposition occurs primarily in the
   A) benthic zone.
   B) littoral zone.
   C) limnetic zone.
   D) profundal zone.

   Answer: A
   Topic: Section 24.2

6) In lakes and ponds, phytoplankton and zooplankton are most abundant in the
   A) benthic zone.
   B) littoral zone.
   C) limnetic zone.
   D) profundal zone.

   Answer: C
   Topic: Section 24.3

7) In lakes and ponds, oxygen concentrations are lowest in the
    A) benthic zone.
    B) littoral zone.
    C) limnetic zone.
    D) profundal zone.

Answer: A
Topic: Section 24.3

8) Which of the following lakes is likely to be the most oligotrophic?
    A) small and shallow
    B) small and deep
    C) large and shallow
    D) large and deep

Answer: D
Topic: Section 24.4

9) In streams and rivers, decomposition occurs primarily in
    A) the benthic zone.
    B) riffles.
    C) pools.
    D) the lotic zone.

Answer: C
Topic: Section 24.5

10) Invertebrates that feed on coarse particulate organic matter, such as leaves that fall into streams and rivers, are referred to as
    A) shredders.
    B) gougers.
    C) grazers.
    D) collectors.

Answer: A
Topic: Section 24.6

11) Invertebrates that feed on the algal coating of stones and rubble in streams and rivers are referred to as
    A) shredders.
    B) gougers.
    C) grazers.
    D) collectors.

Answer: C
Topic: Section 24.6

12) As a stream or river descends, it generally grows
    A) faster and cooler.
    B) slower and warmer.
    C) faster and warmer.
    D) slower and cooler.

Answer: B
Topic: Section 24.7

13) Semi-enclosed areas of the coastal ocean where seawater is diluted and partially mixed with freshwater coming from the land are referred to as
    A) eddies.
    B) coastal reservoirs.
    C) tidal basins.
    D) estuaries.

Answer: D
Topic: Section 24.8

14) The oxygen-minimum layer of an ocean occurs in the
    A) abyssalpelagic zone.
    B) bathypelagic zone.
    C) epipelagic zone.
    D) mesopelagic zone.

Answer: D
Topic: Section 24.9

15) In the ocean, phytoplankton are most abundant in the
    A) abyssalpelagic zone.
    B) bathypelagic zone.
    C) epipelagic zone.
    D) mesopelagic zone.

Answer: C
Topic: Sections 24.9 and 24.10

16) The dominant autotrophs of the open water are
    A) phytoplankton.
    B) kelp.
    C) seagrasses.
    D) stromatolites.

Answer: A
Topic: Section 24.10

17) In the ocean, swimming organisms that can move at will in the water column are referred to as
    A) periphyton.
    B) zooplankton.
    C) megaplankton.
    D) nekton.

Answer: D
Topic: Section 24.10

18) The organisms living on the bottom of the ocean are collectively referred to as
    A) nekton.
    B) benthos.
    C) meiofauna.
    D) epifauna.

Answer: B
Topic: Section 24.11

19) The benthic community of an ocean, with the exception of hydrothermal vents, is best described as
    A) completely heterotrophic and very diverse.
    B) completely autotrophic and very diverse.
    C) completely phototrophic and not very diverse.
    D) mostly heterotrophic and not very diverse.

Answer: A
Topic: Section 24.11

20) In hydrothermal vent communities, autotrophic organisms obtain energy by oxidizing
    A) reduced sulfur compounds.
    B) carbon dioxide.
    C) sodium chloride.
    D) metals such as copper and iron.

Answer: A
Topic: Section 24.11

21) The cells of reef-building corals are inhabited by symbiotic species of
    A) algae.
    B) fungi.
    C) bacteria.
    D) cyanobacteria.

Answer: B
Topic: Section 24.12

22) Coral reefs grow best where water is
    A) warm, shallow, and clear.
    B) warm, deep, and clear.
    C) cold, shallow, and clear.
    D) cold, deep, and murky.

Answer: A
Topic: Section 24.12

23) The productivity of oceans is greatest in the
    A) neritic province at tropical latitudes.
    B) oceanic province at tropical latitudes.
    C) neritic province at temperate latitudes.
    D) oceanic province at temperate latitudes.

Answer: C
Topic: Sections 24.9, 28.16

True/False Questions

1) Non-flowing water bodies, such as lakes, are referred to as lotic ecosystems.

Answer: FALSE
Topic: Introduction to Chapter 24

2) Lakes and ponds are often formed through nongeological activities.

Answer: TRUE
Topic: Section 24.1

3) In the profundal zone of a lake or pond, the rate of photosynthesis exceeds the rate of respiration.

Answer: FALSE
Topic: Section 24.2

4) Phytoplankton thrive in the limnetic zone of lakes and ponds.

Answer: TRUE
Topic: Section 24.3

5) Decomposition in lakes and ponds occurs primarily in the benthic zone.

Answer: TRUE
Topic: Section 24.3

6) Oxygen concentrations are relatively high in the bottom ooze of lakes and ponds.

Answer: FALSE
Topic: Section 24.3

7) Eutrophic lakes typically are very clear, with little algal growth.

Answer: FALSE
Topic: Section 24.4

8) In rivers and streams, decomposition takes place mostly in riffles.

Answer: FALSE
Topic: Section 24.5

9) In rivers and streams, the invertebrates that scrape algae off of rocks are referred to as shredders.

Answer: FALSE
Topic: Section 24.6

10) As a stream flows down its course, it generally becomes warmer and slower.

Answer: TRUE
Topic: Section 24.7

11) Most estuarine organisms are benthic.

Answer: TRUE
Topic: Section 24.8

12) Photosynthesis in the ocean takes place mostly in the mesopelagic zone.

Answer: FALSE
Topic: Section 24.9

13) The deepest water of an ocean in deep-sea trenches and canyons is referred to as the hadalpelagic zone.

Answer: TRUE
Topic: Section 24.9

14) Unlike phytoplankton, which are at the mercy of currents, zooplankton can move at will within a current.

Answer: FALSE
Topic: Section 24.10

15) Many zooplankton migrate to the surface to graze on phytoplankton during the day and retreat to deeper water during the night.

Answer: FALSE
Topic: Section 24.10

16) Swimming organisms in the ocean that are able to move at will in the water column are referred to as nekton.

Answer: TRUE
Topic: Section 24.10

17) Bioluminescence reaches its greatest development in the mesopelagic zone of an ocean.

Answer: TRUE
Topic: Section 24.10

18) Because of the high pressure and cold temperatures, few species of organisms survive in the deep benthic zone of the ocean.

Answer: FALSE
Topic: Section 24.11

19) Organisms living in deep-sea hydrothermal vents do not need light to obtain their energy.

Answer: TRUE
Topic: Section 24.11

20) Coral reefs occur in nutrient-poor areas of the ocean.

Answer: TRUE
Topic: Section 24.12

21) Barrier reefs are separated from land by shallow lagoons.

Answer: TRUE
Topic: Section 24.12

22) Because the thermocline is permanent in tropical oceans, little vertical mixing occurs, resulting in low productivity.

Answer: TRUE
Topic: Section 24.13

23) The Colorado River in western North America is so overused that it disappears before it reaches the mouth of the Gulf of California.

Answer: TRUE
Topic: Ecological Issues: Dams: Regulating the Flow of River Ecosystems

24) The velocity of water in a stream channel is greater along the margins of the channel than in the center of the channel.

Answer: FALSE
Topic: Quantifying Ecology 24.1: Streamflow

Essay Questions

1) Describe three different processes that can lead to the formation of a lake or pond.

Topic: Section 24.1

2) Describe the types of organisms and biological activities that occur within the littoral, limnetic, and benthic zones of a lake.

Topic: Section 24.3

3) Describe the differences between eutrophic and oligotrophic lakes. What conditions lead to the formation of each?

Topic: Section 24.4

4) Based on their feeding behavior, describe three major groups of invertebrates that inhabit flowing water.

Topic: Section 24.7

5) Describe the physical conditions to which organisms living in an estuary must be adapted.

Topic: Section 24.8

6) Describe the differences between phytoplankton, zooplankton, and nekton. How do they interact with each other?

Topic: Section 24.10

7) Describe three different types of reefs and how they are formed.

Topic: Section 24.12

Chapter 25 Coastal and Wetland Ecosystems

Short Answer Questions

1) All coastal shores have one feature in common: they are alternately exposed and submerged by the

   _____.

   Answer: tides
   Topic: Section 25.1

2) The _____ fringe occurs above the ocean along a rocky shoreline and is contacted by salt water only once every two weeks during spring tides.

   Answer: supralittoral
   Topic: Section 25.2

3) The littoral, or _____, zone of a rocky shoreline is submerged daily and is exposed by tides.

   Answer: intertidal
   Topic: Section 25.2

4) Organisms living on the sediment surface of sandy and muddy beaches are collectively referred to as

   _____.

   Answer: epifauna
   Topic: Section 25.3

5) Tiny organisms living between the particles of sand and mud on beaches are collectively referred to as

   _____.

   Answer: meiofauna
   Topic: Section 25.3

6) A salt _____ refers to a herbaceous plant community thriving in the intertidal zone, typically along the fringe of estuaries or in the shelter of spits, offshore bars, and islands along the coast at temperate latitudes.

   Answer: marsh
   Topic: Section 25.4

7) _____ forests typically grow in the intertidal zone of tropical coasts where wave action is absent, sediments accumulate, and the muds are anoxic.

   Answer: Mangrove
   Topic: Section 25.5

8) The root extensions of mangroves are called _____.

   Answer: pneumatophores
   Topic: Section 25.5

9) _____ plants are adapted to grow in water or on soil that is periodically anaerobic because of excess water.

   Answer: Hydrophytic
   Topic: Section 25.6

10) Freshwater wetlands dominated by emergent herbaceous vegetation are called _____.

   Answer: marshes
   Topic: Section 25.6

11) Seasonally flooded, forested wetlands along river systems are referred to as bottomlands, or _____ woodlands.

Answer: riparian
Topic: Section 25.6

12) Wetlands in which considerable amounts of water are retained by an accumulation of partially decayed organic matter are referred to as mires, or _____.

Answer: peatlands
Topic: Section 25.6

13) The duration, frequency, depth, and season of flooding of a freshwater period are collectively referred to as the _____.

Answer: hydroperiod
Topic: Section 25.7

Multiple-Choice Questions

1) The part of a rocky shore in which barnacles, oysters, mussels, limpets, and brown algae are most common is called the
   A) littoral, or intertidal zone.
   B) infralittoral, or subtidal zone.
   C) supralittoral, or supratidal zone.
   D) superlittoral, or supertidal zone.

Answer: A
Topic: Section 25.2

2) In tidal pools,
   A) oxygen concentrations are usually greater during the day than during the night.
   B) carbon dioxide concentrations are usually greater during the day than during the night.
   C) salinity is usually greater during the night than during the day.
   D) temperature is usually greater during the night than during the day.

Answer: A
Topic: Section 25.2

3) The epifauna of sand and muddy beaches refers to organisms
   A) living on the surface of sediments.
   B) attached to grains of sand and mud.
   C) migrating seasonally between the subtidal and intertidal zones.
   D) living between particles of sand and mud.

Answer: A
Topic: Section 25.3

4) In comparison to rocky coasts, intertidal organisms living on sandy or muddy beaches
   A) experience greater variability in salinity.
   B) experience greater variability in temperature.
   C) are more likely to be attached to the substrate.
   D) are more likely to move back and forth with the tides.

Answer: D
Topic: Section 25.3

5) Salt marshes
    A) occur mostly in temperate latitudes.
    B) are inhabited by plants that often have root extensions rising above the water.
    C) are always submerged, except during the lowest of low tides.
    D) are important nurseries for fishes.

Answer: A
Topic: Section 25.4

6) In salt marshes, predatory fish move in when
    A) the tide is high.
    B) migratory fishes are spawning.
    C) the sun goes down.
    D) salinity is low.

Answer: A
Topic: Section 25.4

7) Intertidal mud flats in tropical regions are typically comprised of
    A) salt marshes.
    B) peatlands.
    C) mangrove forests, or mangals.
    D) oysterbeds.

Answer: C
Topic: Section 25.5

8) Mangrove swamps
    A) are formed by a single species of tree adapted to variable salinities.
    B) have relatively anoxic soils.
    C) occur mostly in temperate latitudes.
    D) typically occur along rocky coastlines subjected to heavy wave action.

Answer: B
Topic: Section 25.5

9) Reeds, sedges, grasses, and cattails typically grow in freshwater
    A) marshes.
    B) swamps.
    C) riparian woodlands.
    D) peatlands, or mires.

Answer: A
Topic: Section 25.6

10) Freshwater wetlands dominated by woody vegetation are referred to as
    A) swamps.
    B) marshes.
    C) mangrove forests, or mangals.
    D) prairie potholes.

Answer: A
Topic: Section 25.6

11) Bogs formed when a lake basin fills in from above rather than from below, creating a floating mat of peat over open water, are called
    A) fens.
    B) blanket mires.
    C) moors.
    D) quaking bogs.

Answer: D
Topic: Section 25.6

12) The hydroperiod of a wetland is longest for
    A) riverine wetlands.
    B) basin wetlands.
    C) fringe wetlands.
    D) coastal wetlands.

Answer: B
Topic: Section 25.7

13) Peatlands differ from other wetlands in that
    A) the rate of organic production exceeds the rate of decomposition.
    B) there is no outflow of water, resulting in increasing salinities.
    C) they are seasonal, filling with water during the wet season and drying out during the dry season.
    D) they have a two-way flow of water due to tidal action.

Answer: A
Topic: Section 25.7

True/False Questions

1) Shoreline communities exhibit strong zonation.

Answer: TRUE
Topic: Section 25.1

2) In rocky shore communities of the ocean, the supralittoral or supratidal zone is covered and uncovered daily by the tides.

Answer: FALSE
Topic: Section 25.2

3) In tidal pools, carbon dioxide concentrations are higher during the day than during the night.

Answer: FALSE
Topic: Section 25.2

4) Most organisms in the intertidal zone of sandy shores burrow into the sand.

Answer: TRUE
Topic: Section 25.3

5) The diversity of organisms is greater in the intertidal zone of rocky shores than in sandy and muddy shores.

Answer: TRUE
Topic: Section 25.3

6) Salinity is more variable in the intertidal zone of rocky shores than in sandy and muddy shores.

Answer: TRUE
Topic: Section 25.3

7) The meiofauna of a sandy beach refers to organisms living on the surface of sediments.

Answer: FALSE
Topic: Section 25.3

8) Salt marshes occur mostly below the intertidal zone and are exposed only during very low tides.

Answer: FALSE
Topic: Section 25.4

9) Bird and mammal predators are more common in salt marshes during low tide than during high tide.

Answer: TRUE
Topic: Section 25.4

10) The soils of mangrove forests are rich in oxygen due to bioturbation of organisms living within the soils.

Answer: FALSE
Topic: Section 25.5

11) The roots of mangrove trees often have extensions called pneumatophores that facilitate oxygen absorption by the roots.

Answer: TRUE
Topic: Section 25.5

12) Hydrophytic plants grow in water or on soil that is periodically anoxic due to excess water.

Answer: TRUE
Topic: Section 25.6

13) Wetlands dominated by emergent herbaceous vegetation are called swamps.

Answer: FALSE
Topic: Section 25.6

14) Because bogs depend on precipitation for nutrient inputs, they are highly deficient in mineral salts and are low in pH.

Answer: TRUE
Topic: Section 25.6

15) Riverine wetlands usually have a longer hydroperiod than basin wetlands.

Answer: FALSE
Topic: Section 25.7

16) Wetlands subjected to a long hydroperiod support more submerged and deep-water emergents than wetlands with a shorter hydroperiod.

Answer: TRUE
Topic: Section 25.7

17) In peatlands, the rate of decomposition exceeds the rate of organic production.

Answer: FALSE
Topic: Section 25.7

18) Riverine wetlands act as natural flood-control reservoirs.

Answer: TRUE
Topic: Ecological Issues: The Continuing Decline of Wetlands

Essay Questions

1) Name three ecological zones within a rocky shore and discuss the different forms of life that occur in each.

   Topic: Section 25.2

2) Compare the physical conditions to which intertidal organisms must be adapted to in sandy and rocky shores.

   Topic: Sections 25.2 and 25.3

3) Describe the effects of tides on the composition of animal communities in salt marshes.

   Topic: Section 25.4

4) Discuss the adaptations of mangrove trees to their environment.

   Topic: Section 25.5

5) Discuss the flow of water and nutrients in three topographic types of wetlands.

   Topic: Section 25.6

6) For what reasons have humans drained wetlands in the past, and what valuable services are we losing when we drain a wetland?

   Topic: Ecological Issues: The Continuing Decline of Wetlands

Chapter 26   Large-Scale Patterns of Biological Diversity

Short Answer Questions

1) Over the past 600 million years, the overall trend in the number of species has been _____.

   Answer: increasing
   Topic: Section 26.1

2) The mass extinction of dinosaurs occurred at the end of the _____ period.

   Answer: Cretaceous
   Topic: Section 26.2

3) A mass extinction of large mammals occurred during the _____ epoch.

   Answer: Pleistocene
   Topic: Section 26.2

4) As latitude increases, the number of terrestrial species _____.

   Answer: decreases
   Topic: Section 26.3

5) As estimates of actual and potential evapotranspiration increase, the number of terrestrial species

   _____.

   Answer: increases
   Topic: Section 26.4

6) As structural diversity within plant communities increases, the number of animal species _____.

   Answer: increases
   Topic: Section 26.4

7) As elevation increases, the number of terrestrial species _____.

   Answer: decreases
   Topic: Section 26.4

8) As latitude increases, the number of marine species _____.

   Answer: decreases
   Topic: Section 26.5

9) As latitude increases, marine productivity _____.

   Answer: increases
   Topic: Section 26.5

10) Total species diversity, or species richness, of individual communities is referred to as _____ diversity.

   Answer: local, or alpha
   Topic: Section 26.6

Multiple-Choice Questions

1) The number of species of living organisms on the planet is probably closest to
   A) 100,000.
   B) 1,000,000.
   C) 10,000,000.
   D) 100,000,000.

   Answer: C
   Topic: Introduction to Chapter 26

2) In the past 100 million years, the number of species of this group of plants has been increasing.
   A) arthrophytes (e.g., horsetails)
   B) pteridophytes (ferns)
   C) gymnosperms (e.g., ginkos, cycads, conifers)
   D) angiosperms (flowering plants)

   Answer: D
   Topic: Section 26.1

3) The end of the Permian period was characterized by a mass extinction of
   A) shallow-water marine invertebrates.
   B) dinosaurs and other large reptiles.
   C) small mammals.
   D) large mammals.

   Answer: A
   Topic: Section 26.2

4) The dinosaurs and many other animals became extinct at the end of the
   A) Cambrian period.
   B) Permian period.
   C) Cretaceous period.
   D) Pleistocene epoch.

   Answer: C
   Topic: Section 26.2

5) The end of the Pleistocene epoch was marked by a mass extinction of
   A) shallow-water marine invertebrates.
   B) dinosaurs and other large reptiles.
   C) small mammals.
   D) large mammals.

   Answer: D
   Topic: Section 26.2

6) Species richness of terrestrial plants and animals increases with
   A) latitude.
   B) the structural diversity of plant communities.
   C) elevation.
   D) flatter terrain.

   Answer: B
   Topic: Sections 26.3 and 26.4

7) Variation in species richness of terrestrial species in North America correlates most strongly with estimates of
   A) actual, or potential, evapotranspiration.
   B) annual temperature.
   C) solar radiation.
   D) precipitation.

Answer: A
Topic: Section 26.4

8) In marine environments,
   A) both species richness and productivity increase with latitude.
   B) species richness increases and productivity decreases with latitude.
   C) species richness decreases and productivity increases with latitude.
   D) both species richness and productivity decrease with latitude.

Answer: C
Topic: Section 26.5

9) As seasonal fluctuations in temperature increase in marine environments,
   A) both species richness and species dominance increase.
   B) species richness increases and species dominance decreases.
   C) species richness decreases and species dominance increases.
   D) both species richness and species dominance decrease.

Answer: C
Topic: Section 26.5

10) Which of the following factors is most likely to shift the geographic ranges of many species, thus altering regional patterns of diversity?
    A) glacial period
    B) fires
    C) earthquakes
    D) hurricanes

Answer: A
Topic: Section 26.6

11) An ecologist samples trees in 50 plots in a forest to determine the number of species in the forest. When a species accumulation curve is used to plot the cumulative number of tree species (y axis) against the number of samples taken (x axis), the optimal sample size needed to determine species richness is represented by the
    A) point at which the curve is steepest.
    B) point at which the curve is highest, after which it dips downward.
    C) point at which the curve flattens.
    D) point at which the curve is lowest.

Answer: C
Topic: Quantifying Ecology 26.1

True/False Questions

1) All living species of organisms have now been described by scientists.

Answer: FALSE
Topic: Introduction to Chapter 26

2) Over the past 600 million years, overall species richness of invertebrates has been increasing.

Answer: TRUE
Topic: Section 26.1

3) Over the past 100 million years, species richness has declined for gymnosperms and has increased for angiosperms.

Answer: TRUE
Topic: Section 26.1

4) About 90% of the shallow-water marine invertebrates became extinct at the end of the Permian period.

Answer: TRUE
Topic: Section 26.2

5) A mass extinction of large mammals occurred at the end of the Pleistocene Epoch.

Answer: TRUE
Topic: Section 26.2

6) Species richness in both terrestrial and marine environments generally declines with latitude.

Answer: TRUE
Topic: Section 26.2

7) In terrestrial habitats, species richness is negatively correlated with primary productivity.

Answer: FALSE
Topic: Section 26.4

8) As the structural diversity of plant communities increases, the species richness of animals also increases.

Answer: TRUE
Topic: Section 26.4

9) The diverse topography of mountainous regions generally supports more species of plants and animals than the consistent terrain of flatlands.

Answer: TRUE
Topic: Section 26.4

10) The species richness of terrestrial plants and animals generally increases with elevation.

Answer: FALSE
Topic: Section 26.4

11) Primary productivity in the oceans is lower in tropical latitudes than in temperate latitudes, primarily due to a permanent thermocline in tropical latitudes.

Answer: TRUE
Topic: Section 26.5

12) Seasonal variation in surface temperatures of the ocean functions to increase primary productivity.

Answer: TRUE
Topic: Section 26.5

Essay Questions

1) Discuss three mass extinction events in Earth's history, including the time when they occurred and the groups of organisms that were most affected.

Topic: Section 26.1

2) Choose one of several mass extinction events of the past or present and discuss the potential cause(s) of the mass extinction.

Topic: Sections 26.2

3) Discuss the major geographical trends in diversity and productivity in marine environments. Give one possible explanation for these patterns.

Topic: Section 26.5

4) What single environmental factor is most likely to shift the geographic ranges of many species, thus altering regional patterns of diversity?

Topic: Section 26.6

Chapter 27 Population Growth, Resource Use, and Sustainability

Short Answer Questions

1) The amount of a resource harvested per unit time is called _____.

   Answer: yield
   Topic: Section 27.1

2) In forest harvest, the time between harvests is called the _____ period, or harvest interval.

   Answer: rotation
   Topic: Section 27.1

3) Harvesting at a level that will ensure a similar yield repeatedly without forcing the population into decline is called _____ yield.

   Answer: sustained
   Topic: Section 27.1

4) A _____ resource is one that is able to regenerate or resupply itself.

   Answer: renewable
   Topic: Section 27.1

5) Ecosystem _____ are the processes by which the environment produces resources (natural capital) such as clean air, water, timber, or fish.

   Answer: services
   Topic: Section 27.2

6) A community that consists of a mixture of crop species is called a(n) _____.

   Answer: polyculture
   Topic: Section 27.4

7) Traditional agriculture is dominated by _____ agriculture in which primarily human labor and draft animals are used to produce only enough crops or livestock for a family to survive.

   Answer: subsistence
   Topic: Section 27.4

8) A method of subsistence farming that is practiced primarily in the tropical forested regions is called shifting cultivation, or _____ agriculture.

   Answer: swidden
   Topic: Section 27.5

9) Different agricultural methods represent a trade-off between sustainability and _____.

   Answer: productivity
   Topic: Section 27.7

10) When chemical fertilizers are transported from agricultural lands into adjacent aquatic habitats, accelerated nutrient enrichment of aquatic habitats leads to major ecological changes termed cultural _____.

    Answer: eutrophication
    Topic: Section 27.7

Copyright © 2009 Pearson Education, Inc.

11) _____ agriculture refers to maintaining agriculture production indefinitely while minimizing environmental impacts.

Answer: Sustainable
Topic: Section 27.8

12) _____-cutting is the complete removal of a forest during harvest.

Answer: Clear
Topic: Section 27.9

13) In _____ cutting, mature single trees or groups of trees scattered through the forest are removed, which produces only small openings or gaps on the forest canopy.

Answer: selection
Topic: Section 27.9

14) The strategy of harvesting a resource at a rate equal to the rate at which it is renewed is referred to as the maximum _____ yield.

Answer: sustainable
Topic: Section 27.10

15) _____ is a technique employed to add and compare costs and benefits that occur at different points in time.

Answer: Discounting
Topic: Section 27.12

16) _____ occur when the actions of one individual (or group of individuals) affect another individual's well-being, but the relevant costs (or benefits) are not reflected in market prices.

Answer: Externalities
Topic: Section 27.12

Multiple-Choice Questions

1) The amount of resource harvested per unit time is called the
   A) crop.
   B) yield.
   C) take.
   D) net harvest.

Answer: B
Topic: Section 27.1

2) In forestry, the period of time between harvests of trees at a site is called the
   A) harvest time.
   B) regrowth period.
   C) rotation time.
   D) fallow time.

Answer: C
Topic: Section 27.1

3) A sustained yield refers to the
   A) rate at which a renewable resource can be used indefinitely without reducing its available supply.
   B) use of only perpetual and renewable resources without using nonrenewable resources.
   C) overuse of common property or resources with free access, leading to depletion of resources.
   D) self-sustaining management of a country's economy to preclude external debt.

Answer: A
Topic: Section 27.1

4) The harvesting of a natural resource based on sustainable yield applies to
   A) renewable resources.
   B) nonrenewable resources.
   C) perpetual resources.
   D) both A and B

Answer: A
Topic: Section 27.1

5) Which of the following is an example of a nonrenewable resource?
   A) groundwater
   B) trees in a forest
   C) tuna
   D) coal

Answer: D
Topic: Section 27.1

6) Which of the following is not a characteristic of swidden agriculture or shifting cultivation?
   A) Some trees are cut but others are left to provide seed for new trees.
   B) Felled trees and brush are burned to clear land for planting.
   C) Ash from fires is high in mineral nutrients.
   D) Productivity declines with each successive crop.

Answer: A
Topic: Section 27.5

7) Different agricultural practices represent a trade-off between
   A) sustainability and economic growth.
   B) productivity and cost.
   C) productivity and sustainability.
   D) sustainability and convenience.

Answer: C
Topic: Section 27.7

8) Cultural eutrophication refers to the
   A) natural decomposition of solid wastes in a landfill.
   B) breakdown of biodegradable wastes by bacteria.
   C) process in which sewage is purified naturally by plants.
   D) accelerated nutrient enrichment of bodies of water due to runoff of chemical fertilizers.

Answer: D
Topic: Section 27.7

9) The silvicultural technique in which mature single trees or groups of trees scattered through the forest are removed is referred to as
    A) the shelterwood, or seed-tree system.
    B) clear-cutting.
    C) selection cutting.
    D) strip cutting.

Answer: A
Topic: Section 27.9

10) When trees are harvested and removed,
    A) soil temperature decreases.
    B) the rate of soil erosion increases.
    C) the rate of decomposition decreases.
    D) the rate of mineralization (transformation of organic compounds into inorganic compounds) decreases.

Answer: B
Topic: Section 27.9

11) The maximum sustainable yield of a fishery occurs at a population level that is at
    A) the carrying capacity.
    B) just below the carrying capacity.
    C) about half of the carrying capacity.
    D) about a quarter of the carrying capacity.

Answer: C
Topic: Section 27.10

12) Marine life that is caught, but is unwanted and discarded, is referred to as
    A) disposable.
    B) excess.
    C) bycatch.
    D) refuse.

Answer: C
Topic: Section 27.11

13) The technique of adding and comparing costs and benefits at different points in time is referred to as
    A) benefit-cost analysis.
    B) discounting.
    C) external analysis.
    D) profit-debt analysis.

Answer: B
Topic: Section 27.11

14) The negative consequences of harvesting a natural resource, such as the soil erosion and sedimentation of a river that occur after a forest is logged, typically are not included in the market price of the resource; these costs are referred to as
    A) externalities.
    B) byproducts.
    C) coincidentals.
    D) unintended consequences.

Answer: A
Topic: Section 27.11

True/False Questions

1) For the exploitation of a resource to be sustainable, the consumption rate must be equal to or greater than the regeneration rate.

   Answer: FALSE
   Topic: Section 27.1

2) The concept of sustained yield applies to nonrenewable resources.

   Answer: FALSE
   Topic: Section 27.1

3) Some nonrenewable resources may be recycled, which extends the effective lifetime of a resource.

   Answer: TRUE
   Topic: Section 27.1

4) The vast majority of human food resources are derived from agriculture.

   Answer: TRUE
   Topic: Section 27.4

5) A field of corn is an example of polyculture.

   Answer: FALSE
   Topic: Section 27.4

6) Although industrialized agriculture produces small quantities of crops, it takes very little energy input to do so.

   Answer: FALSE
   Topic: Section 27.4

7) Swidden agriculture involves burning, which clears space for crops and produces ash that is high in nutrients.

   Answer: TRUE
   Topic: Section 27.5

8) Industrialized agriculture depends on crop rotation to naturally maintain concentrations of plant nutrients in the soils and to sustainably maintain productivity.

   Answer: FALSE
   Topic: Section 27.6

9) Industrialized agriculture uses pesticides to control pest species and increase productivity.

   Answer: TRUE
   Topic: Section 27.6

10) Industrialized agriculture produces a higher yield than traditional agriculture but also requires more energy per unit of food produced.

    Answer: TRUE
    Topic: Section 27.7

11) Nitrate is a commonly used chemical fertilizer that is harmless to human health.

    Answer: FALSE
    Topic: Section 27.7

12) In recent decades, the per capita land area under agricultural production has declined.

Answer: TRUE
Topic: Section 27.7

13) Increased pesticide use is one component of efforts toward sustainable farming practices today.

Answer: FALSE
Topic: Section 27.8

14) Selective cutting usually involves leaving a small number of seed-bearing trees, which are a source of seed for establishment of natural vegetation after harvest.

Answer: FALSE
Topic: Section 27.9

15) As biomass in a forest increases, the density of trees decreases, while the average tree size increases as a result of self-thinning.

Answer: TRUE
Topic: Section 27.9

16) Trees harvested for timber require a longer rotation period than trees harvested for paper products.

Answer: TRUE
Topic: Section 27.9

17) Soil erosion increases when trees are removed from a forest.

Answer: TRUE
Topic: Section 27.9

18) Soil temperature increases when trees are removed from a forest.

Answer: TRUE
Topic: Section 27.9

19) In some parts of our national forests, forest managers are mandated by the government to sell timber at prices that do not meet the costs of management and harvest.

Answer: TRUE
Topic: Section 27.9

20) The maximum sustainable yield of a fishery occurs at a population level that is at the carrying capacity.

Answer: FALSE
Topic: Section 27.10

21) Species characterized by a very high rate of population growth often lose much of their production due to high density-independent mortality.

Answer: TRUE
Topic: Section 27.10

22) One of the strengths of traditional models of sustainable harvest in fisheries is that they see stocks of fish species as components of a larger ecological system.

Answer: FALSE
Topic: Section 27.11

23) The technique of discounting often runs counter to the objectives of sustainable resource management.

Answer: TRUE
Topic: Section 27.12

24) Externalities occur when the actions of one individual affect another individual's well-being, and the relevant costs are reflected in market prices.

Answer: FALSE
Topic: Section 27.12

25) Genetically modified crops rely on the insertion of a beneficial gene from a closely related species because genes from distantly related species are incompatible.

Answer: FALSE
Topic: Ecological Issues: Genetically Modified Crops

26) The research of Deborah Lawrence found that shifting cultivation practices in Indonesia result in increased levels of soil phosphorus with each successive cultivation cycle during the first 80 years of cultivation.

Answer: TRUE
Topic: Field Studies: Deborah C. Lawrence

Essay Questions

1) Distinguish between renewable and nonrenewable resources, and give two examples of each.
Topic: Section 27.1

2) Discuss the advantages and disadvantages of using chemical fertilizers such as nitrates and phosphates.
Topic: Section 27.7

3) List and describe three examples of sustainable farming practices being used today.
Topic: Section 27.8

4) Describe two different forest harvest practices, and explain the pros and cons of each.
Topic: Section 27.9

5) Discuss the theorized relationship among maximum sustainable yield, carrying capacity, and rate of population growth of a harvested species.
Topic: Section 27.10

6) Using an example from farming, forestry, or fisheries, discuss the concept of discounting and how it is used to economically justify the overexploitation of a resource.
Topic: Section 27.12

7) Discuss the relationship between externalities and the market prices of a natural resource.
Topic: Section 27.12

Chapter 28 Habitat Loss, Biodiversity, and Conservation

Short Answer Questions

1) The mass extinction event at the end of the Cretaceous period is thought to have been caused by the impact of a _____.

    Answer: meteor, asteroid, or comet
    Topic: Introduction to Chapter 28

2) The primary cause of current species extinctions is the destruction of _____.

    Answer: habitat
    Topic: Introduction to Chapter 28 and Section 28.1

3) Species living on _____ are especially vulnerable to extinction by the introduction of exotic, alien, or invasive species.

    Answer: islands
    Topic: Section 28.2

4) A species found to naturally occur in a single geographic area and nowhere else is regarded as _____ to that location.

    Answer: endemic
    Topic: Section 28.3

5) A species with a 20% or greater probability of extinction within 20 years or five generations, whichever is longer, is considered to be a(n) _____ species.

    Answer: endangered
    Topic: Section 28.4

6) Designation of a region as a _____ is based on supporting 1500 or more endemic species of plants and more than 70% of the original habitat lost.

    Answer: hotspot
    Topic: Section 28.5

7) The number of individuals necessary to ensure the long-term survival of a species is called the minimum _____ population.

    Answer: viable
    Topic: Section 28.6

8) The area of suitable habitat necessary to ensure the long-term survival of a species is called the minimum _____ area.

    Answer: dynamic
    Topic: Section 28.6

9) Conservations often attempt to restore a locally extinct population of a species through _____ into the wild of individuals from captive-bred populations

    Answer: reintroduction
    Topic: Section 28.7

10) Isolated protected areas should be linked together by habitat _____, which facilitate the dispersal of plants and animals between protected areas.

    Answer: corridors
    Topic: Section 28.9

11) The goal of _____ ecology is to return an ecosystem to a close approximation of its conditions prior to disturbance through the application of ecological principles.

Answer: restoration
Topic: Section 28.10

Multiple-Choice Questions

1) The mass extinction of dinosaurs and other animals at the end of the Cretaceous period is believed by most scientists to have been caused by
    A) a massive asteroid or comet impact.
    B) a massive volcanic eruption.
    C) gamma radiation released from a supernova explosion.
    D) overhunting by expanding populations of Neolithic humans.

Answer: A
Topic: Introduction to Chapter 28

2) The primary cause of modern extinctions is
    A) overhunting.
    B) introduction of non-native species.
    C) pollution.
    D) habitat destruction.

Answer: D
Topic: Introduction to Chapter 28 and Section 28.1

3) Species living on isolated islands are especially vulnerable to extinction by
    A) overhunting.
    B) pollution.
    C) the introduction of exotic species.
    D) habitat destruction.

Answer: C
Topic: Section 28.2

4) An endemic species is best defined as a species that
    A) is a habitat specialist with a large geographical distribution.
    B) has so few individuals remaining that it ceases to perform its role within an ecosystem.
    C) no longer occurs in a given area yet still survives elsewhere.
    D) occurs in a single geographic area and nowhere else.

Answer: D
Topic: Section 28.3

5) A species with this trait is vulnerable to extinction.
    A) short life span
    B) large home range
    C) habitat generalist
    D) non-migratory

Answer: B
Topic: Section 28.3

6) This group of organism is the most vulnerable to extinction based on the number of threatened species as a percentage of the number of species described and evaluated.
   A) mammals
   B) insects
   C) crustaceans
   D) monocotyledonous plants

Answer: A
Topic: Section 28.4

7) The minimum viable population size is highest for this group of organisms.
   A) large birds and mammals
   B) small birds and mammals
   C) perennial plants
   D) annual plants

Answer: D
Topic: Section 28.6

8) The area of suitable habitat necessary for maintaining the number of individuals and ensuring the long-term survival of a species should be highest for a
   A) small herbivore.
   B) large herbivore.
   C) small carnivore.
   D) large carnivore.

Answer: D
Topic: Section 28.6

9) Which of the following is NOT an advantage for preserving a large reserve rather than a small reserve?
   A) A large reserve has more species.
   B) A large reserve supports larger populations.
   C) A large reserve exposes organisms to proportionately more habitat edges.
   D) A large reserve has a greater diversity of habitats.

Answer: C
Topic: Section 28.8

10) The dispersal of plants and animals from one reserve to another within a network of reserves is best accomplished by
   A) establishing buffer zones around reserves.
   B) linking reserves by habitat corridors.
   C) reintroducing individuals born and raised in captivity.
   D) relocating individuals captured within their natural habitat.

Answer: B
Topic: Section 28.9

11) Which of the following would not be considered a goal of restoration ecology?
   A) eliminating exotic or invasive species
   B) replanting native species
   C) suppressing lightning-strike fires
   D) reintroducing individuals of a locally extinct animal species

Answer: C
Topic: Section 28.10

True/False Questions

1) The mass extinction of dinosaurs and other animals at the end of the Cretaceous period is believed by most scientists to have been caused by massive volcanic activity causing an ice age.

    Answer: FALSE
    Topic: Introduction to Chapter 28

2) The primary cause of modern extinctions is habitat destruction.

    Answer: TRUE
    Topic: Section 28.1

3) The species most vulnerable to the introduction of exotic species are those living on isolated islands.

    Answer: TRUE
    Topic: Section 28.2

4) Aquatic environments are not affected by the introduction of exotic species.

    Answer: FALSE
    Topic: Section 28.2

5) Endemic species are in imminent danger of becoming extinct.

    Answer: FALSE
    Topic: Section 28.3

6) A species that migrates seasonally is more vulnerable to extinction than a sedentary species that does not migrate.

    Answer: TRUE
    Topic: Section 28.3

7) Small species of mammals are more vulnerable to extinction than large species of mammals.

    Answer: FALSE
    Topic: Section 28.3

8) Most species of plants and animals have small, restricted geographic ranges.

    Answer: TRUE
    Topic: Section 28.5

9) Conservations refer to the number of individuals necessary to ensure the long-term survival of a species as the effective population size.

    Answer: FALSE
    Topic: Section 28.6 and Quantifying Ecology 28.1

10) Genetic models suggest that the size of a population required to ensure the long-term survival of a species is higher for annual plants and invertebrates than for mammals.

    Answer: TRUE
    Topic: Section 28.6

11) The home range of a carnivore is usually larger than that of a herbivore of the same size.

    Answer: TRUE
    Topic: Section 28.6

12) A small area has proportionately more habitat edges than a large area.

Answer: TRUE
Topic: Section 28.8

13) The establishment of habitat corridors between protected areas may have some negative consequences.

Answer: TRUE
Topic: Section 28.9

14) Degraded habitats cannot be restored even close to their original condition.

Answer: FALSE
Topic: Section 28.10

15) The genetically effective population size is smaller than the actual population size.

Answer: TRUE
Topic: Quantifying Ecology 28.1

Essay Questions

1) Discuss three major causes of modern species extinctions. Which is the primary cause?

Topic: Sections 28.1 and 28.2

2) Explain why exotic species represent a threat to native species. Give an example of an exotic species threatening the survival of one or more native species.

Topic: Section 28.3

3) Explain why the minimum viable population size varies greatly among species.

Topic: Section 28.6

4) Explain why the minimum dynamic area varies greatly among species.

Topic: Section 28.6

5) What are the three major reasons that biodiversity should be preserved?

Topic: Section 28.11

6) What are the ecological benefits of introducing large carnivores, such as wolves and grizzly bears, to areas where they had been extirpated?

Topic: Ecological Issues: The Wolves of Yellowstone National Park

Chapter 29 Global Climate Change

Short Answer Questions

1) The absorption of thermal (long-wave) radiation emitted by the Earth's surface and atmosphere by naturally occurring chemical compounds in the atmosphere is a phenomenon referred to as the _____ effect.

Answer: greenhouse
Topic: Section 29.1

2) The atmospheric concentration of _____ has increased by more than 25% of the past century, due largely to the burning of fossil fuels.

Answer: carbon dioxide
Topic: Section 29.2

3) Deforestation is a major cause of the recent rise in concentrations of the atmospheric gas _____.

Answer: carbon dioxide
Topic: Section 29.2

4) The process of _____ controls uptake of carbon dioxide from the atmosphere into the oceans.

Answer: diffusion
Topic: Section 29.3

5) When carbon dioxide dissolves in ocean water, much of it is transformed into _____.

Answer: carbonates, or bicarbonates
Topic: Section 29.4

6) Plants usually react to increased atmospheric carbon dioxide by increasing their rate of _____.

Answer: photosynthesis
Topic: Section 29.5

7) Plants exposed to higher atmospheric carbon dioxide often partially close the _____ in their leaves to reduce water loss.

Answer: stomata
Topic: Section 29.5

8) Atmospheric scientists have developed complex computer models of Earth's climate system called general _____ models.

Answer: circulation
Topic: Section 29.6

9) General circulation models consistently predict an increase in both average global _____ and average global precipitation.

Answer: temperature
Topic: Section 29.6

10) According to general circulation models, warming is expected to be most significant during the _____ season and in northern latitudes.

Answer: winter
Topic: Section 29.6

11) A major source of aerosols resulting from human activities is sulfates and soot from the burning of _____ fuels.

Answer: fossil
Topic: Section 29.6

12) Decomposition proceeds faster under warm and _____ conditions.

Answer: wet, or humid
Topic: Section 29.7

13) Samples of pollen taken from _____ cores in lake beds have allowed scientists to reconstruct the vegetation of many regions exist during the past 20,000 years.

Answer: sediment
Topic: Section 29.8

14) _____ levels were about 100 meters lower during the last glacial maximum than they are today, and are expected to rise higher in the future as a consequence of global warming.

Answer: Sea
Topic: Section 29.9

15) Albedo, an index of the ability of a surface to reflect solar radiation back to space, is relatively high for vegetation and low for _____.

Answer: snow or ice
Topic: Section 29.12

Multiple-Choice Questions

1) Which of the following gases in the atmosphere is not considered a greenhouse gas?
   A) carbon dioxide
   B) nitrogen
   C) water vapor
   D) ozone

Answer: B
Topic: Section 29.1

2) Deforestation is a major cause of increased atmospheric concentrations of
   A) carbon dioxide.
   B) ozone.
   C) oxygen.
   D) chlorofluorocarbons.

Answer: A
Topic: Section 29.2

3) Within the past century, the major source of carbon emissions into the atmospheric has been
   A) deforestation.
   B) volcanic eruptions.
   C) the combustion of fossil fuels.
   D) forest fires.

Answer: C
Topic: Section 29.3

4) Which of the following is not true?
   A) A large proportion of the ocean water is not available for carbon dioxide uptake.
   B) As the concentration of atmospheric carbon dioxide increases, the oceans take up more carbon dioxide.
   C) When carbon dioxide dissolves in water, some of it is transformed into carbonates.
   D) The thermocline causes the ocean to have a higher capacity for absorbing carbon dioxide.

Answer: D
Topic: Section 29.4

5) In response to an increase in atmospheric carbon dioxide, plants generally
   A) decrease their water-use efficiency.
   B) increase their rate of photosynthesis.
   C) open their stomata more.
   D) increase water loss from transpiration.

Answer: B
Topic: Section 29.5

6) Which of the following biomes is most likely to increase its primary productivity in response to an increase in atmospheric carbon dioxide?
   A) temperate coniferous forest
   B) tropical rainforest
   C) temperate grassland
   D) temperate deciduous forest

Answer: C
Topic: Section 29.5

7) The general circulation models developed by atmospheric scientists predict that in the future,
   A) temperatures, sea levels, variability of climate, and precipitation will all increase.
   B) temperatures, sea levels, and variability of climate will increase while precipitation will decrease.
   C) temperatures and sea levels will increase while variability of climate and precipitation will decrease.
   D) temperatures and precipitation will increase while sea levels and variability of climate will decrease.

Answer: A
Topic: Section 29.6

8) As aerosol concentrations increase,
   A) the amount of radiation reaching the Earth's surface increases.
   B) temperatures decrease.
   C) ozone is formed more rapidly in the stratosphere.
   D) the polar ice caps melt.

Answer: B
Topic: Section 29.6

9) Which of the following is most likely to occur as a consequence of global climate change?
   A) The distributions of plants and animals will move closer toward the equator.
   B) The distributions of plants and animals in mountains will move downward to lower elevations.
   C) The rates of decomposition and microbial will increase, thus increasing emissions of carbon dioxide.
   D) The distribution of tropical rain forests will increase.

Answer: C
Topic: Sections 29.7, and 29.8

10) Which of the following is most likely to occur as a consequence of global climate change?
    A) increases in sea levels, coastal erosion, flooding, and salinity of aquifers
    B) increases in sea levels, coastal erosion, and flooding, and a decrease in salinity of aquifers
    C) increases in sea levels and coastal erosion and decreases in flooding and salinity of aquifers
    D) an increase in sea levels and decreases in coastal erosion, flooding, and salinity of aquifers

Answer: A
Topic: Section 29.9

11) As a consequence of global climate change, crop production is likely to
    A) increase in both developed and developing countries.
    B) increase in developed countries and decrease in developing countries.
    C) decrease in developed countries and increase in developing countries.
    D) decrease in both developed and developing countries.

Answer: B
Topic: Section 29.9

True/False Questions

1) Humans are causing the first instances of significant climate change in Earth's history.

Answer: FALSE
Topic: Introduction to Chapter 29

2) Greenhouse gases existed naturally in the atmosphere before the industrial revolution.

Answer: TRUE
Topic: Section 29.1

3) Atmospheric concentrations of carbon dioxide are rising.

Answer: TRUE
Topic: Section 29.2

4) Deforestation causes a decrease in atmospheric carbon dioxide concentrations.

Answer: FALSE
Topic: Section 29.2

5) The Earth's terrestrial ecosystems are net producers of carbon.

Answer: FALSE
Topic: Section 29.3

6) Most plants respond to elevated atmospheric carbon dioxide by increasing their photosynthetic rate.

Answer: TRUE
Topic: Section 29.5

7) Most plants respond to elevated atmospheric carbon dioxide by partially closing their stomata, reducing water loss due to transpiration.

Answer: TRUE
Topic: Section 29.5

8) In response to elevated atmospheric carbon dioxide, primary productivity is more likely to increase in seasonally dry environments than in seasonally moist environments.

Answer: TRUE
Topic: Section 29.5

9) Carbon dioxide is the only greenhouse gas that is increasing as a result of human activities.

Answer: FALSE
Topic: Section 29.6

10) Several greenhouse gases are more effective at trapping heat than carbon dioxide.

Answer: TRUE
Topic: Section 29.6

11) General circulation models predict that global warming will be greatest during the winter months and in northern latitudes.

Answer: TRUE
Topic: Section 29.6

12) Aerosols reduce the amount of radiation reaching Earth's surface and thus have a cooling effect.

Answer: TRUE
Topic: Section 29.6

13) As a consequence of global climate change, plant and animal distributions will generally shift toward higher latitudes and elevations.

Answer: TRUE
Topic: Section 29.7

14) As a consequence of global climate change, human populations in low-lying coastal areas will become threatened by rising sea levels.

Answer: TRUE
Topic: Section 29.9

15) Most species of agricultural crops will benefit from a rise in carbon dioxide concentrations by increasing crop yields.

Answer: TRUE
Topic: Section 29.10

16) The proportion of the world's population exposed to malarial infection is expected to increase as a consequence of global climate change.

Answer: TRUE
Topic: Section 29.11

17) The albedo of vegetation is higher than it is for snow and ice.

Answer: FALSE
Topic: Section 29.12

18) Minimum, or night, temperatures have increased more dramatically than maximum, or day, temperatures within the past century.

Answer: TRUE
Topic: Ecological Issues: Who Turned Up the Heat?

19) Species diversity tends to decrease in plant communities subjected to increases in carbon dioxide, temperature, precipitation, and nitrogen deposition.

Answer: TRUE
Topic: Field Studies: Erika Zavaleta

Essay Questions

1) What are thought to be the major causes of the recent rise in atmospheric concentrations of carbon dioxide?

   Topic: Sections 29.2 and 29.3

2) Discuss the roles of terrestrial and oceanic ecosystems in absorbing carbon dioxide.

   Topic: Sections 29.3 and 29.4

3) How do plants respond to elevated atmospheric carbon dioxide? Do all plants respond the same?

   Topic: Section 29.5

4) Discuss the major trends expected to occur in the global climate as greenhouse gases in the atmosphere continue to rise.

   Topic: Section 29.6

5) Discuss the anticipated changes in the distribution of plants, animals, and ecosystems in response to global climate change.

   Topic: Sections 29.7, and 29.8

6) Describe the potential impacts of global climate change on coastal environments.

   Topic: Section 29.9

7) Describe the potential impacts of global climate change on agricultural production.

   Topic: Section 29.10